The Excretory Function of Bile

THE ELIMINATION OF DRUGS AND TOXIC SUBSTANCES IN BILE

The Excretory Function of Bile

THE ELIMINATION OF DRUGS AND TOXIC SUBSTANCES IN BILE

R. L. SMITH

Reader in Biochemistry
St Mary's Hospital Medical School, London

CHAPMAN AND HALL
LONDON

First published 1973
by Chapman and Hall Ltd
11 New Fetter Lane, London EC4P 4EE

© *1973 R. L. Smith*

Typeset by
Santype Limited (Coldtype Division)
Salisbury, Wiltshire
and printed in Great Britain by
T. & A. Constable Ltd, Edinburgh

Distributed in the U.S.A.
by Halsted Press, a Division
of John Wiley & Sons, Inc., New York

Library of Congress Catalog Card Number 73-6354

Contents

Foreword

The elimination from the body of drugs and other foreign compounds such as food additives and pesticides is a process of considerable importance to the organism. With most drugs, their elimination is an indication of the termination of their activity and with other foreign compounds used in various aspects of food technology it is an indication that they are not accumulating in the body. The excretion of foreign compounds is therefore an important factor in the study of their pharmacology and toxicology. Foreign compounds can be eliminated from the body by several routes, and they, or their metabolites, may appear consequently in the urine, faeces, expired air, sweat, saliva and milk. The urine is usually the main vehicle of excretion, but considerable amounts of some compounds can appear in the faeces. For many years this department (Department of Biochemistry, St. Mary's Hospital Medical School), investigated the fate of foreign compounds in animals. It was frequently observed that excretion of compounds in the faeces was often greater in the rat than in the rabbit. It was surmized that this difference could be due in part to the rat being a better excretor of foreign compounds in the bile than the rabbit. A systematic study of the excretion of foreign compounds in the bile of various animals was therefore initiated in this department some ten years ago. Dr Smith has now drawn together in this book the results of these researches and those of other workers elsewhere. He shows that the excretion in the bile of foreign compounds and their metabolites is a process of great importance which follows certain principles depending upon the chemical nature and the molecular weight of the compound, and the species of the animal studied. A knowledge of the extent of the biliary excretion of a compound is now essential, from a variety of points of view, in the assessment of its value to those interested in the therapeutic use, the pharmacology, toxicology, biochemistry and pathology of foreign compounds used for medical or technological purposes or which occur in the environment naturally or accidentally.

R. Tecwyn Williams

Preface

Excretion is the process whereby waste and potentially harmful substances are eliminated from the body. It is essential for life since in its absence poisonous substances would accumulate to exert deleterious effects. Traditionally the kidney is considered to be the most important organ concerned with excretion and the role of bile in this respect has been relatively neglected. The main physiological function attributed to bile is its role in fat digestion. Its role as a physiological excretion has been recognized but on the whole this has been viewed as a somewhat circumscribed function, limited to the elimination of a few compounds of physiological interest, in particular the bile salts and bilirubin. The main purpose of this book is to show that the excretory function of bile is much wider than this and that it is important for the elimination of many compounds arising from intermediary metabolism and of numerous foreign chemicals that are encountered and enter the organism. Thus, besides the bile salts and bilirubin many other substances of physiological interest are eliminated in bile including the steroid and thyroid hormones, the catecholamines, porphyrins and vitamins, to name but a few. Undoubtedly as more investigations on bile are made it is safe to predict that many other compounds arising from intermediary metabolism will be found to undergo biliary elimination. Much has already been written about the hepatic elimination of bilirubin and the bile acids and for this reason discussion of these substances has been omitted.

The first part of the book provides an historical background to the subject, and briefly reviews the anatomy and physiology of the liver and the process of bile formation. There then follows an account of the influence of various physico-chemical and biological factors on the biliary excretion of organic compounds. The greater part of the book, however, is given over to a consideration of biliary elimination and its implications for chemicals that are foreign to the body. Such substances may be naturally occurring in the diet or they may be encountered in the form of drugs, food additives, pesticides, or environmental pollutants. The question of their metabolic fate and excretion has an important bearing on the biological properties of such chemicals. For many of these compounds hepatic excretion is a dominant aspect of their overall fate and this in itself gives rise to a number of important implications.

It remains for me to thank the many contributors and friends who have made this work possible. Firstly, I would like to thank Professor R. Tecwyn Williams; it has been a great privilege to have been associated, first as a student and later as a collaborator, with one of the pioneers of biochemical pharmacology. I would also like to acknowledge the considerable help received over the years from Dr Peter Millburn; he has played an important role in the development of some of the views concerning the biliary excretion of foreign compounds expressed in this book. Further special thanks are due to Dr Paul Hirom with whom I have worked closely over the last few years. I should also like to thank a number of visiting scientists, particularly Dr M. M. Abou-El-Makarem (Egypt), Dr A. J. Clark (New Zealand), and Dr W. G. Levine (U.S.A.).

For their work in the latter stages of the preparation of this book, I should like to thank my wife, Judith, Peter Millburn and Paul Hirom for reading proofs, Elayne Storeck for checking the references, and Anita Cassidy for helping with the index. Marie Rees and Sally Ashford typed the manuscript, and Harold Downer and John Moffat helped generally at various times; my thanks finally to all these.

Department of Biochemistry,   R. L. Smith
St Mary's Hospital Medical School,
London W2

PART ONE

The Principles of Biliary Excretion

CHAPTER ONE

Functions of Bile: Historical Aspects

Various functions have been attributed to bile. In Hippocratic medicine, bile was one of the four cardinal humours, these being blood, phlegm, yellow bile and black bile. Each of the humours represented certain characteristics; blood represented hot moist humour; phlegm from the brain, cold moist humour; yellow bile from the liver, hot dry humour and black bile from the spleen and stomach, cold dry humour. When these humours were properly mingled, the body was in a state of health and disease was viewed as a defect or irregularity in the mixture of the four humours. Galen also maintained a humoral view of some diseases; fevers of long duration for example were attributed to irregularities of yellow and black bile.

The view that the liver and the bile are of importance in determining temperament and health is found in the works of many writers including Shakespeare. In Twelfth Night for example, the roisterous knight Sir Toby Belch declares contemptuously of his adversary, Viola:

> If he were opened and you will find so much blood in his liver as will clog the foot of a flea, I'll eat the rest of the anatomy.

While Falstaff in King Henry IV Part 2 is even more explicit about the influence of the liver upon temperament:

> The second property of your excellent sherris is, the warming of the blood; which, before cold and settled, left the liver white and pale, which is the badge of pusillanimity and cowardice: but the sherris warms it and makes it course from the inwards to the parts extreme.

The view of the importance of bile in determining temperament is retained today in the use of the word melancholy to describe a condition of sadness and depression of the spirit. The term is derived from the Greek words melas (black) and chole (bile), and the term originated from the belief that mental depression arose from having too much 'black bile'.

These early views on the function of bile are retained in the writings of several writers of the nineteenth century. Thus Sir Walter Scott wrote mockingly

> what poor things does a fever-fit or an overflowing of the bile make of the master of creation

while Ralph Emmerson wrote with more humour,

> I knew a witty physician who found the creed in the biliary duct, and used to affirm that if there was disease in the liver, the man became a Calvinist, and if that organ was sound, he became a Unitarian.

The first scientific studies on the bile were probably those of the seventeenth century anatomist and physiologist Regnier de Graaf, who was celebrated for his work on digestion and the discovery of the ovarian follicle ('Graafian follicle'). In his publication, *In De natura et usu succi pancreatici* he described the collection of both bile and pancreatic juice from experimental fistulae. Progress in understanding the physiological functions of bile however depended on the development of appropriate techniques for establishing biliary fistulae thus allowing the collection of bile. Schwann (1844) is believed to have been the first to have established permanent biliary fistulae in dogs and a full account of the technique is given by Gamgee (1893). Schwann did not use cannulae as his operation consisted in principle of exteriorizing the gall bladder after ligaturing of the common bile duct. According to Gamgee, Blondlot in 1846 was the first to use cannulae in bile fistula operations.

In man, knowledge of bile formation depended on those rare occasions which accidentally led to the formation of a biliary fistula and at the same time hindered the flow of bile into the intestine. Harley (1866) described a case of ecchinococcus of the liver in which, for a week or so, bile was absent from the stools and was discharged from a fistulous opening, to the amount of 16–20 oz per day. Several other such cases are described by Gamgee and which together suggested that the average daily output in man of hepatic bile from a fistula is about 600–1000 ml. The surgical establishment of a biliary fistula was described by Professor Yeo and Mr E. F. Herroun at Kings College Hospital, London in 1883 in a case of a man with carcinoma of the bile duct, and a second case involving a woman with bile-duct occlusion due to an impacted calculus was described by Copeman and Winston in 1889.

Much of the work of the late nineteenth century was concerned with the physiological chemistry of bile i.e. description of its qualitative and quantitative composition and it was, on the whole, viewed as a secretion of little import. In fact Gamgee (1893) writes that 'the bile is to be looked upon as a comparatively insignificant byproduct'. Thenard (1807) and Berzelius (1808) isolated crude forms of the bile salts while Gmelin (1826) was the first to obtain a pure sample of glycocholic acid although he did not know its composition. Gmelin also isolated taurine from preparations of bile but its structure was not established until 1846 by Redtenbacher. Demarcay was the first to establish the conjugate nature of the bile acid and he showed the so called 'choleic acid' of bile could be split on hydrolysis into taurine and a second non-nitrogenous acid, termed choloidic acid. Strecher (1848a, 1848b) subsequently showed that choloidic acid could occur in bile conjugated with either taurine or glycine. The structures of the bile acids were eventually worked out by Wieland in a series of papers beginning in 1912 (e.g. Wieland and Weil, 1912; Wieland and Dane, 1932a, 1932b, 1933; Wieland, 1934).

The colour of the bile had attracted the attention of the physicians of antiquity and many early observations were recorded of the changes of colour that bile undergoes when exposed to air and acids or when undergoing putrefaction (Heuerman, 1753). Thenard (1807) described a yellow colouring matter in bile and Gmelin and Tiedman studied the properties of this material in dog bile. Gmelin discovered that the addition of nitric acid to bile resulted in the formation of a rapid succession of tints and this forms the basis of the well known test for bile named after the discoverer. Berzelius (1842) attempted to isolate bile pigment and he became aware that it could exist in the two forms, now known as biliverdin, coloured green, and the yellow bilirubin. The chemistry of the bile pigments was studied by both Städeler (1864) and by Hoppe—Seyler (1893) but their constitution was not established until the brilliant researches of Fischer (Fischer and Orth, 1937; Fischer and Plieninger, 1942) and his colleagues.

THE EXCRETORY FUNCTION OF BILE

At the end of the nineteenth century physiologists viewed bile largely as a physiological secretion of importance in the digestive processes particularly in relation to fat absorption (Gamgee, 1893; Schäfer, 1898). There was some dispute as to whether bile should also be considered an excretion. Gamgee considered that it was an excretion in respect of certain constituents particularly cholesterol and the bile pigments. This view was at variance with the earlier views of Bunge (1889) who argued that bile was not an excretion and was a secretion. This view was partly based upon the argument that if bile were an excretion we might expect the bile duct to open into the lower end of the rectum and not into the duodenum, the commencement of the intestine.

Even today the dominant physiological function attributed to bile is its role in the digestion and absorption of fats. Its excretory function is recognized but has been circumscribed to the elimination of a few physiologically important compounds, namely the conjugates of bilirubin and cholesterol. In recent years studies on the elimination of many compounds of endogenous and exogenous origin have shown that the bile may function as a channel for their excretion. Thus, as far as endogenous compounds are concerned, the bile can be important for the elimination of steroid and thyroid hormones, catecholamines, porphyrins and vitamins. Further work will undoubtedly show that many other compounds arising from intermediary metabolism are also excreted in bile.

THE EXCRETION OF FOREIGN COMPOUNDS IN BILE

Probably the first to point out a possible role of bile in the elimination of foreign compounds was M. J. B. Orfila, the founder of the science of toxicology. He directed attention in his work *Traité de toxicologie générale (1813–1815)* to the fact that many metallic poisons are taken up by the liver and either retained by that organ or are excreted in the bile. Subsequently, Claude Bernard found that copper sulphate, potassium iodide, turpentine spirit and fructose, when injected into the blood, rapidly pass into the bile. Mosler (1858) also detected turpentine in bile, (by its smell) following its administration to dogs. The biliary excretion of the two dyestuffs, aniline red and indigo carmine was observed by Chrzonszczewsky (1866) and was developed as the basis of the means to visualize the bile duct system. Later, Wertheimer (1893) showed that phyllocyanic acid, a derivative of chlorophyll, is also rapidly eliminated in the bile when introduced into blood. All of these early studies were, in the absence of suitable analytical techniques, largely qualitative in character and therefore the quantitative significance of the bile as a channel of excretion remained obscure for many years.

During the second half of the nineteenth century it was discovered that many foreign compounds undergo chemical transformations in the body and are excreted in the urine as the so called detoxication products (Williams, 1947; Smith and Williams, 1970). In these transformations, compounds underwent oxidation or reduction and the products were paired or conjugated with, for example, glucuronic acid, sulphate or glycine, and excreted as a conjugate in the urine. At the beginning of the nineteenth century such conjugates were found to be excreted in the bile as well as the urine. Thus, the glucuronic acid conjugate of menthol was isolated in 1905 by Bial from the bile of dogs given the terpene and a year later Blumenthal found cresol in the form of a glucuronic acid conjugate also in the bile of dogs.

In 1909 Abel and Rowntree published an important paper showing that a number of phthalein dyes undergo extensive biliary excretion. This empirical observation was of considerable significance since it laid the basis for the development of the diagnostic agents for the hepatobiliary system that are familiar to us today. Graham conceived the original idea of using the substance tetraiodophenolphthalein, which is extensively excreted in bile and opaque to X-rays, for the X-ray visualization of the gall-bladder, and with his two associates Copher and Cole introduced the compound for this purpose in 1925. In the same year Rosenthal and White introduced bromsulphthalein as the basis for a simple test of liver excretory function.

Between 1900 and 1950 relatively little attention was given to the biliary elimination of foreign compounds and work was on the whole concerned with the qualitative and quantitative aspects of their urinary excretion (see Williams, 1947). There were a few isolated observations recording the hepatic elimination of various organic mercurial and arsenical compounds, the phthalein dyestuffs and the quinoline carboxylic acids cinchophen and neocinchophen. From about 1950 the significance of bile as an important channel of excretion for many compounds became more generally realized. This coincided with the fact that synthetic chemicals being introduced during this period as drugs, food additives and pesticides were on the whole more complex and of higher molecular weight than those previously used. The affinity for such compounds to undergo biliary elimination is much greater than that for compounds of relatively low molecular weight and consequently metabolic studies established the importance of biliary, as opposed to urinary excretion, for the elimination of such compounds. Thus, during the decade 1950–1960 the hepatic excretion of numerous diverse groups of chemicals was described: antibiotics such as penicillin, chloramphenicol, erythromycin and the tetracyclines, cardiac glycosides, azo dyestuffs, steroids and the phenothiazines. Smith (1966) in a comprehensive review of biliary excretion reviews the hepatic elimination of many drugs and foreign compounds and discusses its implications.

REFERENCES

Abel, J. J. and Rowntree, L. G. (1909) *J. Pharmacol. exp. Ther.*, **1**, 231.
Berzelius, J. J. (1808) *Föreläsningar i Djurkemine*, Vol. 2, p. 243, Stockholm.
Berzelius, J. J. (1842) in *Handwörterbuch der Physiologie mit Rücksicht auf*

Physiologische Pathologie, quoted by Berzelius (1842), edited by R. Wagner, Vol 1, p. 516, F. Vieweg and Sohn, Braunschweig.

Bial, M. (1905) *Hoppe-Seyler's Z. physiol. Chem.,* **45**, 258.

Blumenthal, F. (1906) *Biochem. Z.,* **1**, 135.

Bunge, G. (1890) *Textbook of Physiological and Pathological Chemistry,* p. 213, translated by L. G. Wooldridge, Kegan Paul, Trench Trübner and Co., London.

Chrzonszezewsky, N. (1866) *Virchows Arch. path. Anat.,* **35**, 153.

Copeman, S. M. and Winston, W. B. (1889) *J. Physiol, (Lond).,* **10**, 213.

Demarcay, H. (1838) *Justus Liebigs Ann. Pharm.,* **27**, 270.

Fischer, H. and Orth, H. (1937) *Die Chemie des Pyrrols.,* **Vol. II,** Akademische Verlagsgesellschaft M. B. H., Leipzig.

Fischer, H. and Plieninger, H. (1942) *Naturwissenschaften,* **30**, 382.

Gamgee, A. (1893) *A Text-Book of the Physiological Chemistry of the Animal Body* Vol. II, p. 267, Macmillan and Co., London.

Graham, E. A., Cole, W. H. and Copher, G. H. (1925) *J. Amer. med. Ass.,* **84**, 1175.

Harley, J. (1866) *Med.-chir. Trans.,* **49**, 79.

Heuermann, G. (1753) in *Der Arzney-Gelahrheit Doktors Physiologie,* Part 3, p. 786, Friedrich Christian Pelt., Copenhagen and Leipzig.

Hoppe-Seyler, F. (1893) *Handbuch ber Physiologisch-und-Pathologisch-Chemischen Analyse für Aerzte und Studivende,* 6th ed., p. 226, Aügust Hirschwald, Berlin.

Mosler, F. (1858) *Virchows Arch. path. Anat.,* **13**, 29.

Redtenbacher, J. (1846) *Justus Liebigs Ann. Chem.,* **57**, 170.

Rosenthal, S. M. and White, E. C. (1925) *J. Amer. Med. Ass.,* **84**, 1112.

Schäfer, E. A. (1898) *Textbook of Physiology,* Vol. 1 p. 444, Young, J. Pentland, Edinburgh and London.

Schwann, T. (1844) *Arch. Anat. Phys.,* p. 127.

Smith, R. L. (1966) *Progress in Drug Research* **9**, 299.

Smith, R. L. and Williams, R. T. (1970) *Metabolic Conjugation and Metabolic Hydrolysis* Vol. 1, p. 1, Ed. W. H. Fishman, Academic Press, New York and London.

Städeler, G. (1864) *Justus Liebigs Ann. Chem.,* **132**, 323.

Strecher, A. (1848a) *Justus Liebigs Ann. Chem.,* **65**, 1.

Strecher, A. (1848b) *Justus Liebigs Ann. Chem.,* **67**, 1.

Thenard, L. J. (1807) *Mémoires de Physique et de Chimie, de la Societe d'Arcueil,* Vol. 1, p. 23.

Wertheimer, E. (1893) *Arch. Physiol.,* Series 5, **5**, 122.

Wieland, H. and Weil, F. J. (1912) *Hoppe-Seyler's Z. physiol. Chem.,* **80**, 287.

Wieland, H. and Dane, E. (1932a) *Hoppe-Seyler's Z. physiol. Chem.,* **210**, 268.

Wieland, H. and Dane, E. (1932b) *Hoppe-Seyler's Z. physiol. Chem.,* **212**, 41.

Wieland, H. and Dane, E. (1933) *Hoppe-Seyler's Z. physiol. Chem.,* **216**, 91.

Wieland, H. (1934) *Ber.* **67**, A27.

Williams, R. T. (1947) *Detoxication Mechanisms* Chapman and Hall, London.

Yeo, G. F. and Herroun, E. F. (1884) *J. Physiol.* (Lond.), **5**, 116.

CHAPTER TWO

Anatomy and Physiology of the Liver and Bile Production

The liver is the largest gland in the body, weighing about 1500 g in adult humans. It functions both as an exocrine gland, secreting bile through a system of ducts into the duodenum and as an endocrine gland, synthesizing many substances which are released directly into the blood stream.

The liver receives venous blood from the intestinal tract via the *portal vein* and a smaller volume of arterial blood via the *hepatic artery*. The organ is drained by the *hepatic veins* which run into the inferior *vena cava* near the heart. The liver is thus interposed between the intestinal tract and the general circulation. It receives in the portal blood most of the materials absorbed from the intestinal tract and therefore orally ingested substances such as drugs and other foreign compounds must first go through the liver on their 'first pass' before they get into the systemic circulation. Compounds in the general circulation will, of course, be presented to the liver via the hepatic artery.

Structurally, the liver is composed of epithelial cells arranged in plates or laminae that are interconnected to form a continuous three-dimensional lattice. The laminae are disposed radially with respect to terminal branches of the hepatic veins which are located in the centres of prismatic units of liver parenchyma that constitute the *liver lobules*. The radially disposed plates of liver cells are exposed on both sides to the blood flowing in a parallel system of blood channels called the *hepatic sinusoids*. The liver lobules are typically hexagonal, each corner of the polygon being occupied by a *portal canal*. This consists of a branch of the portal vein and one of the hepatic artery together with a bile ductule enclosed in a common investment of connective tissue. Blood enters the blood sinusoids (which are interconnecting) from small branches of the hepatic artery and portal vein. It flows through the lobule

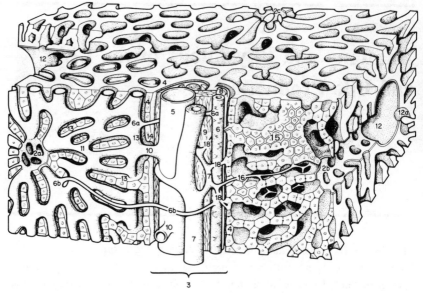

Fig. 1.
Synopsis of the structure of the normal human liver.
1, Lacuna; 2a,b,c, central veins; 3, portal canal; 4, limiting plate; 5, portal vein; 6, hepatic artery, 6a, arterial capillary emptying into paraportal sinusoid, 6b, arterial capillary emptying into intralobular sinusoid; 7, bile ducts; 8, lymph vessel; 9, periportal connective tissue; 10, inlet venules. 11, sinusoids; 12, sub-lobular vein, 12a, lacuna connecting with sub-lobular space; 13, perisinusoidal space of Disse; 14, periportal space of Mall; 15, bile canaliculi within liver plates. 16, intralobular cholangiole; 18, tributary of bile duct 7. (After Hans Elias, *Functional Morphology of the Liver*, G. D. Searle & Co.)

centripetally and is collected in the central vein. In the larger portal canals, fine branches of both the portal vein and the hepatic artery supply an elaborate capillary network to branches of the bile duct – the *peribiliary plexus*. From this network connecting venules re-enter the portal vein. It is thought that the main function of the hepatic artery is in relation to the peribiliary plexus.

The hepatic sinusoids are larger than the capillaries and are more irregular in shape. The lining of the sinusoids consists of a thin layer of cells that are unlike typical capillary endothelial cells since they are markedly phagocytic. There may be two types of cells in the endothelium. One type is an *endothelial cell* and the other a fixed macrophage, the *stellate cell of Kupfer*. The latter frequently contain granules of pigment and they are able to phagocytose particulate materials such as carbon particles of India ink injected into the circulation. The sinusoid epithelium has openings in it that permit the passage of blood plasma but not red cells to pass freely through to the underlying parenchymal cells. The sinusoid lining is therefore presumably freely permeated by drugs and their metabolites. Between the sinusoid wall and the underlying parenchymal cells there is a perivascular space called the space of Disse. Microvilli from the parenchymal cells project into the space and make contact with the sinusoid lining.

The bile canaliculi are minute canals that run between liver cells throughout the parenchyma. Generally, a single canaliculus runs between each adjacent pair of cells. In a plate of liver cells the bile canaliculi form a network of hexagonal meshes with a single cell in each mesh. The canaliculi branch to form a three-dimensional net with polyhedral meshes. The meshes

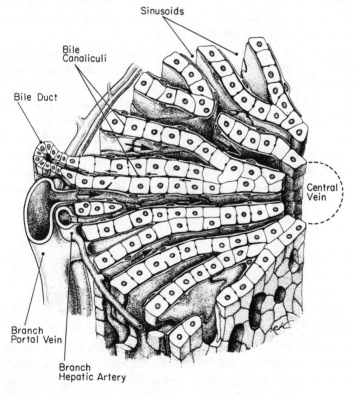

Fig. 2.
Relationship of liver cell plates and sinusoids to blood and bile flow. (Redrawn and modified from Ham, Textbook of Histology. Philadelphia, J. B. Lippincott Co.)

run together to form a continuous network throughout the entire parenchyma. Electron microscopy has shown that the lumen of the bile canaliculus
is merely an expansion of the intercellular space and that its wall is a local
specialization of the surfaces of adjoining hepatic cells. The part of the cell
membrane making up the wall of the canaliculus bears short microvilli which
project into the lumen. High concentrations of adenosine triphosphatase are
associated with the membrane.

The bile canaliculi vary in diameter, being distended during active
secretion and more or less in a collapsed state with decreasing activity. They
eventually drain into the very finest terminal branches of the bile duct which
are called *cholangioles*. The canaliculi communicate with the interlobular bile
ducts by the so-called canals of Hering. Closer to the porta, the lumina of the
ducts gradually become larger. At the transverse fossa of the liver, the main
ducts from the different lobes of the liver fuse to form the *hepatic duct*,
which after receiving the *cystic duct,* continues from the gall-bladder to the
duodenum as the *common bile duct.*

The *gall-bladder* is a pear-shaped organ closely attached to the posterior
surface of the liver. It consists of a blindly ending fundus, a body, and a neck
which passes into the cystic duct. In an adult man it measures about
10 x 4 cm and in most animals it has a capacity of 1−2 ml per kg body wt.
The gall-bladder serves as a reservoir for bile which is probably continuously
secreted by the liver. Ingestion of a meal causes contraction of the
gall-bladder musculature thereby expelling the bile into the duodenum. The
gall-bladder is able to concentrate bile by the absorption of water and organic
ions. In some species e.g. the rat, whale and deer the gall-bladder is absent.

COMPOSITION OF BILE

The composition of both hepatic and gall-bladder bile is very variable. The
data given in Table 1 which summarizes the chemical composition of human
bile is taken from Dittmer (1961) who quotes values found by several
investigators. The average water content in liver bile is 97 to 98% and of the
remaining 2 to 3% of solids, almost half consists of the bile salts. The latter
consist mainly of the glycine and taurine conjugates of cholic and
chenodeoxycholic acid. In gall-bladder bile the water content is about 86%,
the remainder being solid material. This difference in composition between
hepatic and gall-bladder bile is due to the concentrating activity of the latter
organ.

The main inorganic anions of bile are bicarbonate and chloride ions, the
concentration of these being much higher in hepatic bile than in gall-bladder

bile. The principal inorganic cations are sodium, potassium and calcium, while small amounts of iron and copper are also present. In general the levels of electrolytes found in hepatic bile are similar or somewhat less than those of the plasma.

The levels of the bile pigment, bilirubin, which is present mainly in the form of its diglucuronic acid conjugate, are about 20–200 mg % in hepatic bile and about 1000 mg % in gall-bladder bile. Bile contains substantial amounts of lipids including cholesterol, fatty acids and lecithin; their concentrations in gall-bladder bile being several times those of hepatic bile. The concentration of cholesterol is well in excess of its solubility in aqueous systems and it is maintained in solution by the solubilizing effect of the bile salts and lecithin (see Hofmann and Small, 1967). Besides these, small amounts of urea, uric acid, creatinine and amino acids occur in bile, the levels being similar to those of the plasma. Also present are traces of proteins including albumin, various γ-globulins and glycoproteins. Whether or not these arise in bile from the parenchymal cells by ductular secretion, or from the gall-bladder, is not known. Small amounts of various enzymes including α-amylase, β-glucuronidase, uricase and alkaline phosphatase can also occur in bile. Finally it should be mentioned that bile contains numerous metabolites arising from the metabolism of steroid and thyroid hormones, porphyrins and vitamins such as vitamins A and D and cyanocobalamin.

There occur marked species variations in bile composition as well as in its rate of formation (p. 89). Thus, there are marked species variations in the nature of the bile salts present in bile. Species differences occur both in the nature of the primary bile acids and in the nature of the conjugating group. As an example of the latter, the rabbit and domestic pig excrete bile acids conjugated with glycine whereas humans and the rat utilize both glycine and taurine for bile acid conjugation (see Haslewood, 1962; Weiner and Lack 1968). Species variations also occur in the lipid content of bile. The bile cholesterol levels, for example, are much lower in the case of both the rat and dog (8–18 mg%) than in the case of human bile (120 mg%)

FORMATION OF BILE

The processes involved in the formation of bile are obscure. It has been proposed that the primary event in bile formation is the active transport of bile acid anions from parenchymal cells into the bile canaliculi (Sperber, 1959). These substances then exert an osmotic effect whereby water and other solutes are 'dragged' into the bile canaliculi. Support for this view comes from the fact that bile salts are choleretics i.e. stimulate bile flow.

Similarly, many acidic compounds or substances giving rise to acidic metabolites, that are highly excreted in bile, also increase the rate of bile formation. In addition to this so called 'bile salt dependent fraction' of the bile flow there may also be an 'inorganic electrolyte dependent fraction' (Wheeler and Ramos, 1960; Sperber 1963). This is because bile flow can be markedly enhanced in dogs given an infusion of the hormone secretin when the bile salt excretion is kept constant. The bile produced by secretin stimulation is rich in bicarbonate and it has been suggested that the secretion of this ion may also be a factor for bringing about bile flow.

The sodium and potassium concentrations of bile are similar to those of the plasma and the ions undergo rapid equilibration between the two fluids.

Table 1
Chemical composition of human bile

	Hepatic bile	Gallbladder bile
General composition (g/100 ml)		
Dry matter	2.3–3.3	18
Inorganic matter	0.2–0.9	0.5–1.1
Bile salts	0.6–1.4	11.5
Total solids	1.0–4.0	4.7–16.5
Water	97.5	85.9
Electrolytes (milliequivalents/l)		
Bicarbonate	40	8–12
Chloride	75–110	15–30
Calcium	2.0–4.5	5–7
Potassium	2.6–12	–
Sodium	131–164	–
Magnesium	1.5	–
Iron (as Fe^{++})	2.4	0.01–0 6
Organic substances (mg %)		
Protein (total	273	315–539
Bilirubin	20–200	1000
Urea	23.6	20–45
Nitrogen		
Total N	67–92	490
Amino acid N	5.4	6.0–21.6
Cholesterol	120	630
Fatty acids	110	970
Lecithin	100–575	3500

(From Dittmer, 1961)

This equilibration could take place across the bile duct epithelium or through the spaces between parenchymal cells or at the level of the peribiliary plexus. Also, the levels of urea, uric acid and creatinine in plasma and hepatic bile are similar suggesting that these may pass into bile by equilibration processes.

REFERENCES

Dittmer, D. S. (1961) Editor, *Blood and Other Body Fluids*, Federation of American Societies for Experimental Biology, Washington, D.C.

Haslewood, G. A. D. (1962) *Comparative Biochemistry*, Vol. 3, p. 205, edited by M. Florkin and H. S. Mason, Academic Press, New York and London.

Hofmann, A. F. and Small, D. M. (1967) *Ann. Rev. Med.,* **18**, 333.

Sperber, I. (1959) *Pharmacol. Rev.,* **11**, 109.

Sperber, I. (1963) Proceedings of the First International Pharmacological Meeting August 22–25, 1961 Vol. 4, p. 137, *Drugs and Membranes*, edited by C. A. M. Hogben, Pergamon Press, Oxford.

Wheeler, H. O. and Ramos, O. L. (1960) *J. clin. Invest.,* **39**, 161.

Weiner, I. M. and Lack, L. (1968) *Handbook of Physiology*, Section 6 Alimentary Canal, Vol. 3, p. 1439, American Physiological Society, Washington D.C.

CHAPTER THREE

Factors Affecting Biliary Excretion

The extent of biliary excretion of a compound is influenced by a number of factors which may conveniently be considered to be of two types, namely, physico-chemical or biological. The former are the physico-chemical characteristics of the compound such as molecular weight, polarity and structural features. The influences of these factors are considered in this chapter. Biological factors include species, sex and genetic factors, the influence of protein binding, renal excretion and metabolism on biliary excretion, as well as the nature of the hepatic excretion process itself. The roles of these factors are discussed in later chapters.

PHYSICO-CHEMICAL FACTORS IN BILIARY EXCRETION

Molecular weight

The idea that molecular weight influences the extent of biliary excretion of a compound is implicit in much of the older literature. Several early studies suggested that fat-soluble substances of relatively high molecular weight were eliminated predominantly via the bile rather than in the urine (for references see Sobotka, 1939). Later the idea was stated more cogently both by Brauer (1959) and Sperber (1963) who pointed out that the molecular weight of those organic carboxylic acids which are highly excreted in bile is usually in the region of 300–400.

Evidence for a molecular weight factor in biliary excretion

Evidence in support of the view that molecular weight has an important bearing on biliary excretion comes from two sources. First, from a consideration of the molecular weights of compounds of both endogenous and exogenous origin which are excreted in the bile. Secondly, from systematic studies on the relationship between molecular weight and the extent of biliary excretion of various groups of chemicals.

Table 2 shows examples of a number of compounds which are known to be highly excreted (30–100% of dose) in the bile, together with their molecular weights. Endogenous metabolites such as the bile salts and the glucuronide conjugates of steroid hormones. bilirubin and thyroxine, which are highly excreted in bile, tend to have relatively high molecular weights (approx. 500–1000). Conversely, simpler intermediary metabolites of low molecular weight such as urea, uric acid, sugars and amino acids are not extensively eliminated in the bile (Dittmer, 1961). Similarly, a consideration of the molecular weights of the excretion forms of various foreign compounds excreted in the bile suggests that these are usually at least 300–400 and upwards. Table 2 shows 28 examples of exogenous compounds which are extensively excreted in the bile. Most of these appear in the bile in the form of polar conjugates such as glucuronides and sulphates, and it is the molecular weights of these which have to be considered. It can be seen that the molecular weights of the excretion forms, ranges from 346 in the case of 4-hydroxybiphenylglucuronide to 1020 for the sulphobromophthalein glutathione conjugate. Some of the compounds e.g. succinylsulphathiazole, dichloromethotrexate, oubain and amaranth are excreted in the bile unchanged and their molecular weights also fall into this range. It should be emphasized that most of the examples given in Table 2 are from studies in the rat. Marked species variations occur in the extent of biliary excretion of foreign compounds and their metabolites, particularly those having molecular weights in the range of about 300–500.

The importance of the molecular weight factor in biliary excretion is also indicated by the fact that the hepatic elimination of foreign organic compounds and their metabolites of molecular weight less than about 300 is low. These substances are in the main excreted by the kidneys and, if volatile or if they give rise to volatile metabolites, are also excreted in the expired air. Thus, the biliary excretion of the few low molecular weight aliphatic derivatives that have been studied, namely, chloroform, dimethylsulphoxide, and methyl methanesulphonate is of a low order. Similarly, the biliary excretion of simple mono- and di-substituted benzene derivatives is also small (Abou-El-Makarem et al, 1967). These compounds and their metabolites are eliminated mainly by the kidneys. Table 3 summarizes the findings of Abou-El-Makarem et al, (1967) and shows that the biliary excretion of benzene and 17 of its simple low molecular weight derivatives and their metabolites accounts for only 1–8% of the dose in the rat.

Table 2

Molecular weight and biliary excretion

Compound	Mol. wt.	Main form excreted in bile	Mol. wt.
Endogenous substances			
Retinoic acid	300	Retinoylglucuronide	476
Pregnane-3,20-diol	321	Pregnane-3,20-diol glucuronide	497
Oestriol	288	Oestriol 3-sulphate 16-glucuronide	544
Cholic acid	409	Glycocholate	466
Bilirubin	585	Bilirubin diglucuronide	937
Thyroxine	777	Thyroxine glucuronide	953
Exogenous substances			
4-hydroxybiphenyl	170	4-hydroxybiphenylglucuronide	346
Isoprenaline	211	3-methoxyisoprenaline glucuronide	387
Diphenylacetic acid	212	Diphenacetylglucuronide	388
Glutethimide	217	Hydroxyglutethimide glucuronide	409
Propanolol	259	Propanolol glucuronide	435
Stilboestrol	268	Stilboestrol glucuronide	445
Dextromethorphan	271	3-hydroxy-N-methylmorphinan glucuronide	433
Imipramine	280	2-hydroxyimipramine glucuronide	472
Morphine	285	Morphine glucuronide	461
Sulphadimethoxine	310	Sulphadimethoxine N^1-glucuronide	486
Phenolphthalein	318	Phenolphthalein glucuronide	495
Chloramphenicol	323	Chloramphenicol 3-glucuronide	499
Ergometrine	325	12-hydroxyergometrine glucuronide	517
Succinylsulphathiazole	355	Unchanged	355
Indomethacin	358	Indomethacin ester glucuronide	534
Glycyrrhetic acid	471	Glycyrrhetic acid glucuronide	647
Dipyridamole	504	Dipyridamole glucuronide	680
Dichloromethotrexate	523	Unchanged	523
Iodopanoic acid	571	Iodopanoic acid glucuronide	747
Oubain	585	Unchanged	585
Amaranth	604	Unchanged	604
Bromophenol blue	670	Unchanged	670
Bromocresol green	698	Unchanged	698
Rifamycin SV	698	Unchanged	698
Indocyanine green	775	Unchanged	775
Bromosulphthalein	794	Sulphobromophthalein glutathione conjugate	1020
Lanatoside A	969	Unchanged	969

Evidence in support for a molecular size hypothesis can also be drawn from the results of studies which show that if simple aromatic compounds are substituted so as to increase their molecular size then their biliary excretion also increases. Thus, the introduction of heavy atoms (e.g. halogen, particularly iodine), or large groups such as cyclic (aromatic, cycloalkyl and heterocyclic) and aliphatic groups into simple aromatic structures can enchance their hepatic elimination. There is a low specificity in this effect in the sense that the introduction of markedly different atoms or groupings into molecules can enhance biliary excretion.

Table 3
Biliary excretion in the rat of some simple mono- and di-substituted benzene derivatives of low molecular weight

Compounds were injected intraperitoneally as solutions; dose level varied from 0.13—0.77 mmol per kg body wt.

(*a*) Monosubstituted benzenes

Compound	R	Mol. wt.	% dose in bile in 24 h
Benzene	H	78	1
Toluene	CH_3	92	2
Aniline	NH_2	93	6
Phenol	OH	94	5
Phenylthiourea	$NHCSNH_2$	152	1

(*b*) *Ortho*-disubstituted benzenes

Compound	R^1	R^2	Mol. wt.	% dose in bile in 24 h
2-aminophenol	NH_2	OH	109	7
2-aminobenzoic acid	NH_2	COOH	137	3
Salicylic acid	OH	COOH	138	2
Orthanilic acid	NH_2	SO_2OH	173	0

Table 3   (*continued*)

(*c*) *Para*-disubstituted benzenes R^1—⟨benzene ring⟩—R^2

Compound	R^1	R^2	Mol. wt.	% dose in bile in 24 h
4-aminophenol	NH_2	OH	109	8
Quinol	OH	OH	110	7
4-aminobenzoic acid	NH_2	COOH	137	6
4-nitrobenzoic acid	NO_2	COOH	167	0
Sulphanilamide	NH_2	SO_2NH_2	172	4
Sulphanilic acid	NH_2	SO_2OH	173	1
Sulphacetamide	NH_2	$SO_2NHCOCH_3$	214	1
Sulphaguanidine	NH_2	$SO_2NHC(=NH)NH_2$	214	1
4-aminophenylglucuronide	NH_2	$C_6H_9O_7$	285	1

(Data from Abou-El-Makarem *et al.*, 1967)

Nevertheless, it appears that certain groups may be more effective than others in certain situations in promoting biliary excretion (see structural factors). The effect on biliary excretion of increase of molecular weight by substitution with various groups, can be illustrated by considering several examples.

(*a*) The iodination of 4-aminohippuric acid (mol. wt. 194) to give the 3-iodo derivative (mol. wt. 320) increases the biliary excretion from 2 to 25%. Similarly, the introduction of two iodine atoms into anthranilic acid (mol. wt. 137) to give 3,5-diiodoanthranilic acid (mol. wt. 389) enhances the biliary excretion of this acid in the rat from 5 to 35% of the dose (Williams, *et al.*, 1965).

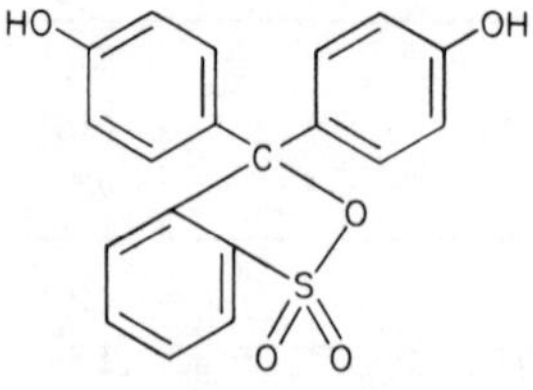

Phenolsulphonphthalein

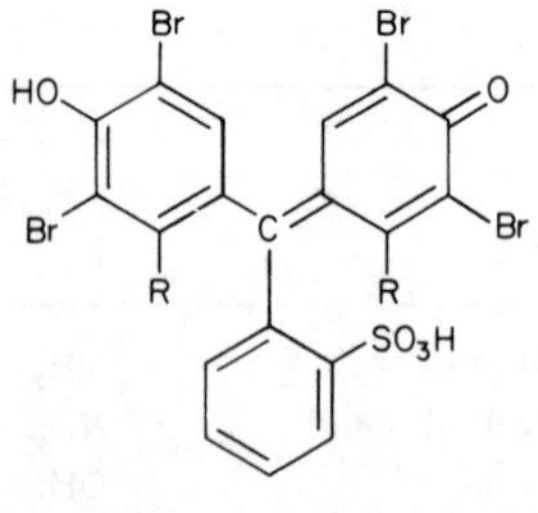

Bromophenol blue R=H
Bromocresol green R=CH_3

The influence of halogenation on biliary excretion is also seen with the halogenated phenolsulphonphthaleins. Phenolsulphonphthalein (mol. wt. 354) is relatively poorly excreted (3% of dose) in dog bile and is rapidly eliminated by the kidneys. Its brominated derivatives, bromophenol blue (mol. wt. 670) and bromocresol green (mol. wt. 698), both having considerably higher molecular weights are, however, excreted predominantly in the bile (Kim and Hong, 1962).

(b) Introduction of the phenyl group into a simple benzene derivative can enhance the biliary excretion. Thus, phenol is poorly excreted in bile; in the rat less than 1% of the dose is excreted by this route in the form of its glucuronide and sulphate conjugates. By contrast both 4-hydroxybiphenyl and 4,4′-dihydroxybiphenyl which have in their structures an additional phenyl and hydroxyphenyl group respectively, are both highly excreted in rat bile as their glucuronide conjugates having molecular weights of 346 and 362 respectively.

	Phenol	4-hydroxybiphenyl	4,4′-dihydroxybiphenyl
Mol. wt.	94	170	186
% in bile	1	37	65

(c) Phenylsulphate is poorly excreted (<1% of dose) in rat bile. The para-substitution of phenylsulphate with a cyclohexyl group gives cyclohexylphenyl-4-sulphate which is highly excreted (70% of dose) in rat bile as a glucuronide conjugate (Hearse et al., 1969). This illustrates the effect upon the biliary excretion of a simple compound, of the introduction of a cyclohexyl group into the structure.

	Phenylsulphate	Cyclohexylphenyl-4-sulphate
Mol. wt.	174	256
% in bile	1	70

(d) The introduction of a heterocyclic group into the structure of a simple aromatic compound may also enhance biliary excretion. This can be

Table 4

Biliary excretion of some sulphanilamide derivatives in the rat

CH_2CONH—⟨ ⟩—SO_2NHR
CH_2COOH

Compound	R	Mol. wt.	% dose in bile
Succinylsulphanilamide	H	272	5
Succinylsulphacetamide	$COCH_3$	314	4
Succinylsulphathiazole	[thiazole ring]	355	50

⟨ ⟩CONH—⟨ ⟩—SO_2NHR
COOH

Compound	R	Mol. wt.	% dose in bile
Phthalylsulphanilamide	H	319	7
Phthalylsulphacetamide	$COCH_3$	363	2
Phthalylsulphathiazole	[thiazole ring]	403	20

Data from Hirom *et al.*, (1972a)

illustrated by considering the effect of the introduction of a thiazole group on the hepatic elimination of some simple sulphanilamide derivatives (Table 4).

When R = H or $COCH_3$, biliary excretion is at a low level (2—7% of dose) but this increases markedly when R is a 2-thiazole group as in the case of both succinyl- and phthalyl-sulphathiazole.

Molecular weight threshold for biliary excretion

It appears that for extensive biliary excretion to occur there is a requirement for a minimum threshold molecular weight below which little (i.e. not more than 5—10% of the dose) hepatic elimination occurs. There is some latitude in the choice of the molecular weight threshold which can also vary markedly with species. Millburn *et al.*, (1967) have proposed from studies on the biliary excretion of diverse aromatic compounds which largely appear in the bile as anions, that for the rat, the threshold molecular weight is about 325 ± 50. This is illustrated in Fig. 3 which shows the extent of biliary excretion of over seventy aromatic compounds in relation to their molecular weight. It must be stressed that the molecular weight factor used here is that of the main form excreted in the bile and is not necessarily that of the compound given unless the latter is excreted in the bile unchanged. It can be seen that when the molecular weight of the compounds reach about 300 there is a tendency for biliary excretion to become significant and above about 400 biliary elimination becomes pronounced.

There is probably an upper limit to the molecular size of compounds which can be excreted in the bile but this remains to be determined. Brauer (1959) has pointed out that macromolecules such as inulin, a polysaccharide of molecular weight about 5000, and proteins are only excreted in trace amounts in bile. Also certain azo dyes are not extensively excreted in bile despite their apparently suitable high molecular weights and polar character. Thus the bisazo dye congo red (mol. wt. 697) is poorly excreted in the bile of the rabbit and cat (Richardson, 1939). The apparently anomalous low biliary excretion of this substance may be due to its existence in solution as an aggregate of apparent molecular weight of about 8000. Similarly, the two polar dyes Evans Blue and its isomer Trypan Blue (mol. wt. 871) are poorly excreted in the bile and this may also be a consequence of their forming in solution high molecular weight aggregates.

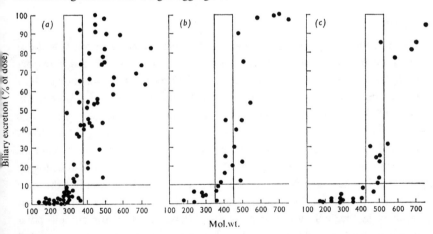

Fig. 3.
Threshold molecular weight for appreciable biliary excretion (>10% of dose) in the female rat, guinea pig and rabbit.
The extent of biliary excretion of 75 compounds (rat), 26 compounds (guinea pig) and 25 compounds (rabbit) is plotted against molecular weight. The vertical boxes show the regions of the molecular-weight thresholds, which are 325 ± 50 for the rat (a), 400 ± 50 for the guinea pig (b) and 475 ± 50 for the rabbit (c). (Reproduced with permission from *Biochem. J.*, **129**, (1972)).

There occur important species variations as regards the threshold molecular weight for biliary excretion (see Fig. 3). Thus, for the guinea pig and the rabbit the threshold molecular weight values for the biliary excretion of anions are 400 ± 50 and 475 ± 50 respectively (Aziz *et al.*, 1971; Hirom *et al.*, 1972*b*). As yet no attempt has been made to define these values for other species though it appears probable that the dog resembles the rat in this respect and the rhesus monkey and humans more closely resemble the rabbit (see Chapter 6).

It should also be stressed that the foregoing applies to the biliary excretion of anions which in fact is the most common form in which foreign compounds and endogenous metabolites appear in the bile. Some quaternary ammonium compounds which exist at physiological pH as cations, are extensively excreted in the bile and it seems that for these compounds, the minimum molecular weight requirements for biliary excretion differ from those for anions (Hughes *et al.*, 1972). Furthermore, the species variations observed in the molecular weight factor for biliary excretion of anions does not appear to be the same for cations. This difference between anions and cations is possibly a reflection that there is some difference in their mechanism of biliary excretion.

Polarity

The presence of a strongly polar group in a molecule appears to be a requirement for extensive biliary excretion to occur. It is difficult in respect to biliary excretion to give any exact definition to the term 'polar'. It is usually, but not always synonymous with the presence of a potentially ionizable group such as a carboxylic or sulphonic acid or sulphate group, or a basic function such as the quaternary ammonium group. Such groups allow a molecule to exist at physiological pH as water-soluble anions or cations. Occasionally, as in the case of the cardiac glycosides which can also be highly excreted in bile, there is no charged anionic or cationic centre, but this may be compensated for by the presence of one or more water-soluble sugar residues in the molecule. For extensive biliary excretion the anionic polar group probably should have a pK_a of about 5 or less since it appears that weaker acids are probably not excreted in the bile in quantity. The majority of compounds eliminated in the bile are usually in the form of polar conjugates such as glucuronides and glycine derivatives which typically show a pK_a of 3–4, and they are at physiological pH more than 99.9% ionized. Substances of even lower pK_a can however be excreted in bile as occurs in the case of cromoglycate (pK_a 1.9) and phenolphthalein disulphate which is a very strong electrolyte.

Quaternary ammonium compounds are strong bases and are also largely ionized at pH 7.4. The quaternary ammonium function may in some cases be replaced by the more weakly basic tertiary amine structure. (Nayak and Schanker, 1969).

Polar groups important in biliary excretion

Group	Structure of ion
Carboxyl	$\overset{\text{O}}{\underset{\ }{\overset{\|}{-}}}\text{C-O}^-$
Sulphate	$-OSO_2-O^-$
Sulphonate	$-SO_2O^-$
Quaternary ammonium	$-N^+(R)_3$
Glycoside	e.g. $-O-(C_6H_{11}O_4)$

Evidence for the necessity of a polar group for biliary excretion

Proof that the presence of a polar group in a compound is a prerequisite for extensive biliary excretion to occur is difficult to obtain. Evidence in support of this view can however be drawn from a number of different sources.

(1) Experience has shown that the majority of compounds known to be extensively excreted in the bile appear in the latter as polar derivatives particularly metabolic conjugates such as glucuronides. A substance may already possess a polar group in its molecule, e.g. a carboxylic acid group, and it may appear in the bile unchanged.

(2) Compounds of relatively high molecular weight but not having a strongly polar group in its structure are not excreted in the bile in quantity. Thus, the non-polar substance dieldrin (mol. wt. 381) is very lipid soluble and is only slowly eliminated in the bile; only 1% appears in the bile of the rat in 24 h (Williams *et al.*, 1965). This slow biliary excretion is a reflection of the difficulty with which its metabolic conversion to polar metabolites, suitable for biliary excretion is effected.

Dieldrin

(3) As previously mentioned many compounds appear in the bile as polar conjugates and this may be crucial for their biliary excretion. Suppression of

the conversion of a compound to its polar metabolic conjugate may be accompanied by reduced biliary excretion. This can be done in two ways, namely chemical alteration of the molecule to prevent conjugation or by the use of an enzyme inhibitor, to suppress the metabolic conjugation. As an example of the first, Jirsa *et al.*, (1968) found that methylation of the carboxyl groups of bilirubin markedly reduces its biliary excretion in rats. In this instance esterification blocks the two carboxyl sites involved in the metabolic transformation of bilirubin to its polar diglucuronide conjugate, a conversion which appears to be necessary for its elimination by the liver. Suppression of the metabolic conjugation of a compound by an enzyme inhibitor can reduce its excretion in bile. Thus, the biliary excretion of stilboestrol and phenolphthalein, both of which are normally extensively excreted in rat bile as their respective glucuronides is depressed by the inhibitor SKF 525A due to inhibition of their glucuronide conjugation (Levine *et al.*, 1970).

(4) Further evidence comes indirectly from studies on species variations in the biliary excretion of foreign compounds. In the cat, both phenolphthalein and stilboestrol glucuronide are well excreted in bile if the preformed conjugates are given, but the aglycones are, by comparison, less well excreted in bile. This may be related to the well-known defective ability of the cat to form glucuronides with certain compounds.

(5) The results of some systematic studies on the biliary excretion in the rat of some sulphathiazole derivatives, particularly N^4-substituted-ω-carboxy-acylsulphathiazoles also indicate the importance of the polar carboxyl group for extensive biliary excretion (Hirom *et al.*, 1972*a*). Some of these findings are summarized in Table 5. It can be seen that sulphathiazole and its

Table 5
Biliary excretion in the rat of some sulphathiazole derivatives

Compound	R	Mol. wt.	% dose in bile
Sulphathiazole	H	255	4
N^4-Acetylsulphathiazole	CH_3CO-	297	2
Oxalylsulphathiazole	$HOOC.CO-$	327	21
Malonylsulphathiazole	$HOOC.CH_2CO-$	341	15
Succinylsulphathiazole	$HOOC(CH_2)_2CO-$	355	54
Glutarylsulphathiazole	$HOOC(CH_2)_3CO-$	369	74

N^4-acetyl conjugate are both poorly excreted in rat bile. Replacement of the acetyl group by various ω-carboxyacyl groups is accompanied by a marked increase in biliary excretion. This can be attributed to the introduction of the polar carboxyl group since the changes in molecular weight are relatively small.

From the point of view of polarity and biliary excretion, two types of compounds may be distinguished: (a) polar substances that are excreted in the bile unchanged and (b) compounds which acquire a polar group by metabolic transformation before undergoing elimination in the bile.

(a) Polar substances excreted in the bile unchanged.   Substances may be eliminated unchanged in the bile in quantity providing that they satisfy the appropriate requirements of molecular weight and polarity *per se*. Examples of such compounds are succinylsulphathiazole and cromoglycate which have one and two polar carboxyl groups respectively in their structures while neoprontosil and amaranth have two and three polar sulphonic acid groups respectively in their molecular structures.

Examples of polar compounds excreted in bile unchanged

Compound	Mol. wt.	Polar group(s) in molecule
Succinylsulphathiazole	355	—COOH
Cromoglycate	468	—COOH (2)
Amaranth	539	—SO₂OH (3)

Examples of polar compounds excreted in bile unchanged   (continued)

Compound	Mol. wt.	Polar group(s) in molecule
 Phenolphthalein disulphate	479	$-OSO_2OH$ (2)
 Tribenzylmethylammonium	302	R_4N^+
 Indocyanine green	775	$-SO_2OH$ (2) and R_4N^+

The compound tribenzylmethylammonium, which is excreted in quantity in bile unchanged, has in its structure the strongly polar quaternary ammonium group. Indocyanine green has in its structure two polar sulphonate groups and a quaternary ammonium group as well.

(b) Compounds excreted in bile after metabolic conversion to a polar conjugate.   The majority of foreign compounds are metabolized in the body

to polar conjugates and this conversion appears to be essential for their efficient excretion both by the kidneys and the liver. One, therefore commonly finds that compounds excreted in the bile appear mainly as polar conjugates with for example glucuronic acid, sulphate, or glutathione. Thus, morphine and phenolphthalein, both of which are extensively excreted in bile appear largely as conjugates with glucuronic acid while sulphobromophthalein is eliminated in the bile mainly conjugated with glutathione. The common polar groups introduced by metabolic conjugation and which are important in biliary excretion are shown in Table 6.

Table 6
Common polar groups introduced into molecules by metabolic conjugation

Group	Structure of anion	Examples
Glucuronide		Found in biliary metabolites of many compounds e.g. morphine and stilboestrol glucuronide
Sulphate	$-OSO_2O^-$	Thyroxine O-sulphate
Glycine	$-NHCH_2COO^-$	Glycocholate
Taurine	$-NHCH_2CH_2SO_2O^-$	Taurocholate
Glutathione		Sulphobromophthalein glutathione conjugate

From the point of view of the metabolic conversion of a compound to a polar conjugate two situations can be distinguished. In the first the compound may undergo a conjugation reaction directly providing it has within its molecular structure a centre at which such a reaction can occur. Thus, stilboestrol can undergo a direct glucuronide conjugation at one of the two hydroxyl groups of its molecular structure and the conjugate formed is excreted in the bile (Fischer *et al*., 1966).

Stilboestrol   Stilboestrol glucuronide

Frequently, however, a compound may undergo preliminary metabolic reactions such as oxidations, reductions or hydrolysis prior to conjugation. These seem to provide in the molecule a suitable centre, e.g. hydroxyl, carboxyl or amino group, at which a conjugation can occur. Biphenyl, for example is excreted in the bile of rats as the glucuronides of 4-hydroxy- and 4-4'-dihydroxy-biphenyl (Millburn *et al.*, 1967). In this case biphenyl undergoes initial oxidation to 4-hydroxy- and 4,4'-dihydroxy-biphenyl and these phenolic metabolites then undergo conjugation to form their respective glucuronides which are excreted in the bile.

Biphenyl

4-hydroxybiphenyl

4-hydroxybiphenylglucuronide

4,4'-dihydroxybiphenyl

4,4'-dihydroxybiphenylglucuronide

Of the known conjugation reactions the processes of glucuronide, sulphate, glycine, taurine and glutathione conjugation are of particular significance from the point of view of biliary excretion and of these by far the most important is glucuronide synthesis. This is because many drugs and other environmental chemicals as well as endogenous substances commonly appear in the bile as glucuronic acid conjugates. This is however probably not due to any special affinity of glucuronic acid conjugates to undergo excretion in the bile. Rather it probably reflects the restricted scope of other conjugations compared to glucuronide synthesis (Smith & Williams, 1966). Glucuronide formation is probably the most versatile of the conjugation mechanisms in terms of the variety of chemical groups which can accept glucuronic acid, the availability of the conjugating agent, and the numerous tissues which can effect glucuronide synthesis.

Structural factors

The previous discussion has stressed the importance of molecular weight and polarity in biliary excretion. Besides these there appears to be a third and, as yet, somewhat undefined structural factor which has also to be considered. Thus it has been found that, in certain situations, the introduction of a group or the change in relative position of certain groups in a molecule may alter the extent of biliary excretion out of all proportion to any effect that the change may have on molecular size or polarity. A number of examples may be quoted to illustrate this effect. Iga *et al*. (1970, 1971) found for a number of sulphonated dyes that the shift of a single SO_3^- group from one position to another in the molecule caused a 4- to 8-fold change in the extent of biliary excretion in rats. Similarly, a marked difference in the extent of hepatic elimination in rats of the azo dye Ponceau SX and its structural isomer Scarlet GN was observed by Ryan and Wright (1961). There also occurs a marked difference in the extent of biliary excretion in rats of the glucuronides of 4-hydroxybiphenyl and 4,4'-dihydroxybiphenyl; the hepatic elimination of the latter being the greater of the two and the conjugates differ from one another only in the presence in one of the phenolic hydroxyl group (Williams *et al*., 1965).

Hirom *et al*. (1972a) have studied the role of a structural factor in the biliary excretion of a number of sulphonamides in the rat in some detail. They have suggested that the structural factor might influence biliary excretion in one or more of three ways, namely, by changing lipid solubility, the shape of the molecule or the relative intramolecular relationship of the polar and non-polar parts of the molecule.

Table 7 shows that the partial or full saturation of the aromatic ring of phthalylsulphathiazole markedly enhances the biliary excretion. The molecular weights and relative lipid solubilities of these three compounds are essentially similar and Hirom *et al.* (1972a) have argued that the structural effect in this situation is related to the shape of the molecule — puckering of the aromatic ring by saturation favouring in some way hepatic excretion.

Also within an homologous series of N^4-ω-carboxyacylsulphathiazoles, differing from each other by a single methylene group $(-CH_2-)$, marked variations in the extent of biliary excretion were found to occur and this was attributed to a structural factor (Table 8). Thus, when $n = 0$ to 3, the extent of biliary excretion increases with chain length i.e. from about 15–20% when $n = 0$ or 1, to 74% where $n = 3$, but when $n = 4-8$ biliary excretion declines to about 40–50% of the dose. The molecular weights and lipid solubilities are of a similar order and the extent of biliary excretion seems to be influenced

Table 7

Structural factors in biliary excretion; excretion in rat bile of some sulphonamides

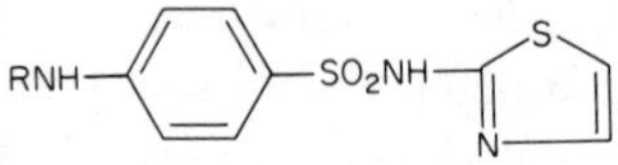

RNH—⟨phenyl⟩—SO_2NH—⟨thiazole⟩

Compound	R	Mol. wt.	% dose in bile
Phthalylsulphathiazole	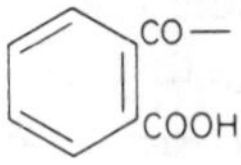 ⟨CO—, COOH⟩	403	19
1,2,3,6-tetrahydrophthalylsulphathiazole	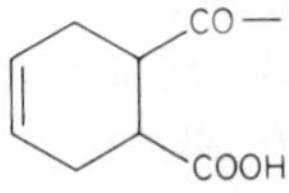 ⟨CO—, COOH⟩	407	54
Hexahydrophthalylsulphathiazole	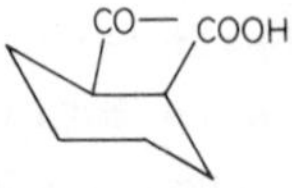 ⟨CO—, COOH⟩	409	66

Table 8

Structural factors in biliary excretion; excretion in rat bile of some N^4-ω-carboxyacylsulphathiazoles

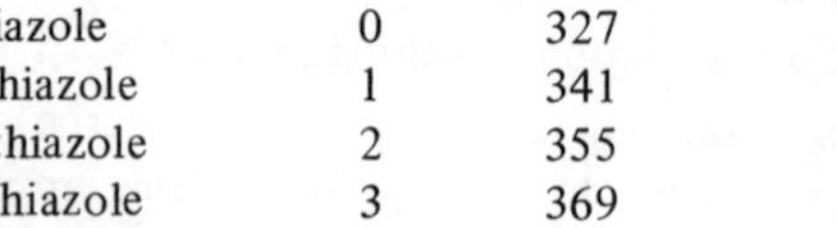

$HO_2C(CH_2)_nCONH$—⟨phenyl⟩—SO_2NH—⟨thiazole⟩

Compound	n	Mol. wt.	% dose in bile in 24 h*
Oxalylsulphathiazole	0	327	21
Malonylsulphathiazole	1	341	15
Succinylsulphathiazole	2	355	54
Glutarylsulphathiazole	3	369	74
Adipylsulphathiazole	4	383	42
Pimelylsulphathiazole	5	397	51
Suberylsulphathiazole	6	411	43
Azeleylsulphathiazole	7	425	41
Sebacylsulphathiazole	8	439	53

*All these sulphonamides are excreted unchanged in bile.

in some way with the number of methylene groups in the molecule. This may be due to the fact that the position of the polar carboxyl group relative to the non-polar part of the molecule will be influenced by the number of methylene groups in the side chain.

INTER-RELATIONSHIP OF MOLECULAR WEIGHT, POLARITY AND STRUCTURAL FACTORS IN BILIARY EXCRETION

That molecular weight, polarity and structural features have a bearing on biliary excretion is clear but their significance is obscure. One striking characteristic of many compounds extensively excreted in bile is their amphipathic character, i.e. they contain both polar and substantially non-polar groups in their molecular structures. In this sense they resemble the bile salts which structurally consist of a large relatively non-polar steroid moiety and a very polar side chain containing a glycine or taurine residue. It is possible that for a compound to undergo extensive biliary excretion a more or less critical balance between the polar and non-polar aspects of its structure is required. This may determine some ability to orientate at a membrane or to interact with a carrier molecule or to undergo aggregation. Substances that are highly polar or non-polar appear in general to be poorly excreted in bile. Thus, the lipophilic compound dieldrin is not excreted in rat bile as such nor are the strongly polar electrolytes such as hippuric acid or phenylsulphate. Although there is no simple relationship between lipid solubility and the extent of biliary excretion there is nevertheless a tendency for substances that undergo hepatic elimination to be more lipophilic in character than those that are not (Hirom et al., 1972a). This is probably a reflection of their greater molecular weight.

The point of view that ampholytic character may be important for biliary excretion is suggested by the findings of Michael (1968) on the metabolism and excretion in the rat of linear and branched-chain alkyl benzene sulphonates. The latter are excreted in bile partly unchanged and also as metabolites which retain considerable lipophilic character whereas, by contrast, the linear alkyl benzene sulphonates undergo extensive metabolic degradation to more polar metabolites of lower molecular weight which are eliminated in the urine.

REFERENCES

Abou-El–Makarem, M. M., Millburn, P., Smith, R. L. and Williams, R. T. (1967) Biochem. J., 105, 1269.

Aziz, F. T. A., Hirom, P. C., Millburn, P., Smith, R. L. and Williams, R. T. (1971) *Biochem. J.,* **125**, 25P.

Brauer, R. W. (1959) *J. Amer. med. Ass.,* **169**, 1462.

Dittmer, D. S. (1961) Editor, *Blood and Other Body Fluids,* p. 409, Federation of American Societies for Experimental Biology, Washington,· D.C.

Fischer, L. J., Millburn, P., Smith, R. L. and Williams, R. T. (1966) *Biochem. J.,* **100**, 69P.

Hearse, D. J., Powell, G. M., Olavesen, A. H. and Dodgson, K. S. (1969) *Biochem. Pharmacol.,* **18**, 181.

Hirom, P. C., Millburn, P., Smith, R. L. and Williams, R. T. (1972a) *Xenobiotica,* **2**, 205.

Hirom, P. C., Millburn, P., Smith, R. L. and Williams, R. T. (1972b) *Biochem. J.,* **129**, 1071.

Hughes, R. D., Millburn, P., Smith, R. L. and Williams, R. T. (1972) *Biochem. J.,* **128**, 144P.

Iga, T., Awazu, S., Hanano, M. and Nogami, H. (1970) *Chem. pharm. Bull.,* **18**, 2431.

Iga, T., Awazu, S. and Nogami, H. (1971) *Chem. pharm. Bull.,* **19**, 273.

Jirsa, M., Dickinson, J. P. and Lathe, G. H. (1968) *Nature (Lond.),* **220**, 1322.

Kim, J. H. and Hong, S. K. (1962) *Amer. J. Physiol.,* **202**, 174.

Levine, W. G., Millburn, P., Smith, R. L. and Williams, R. T. (1970) *Biochem. Pharmacol.,* **19**, 235.

Michael, W. R. (1968) *Toxicol. appl. Pharmacol.,* **12**, 473.

Millburn, P., Smith, R. L. and Williams, R. T. (1967) *Biochem. J.,* **105**, 1275.

Nayak, P. K. and Schanker, L. S. (1969) *Amer. J. Physiol.,* **217**, 1639.

Richardson, A. P. (1939) *Amer. J. med. Sci.,* **198**, 82.

Ryan, A. J. and Wright, S. E. (1961) *J. Pharm. Pharmacol.,* **13**, 492.

Smith, R. L. and Williams, R. T. (1966) *Glucuronic Acid Free and Combined,* p. 457, edited by G. J. Dutton, Academic Press, New York and London.

Sobotka, H. (1937) *Physiological Chemistry of the Bile,* Baillière, Tindall and Cox, London.

Sperber, I. (1963) In Proceedings of the First International Pharmacological Meeting August 22-25, 1961, Vol. 4, p. 137, *Drugs and Membranes,* edited by C. A. M. Hogben, Pergamon Press, Oxford.

Williams, R. T., Millburn, P. and Smith, R. L. (1965) *Ann. N. Y. Acad, Sci.,* **123**, 110.

CHAPTER FOUR

Metabolism and Biliary Excretion

Although many studies on the biliary excretion of foreign compounds have been made in the past, few were directed towards identifying the actual chemical form of the compound appearing in the bile. In retrospect this seems surprising in view of the knowledge from urinary excretion studies that the majority of foreign chemicals undergo metabolic transformations prior to excretion. It is now clear that the majority of compounds excreted in bile are eliminated in the form of transformation products and that these changes are usually crucial for their elimination by this route.

From the point of view of excretion in the bile, metabolic reactions, or at least some of them, are important for two reasons: (a) they may introduce a polar centre into the molecule – a factor of importance in biliary excretion and (b) they increase the molecular weight of the compound; this is also of importance as far as biliary excretion is concerned. This can be illustrated by considering the case of biphenyl which is converted metabolically to the glucuronic acid conjugates of 4-hydroxybiphenyl and 4,4'-dihydroxybiphenyl both of which are extensively excreted in the bile.

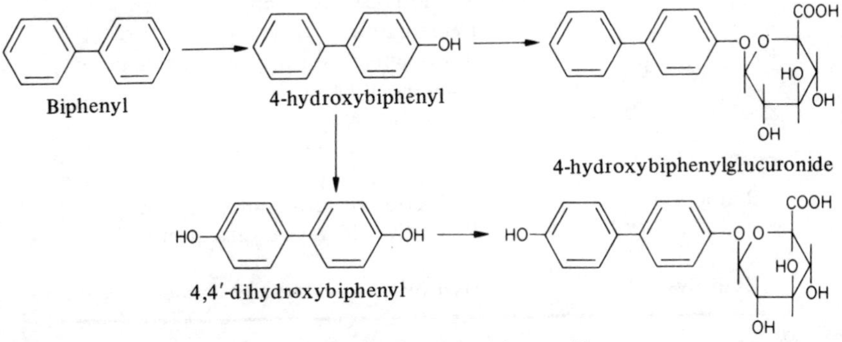

Biphenyl

4-hydroxybiphenyl

4-hydroxybiphenylglucuronide

4,4'-dihydroxybiphenyl

4,4'-dihydroxybiphenylglucuronide

The importance of metabolism in the biliary excretion of a compound is further illustrated by the fact that the biliary elimination of biphenyl is altered by factors which influence its rate of metabolism. Thus, acceleration of its rate of conversion to glucuronic acid conjugates by the use of the enzyme-inducing agent phenobarbitone speeds up its rate of excretion in the bile, while suppression of its metabolism using the enzyme inhibitor SKF 525A slows its rate of excretion (Levine *et al.*, 1970). Similarly, the biliary excretion of *N*-2-fluorenylacetamide is enhanced in rats treated with a microsomal enzyme inducer which accelerates the rate of metabolic conversion of the carcinogen (Levine, 1971). In this chapter an outline of the main pathways of metabolism is given particularly in relation to the excretion of drugs and foreign compounds in bile. There is a very large literature on drug metabolism and for more information the reader is referred to the classical text of Williams (1959). Other more recent sources of information are those of Parke (1968) and the edited works of Brodie and Gillette (1971) and Fishman (1970).

THE GENERAL PATTERN OF METABOLISM

In the body drugs and other foreign compounds can undergo a large number of biochemical transformations which can be conveniently classified into four main groups as follows: (1) oxidations (2) reductions (3) hydrolyses and (4) synthetic reactions. Typically a compound may be considered to undergo

Phase I
Biochemical reactions of foreign compounds

Reaction class	Example
Oxidation	Hydroxylation
	N- and *O*-dealkylation
	Deamination
	Replacement of sulphur by oxygen
	Cleavage of ethers
	Aromatization
	Oxidation of thioethers to sulphoxides
Reduction	Reduction of nitro and keto groups
	Reductive cleavage of azo groups
Hydrolysis	Hydrolysis of esters and amides

metabolism in two stages (biphasic metabolism) (Williams, 1959). In the first stage, or phase I the compound undergoes an oxidative, reductive or hydrolytic reaction or a combination of these reactions, whilst in the second phase the products of the first phase undergo a synthetic reaction which is usually referred to as a conjugation. The phase I metabolic reactions introduce into the molecule groups such as hydroxyl (OH), carboxyl (COOH), and amino (NH_2) at which conjugation reactions can subsequently occur. During each of these two phases, the products are usually more polar than their precursors while the products of conjugation are in the main strong organic acids. This biphasic metabolism may be illustrated by considering one of the major biliary metabolites of the antidepressive drug, imipramine, namely, the glucuronic acid conjugate of 2-hydroxyimipramine. One of the metabolic reactions of imipramine is hydroxylation in the 2-position (phase I oxidation) followed by the conjugation of the metabolite produced with glucuronic acid (phase II, synthetic).

Imipramine   2-hydroxyimipramine

Glucuronide of
2-hydroxyimipramine

Such a biphasic pattern is common to the metabolism of many foreign compounds. Some substances may already have within their molecular structures groups at which a conjugation reaction can occur, e.g. hydroxy or amino. In this case the compound may undergo a synthetic reaction directly. Stilboestrol for example has in its structure two phenolic hydroxyl groups which are potentially available as sites for conjugation. The drug is in fact conjugated through one of these groups with glucuronic acid to give stilboestrol monoglucuronide which is extensively excreted in bile.

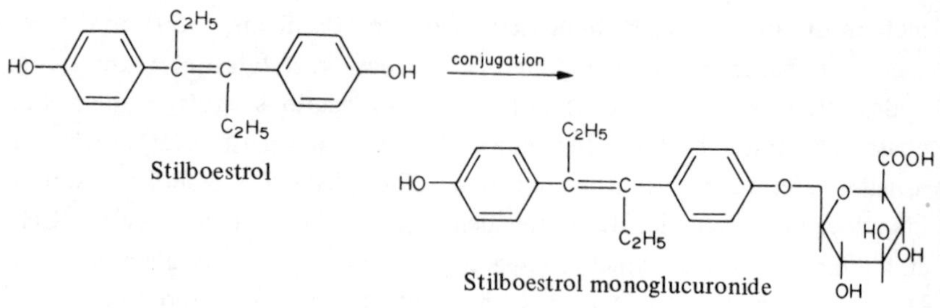

Stilboestrol

conjugation

Stilboestrol monoglucuronide

PATHWAYS OF DRUG METABOLISM

The phase I reactions

1. Oxidative reactions.

The oxidative biochemical reactions of drugs are numerous and varied and include the oxidation of aromatic rings (aromatic hydroxylation), the oxidation of alkyl chains and cycloalkyl groups, oxidative dealkylation, *N*-oxidation, sulphoxidation, the replacement of S by O and epoxidations.

(a) Aromatic hydroxylation.   Aromatic rings can be oxidized to produce phenols by a reaction usually referred to as aromatic hydroxylation. It occurs with both carbocyclic and heterocyclic aromatic systems and the main site of oxidation is usually, but not always, that of highest electron density and as a consequence the oxidation is orientated. Hydroxylation may also occur at more than one site so that more than one monophenol and some polyphenols may be produced. Aniline, for example is hydroxylated in both the *ortho* and *para* positions thus giving rise to two monophenols:

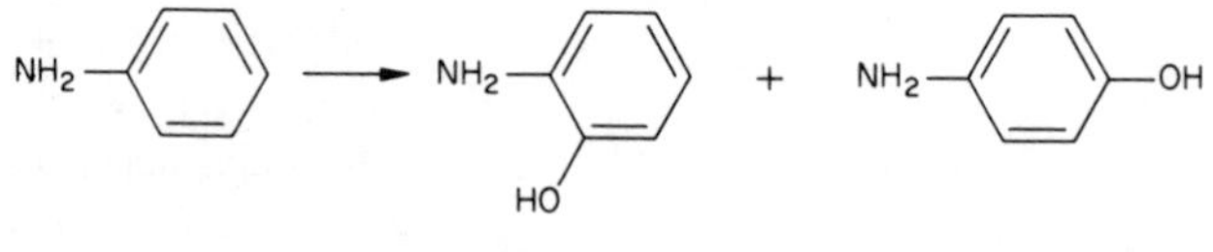

Benzene is hydroxylated to phenol and to a lesser extent to the polyphenols, catechol, quinol and hydroxyquinol:

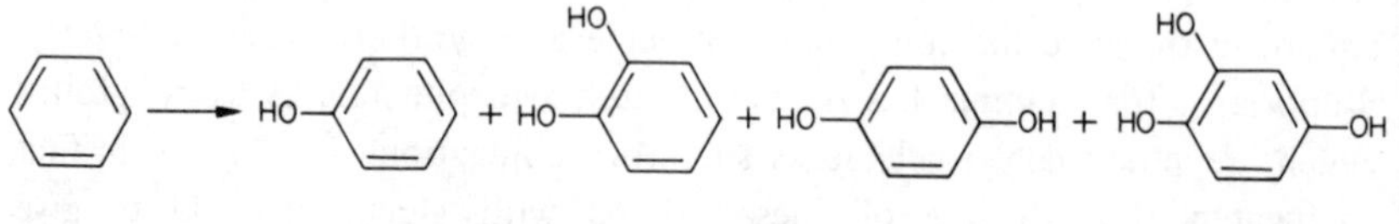

(b) The oxidation of alkyl chains.   Compounds containing alkyl chains can be oxidized in the body with the formation of primary, secondary or tertiary

alcohols, the nature of the alcohol produced depending upon the location of the oxidation in the alkyl chain and upon the nature of the alkyl group. Oxidation usually occurs at the ω or ($\omega - 1$) carbon atom. If oxidation occurs at the ω position of the chain, then further oxidation to a carboxylic acid can occur. These reactions can be summarized as follows:

(*a*) ω-oxidation: $RCH_2CH_3 \longrightarrow RCH_2CH_2OH$

(*b*) ω-1 oxidation: $RCH_2CH_3 \longrightarrow RCHOHCH_3$

(*c*)   tertiary alcohol formation: $RR'R''CH \longrightarrow RR'R''COH$
where R, R', R" are alkyl groups.

ω-oxidation. ω-oxidation is a common metabolic reaction of aliphatic groups. The product of this reaction, namely the primary alcohol is usually further metabolized to the corresponding aldehyde and acid by the action of soluble dehydrogenases. ω-oxidation products are minor metabolites of barbiturates such as barbitone, thiopentone and pentobarbitone.

| Barbitone | 5-ethyl-5-hydroxyethylbarbituric acid |

A common example of this type of oxidation is the hydroxylation of a methyl group attached to aromatic or heterocyclic ring systems. The initial product is a primary alcohol which may be further oxidized first to the aldehyde and then to the acid. Thus, the methyl group in tolbutamide is oxidized first to the primary alcohol metabolite and ultimately to the carboxylic acid.

Tolbutamide

ω-1 oxidation. In addition to oxidation at the terminal methyl group, alkyl functions are commonly oxidized at the $\omega - 1$ methylene position. Frequently this site of oxidation is favoured over ω-oxidation. The alkyl side

chains of several barbiturate drugs such as amylobarbitone and hexethal are hydroxylated in the $\omega - 1$ position and it also occurs with the drug meprobamate.

Meprobamate   Hydroxymeprobamate

Tertiary alcohol formation.   This occurs during the metabolism of amylobarbitone which is hydroxylated to form the corresponding tertiary alcohol, namely, 5-ethyl-5-(3'-hydroxyisoamyl)barbituric acid.

Amylobarbitone   Hydroxyamylobarbitone

As might be expected the tertiary carbinol group is resistant to further oxidation and compounds and metabolites containing such groups are not further oxidized and are usually excreted in a conjugated form.

Oxidation of cycloalkane rings.   Alicyclic structures may be hydroxylated to the corresponding alcohols. Thus, cyclohexane is converted to cyclohexanol

Cyclohexane   Cyclohexanol

There is a tendency for alicyclic compounds to undergo hydroxylation in the axial position.

(c) Oxidative dealkylation.   Alkyl groups, particularly methyl groups can be oxidatively removed from compounds when they are attached through oxygen (*O*-methyl), nitrogen (*N*-methyl) or sulphur (*S*-methyl). These

reactions can be represented as follows

$$ROCH_3 \longrightarrow ROCH_2OH \longrightarrow ROH + HCHO$$

$$RR'NCH_3 \longrightarrow RR'NCH_2OH \longrightarrow RR'NH + HCHO$$

where $R' = H$ or CH_3. The initial step is apparently the oxidation of the methyl group to hydroxymethyl which is then lost as formaldehyde which is ultimately oxidized to carbon dioxide. Other alkyl groups can also be oxidatively removed presumably as their respective aldehydes. The O-dealkylation of drugs containing alkoxy groups is a common metabolic reaction of such compounds. Thus, codeine is converted to morphine by O-demethylation; a second important example of O-dealkylation is the metabolic conversion of phenacetin to N-acetyl-p-aminophenol.

Phenacetin   N-acetyl-p-aminophenol

Some drugs are excreted in bile as their O-dealkylated products or conjugates of such metabolites. Thus, dextromethorphan is excreted in rat bile as conjugates of its O-demethylated metabolite, 3-hydroxy-N-methylmorphinan.

Dextromethorphan   3-hydroxy-N-methylmorphinan

Another example is griseofulvin which appears in rat bile as 4-demethyl-griseofulvin

Griseofulvin   4-demethylgriseofulvin

N-dealkylation, that is the oxidative removal of alkyl groups attached to nitrogen is also a very common metabolic reaction of compounds containing such groups. Although *N*-demethylation is the most frequently encountered dealkylation reaction other dealkylations such as the removal of ethyl, propyl, isopropyl, t-butyl groups can occur. A number of drugs appear in bile as their *N*-desalkyl derivatives or conjugates of such metabolites. Thus erythromycin is excreted in bile as *N*-desmethylerythromycin and imipramine appears in bile as desmethylimipramine and derivatives derived from this metabolite.

$CH_2CH_2CH_2N(CH_3)_2$	$CH_2CH_2CH_2NHCH_3$
Imipramine	Desmethylimipramine

(*d*) *N*-oxidations.   Primary and secondary amines can be *N*-hydroxylated to give hydroxylamines and tertiary amines can be oxidized to amine oxides (see Bickel 1969). These reactions can be represented as follows:—

(1)   Primary amines: RNH_2 ⟶ $RNHOH$
(2)   Secondary amines: R R′NH ⟶ R R′NOH
(3)   Tertiary amines: RR′R″N ⟶ RR′R″NO

where R, R′ and R″ are usually alkyl groups although one of them can be an aryl group.

In addition to these reactions two others can be mentioned here. Firstly, the hydroxylation of an amide group as occurs with urethane and secondly the *N*-hydroxylation of an acetamido group as occurs with acetamidofluorene

(4) $ROCONH_2$ ⟶ $ROCONHOH$
(5) $ArNHCOCH_3$ ⟶ $ArN(OH)COCH_3$

The first reaction, namely, the conversion of primary amines to hydroxylamines occurs with arylamines such as aniline and *p*-phenetidine and carcinogenic amines such as 2-naphthylamine, 4-aminobiphenyl and 4-aminostilbene.

p-phenetidine	*p*-ethoxyphenylhydroxylamine

The hydroxyl group introduced by *N*-hydroxylation can undergo the usual conjugation reactions so that the hydroxylamines formed are usually excreted as their conjugates with glucuronic or sulphuric acid. An example of an *N*-hydroxyl metabolite undergoing excretion in bile is provided by the carcinogen *N*-2-fluorenylacetamide which is eliminated in rat bile as the glucuronide conjugate of its *N*-hydroxylation product, namely, *N*-hydroxy-*N*-2-fluorenylacetamide, a potent carcinogen (Irving *et al*, 1967).

N-2-fluorenylacetamide

N-hydroxy-*N*-2-fluorenylacetamide

Glucuronide of
N-hydroxy-*N*-2-fluorenylacetamide

In contrast to many other oxidative reactions which lead to the formation of less toxic, readily excreted products, *N*-hydroxylation generally gives rise to more toxic intermediates. Indeed several of the toxic effects of aromatic amino and nitro compounds such as blood disorders and carcinogenesis have been attributed to the formation from these compounds of toxic hydroxylamines.

N-oxide formation can occur with tertiary amines and the best known example of this is the formation of the *N*-oxide of trimethylamine:

Trimethylamine   Trimethylamine *N*-oxide

It is a common reaction of drugs containing aliphatic tertiary amine side chains such as chlorpromazine and imipramine. The latter, for example, is extensively (70% of dose) excreted in rat bile mainly as conjugates of hydroxylated metabolites together with a small amount of imipramine N-oxide formed by oxidation of the tertiary amine group:

Imipramine → N—oxidation → Imipramine N-oxide

(e) *Sulphoxidation.* In this reaction divalent sulphur is oxidized to the sulphoxide and perhaps to the sulphone:

$$\text{S} \longrightarrow \text{SO} \longrightarrow \text{SO}_2$$

Sulphoxide formation is a minor but common metabolic reaction of phenothiazines such as chlorpromazine and small amounts of such sulphoxides occur in the bile of animals treated with these drugs.

Chlorpromazine → sulphoxidation → Chlorpromazine sulphoxide

(f) *Replacement of S by O.* The replacement of sulphur by oxygen can occur with compounds containing P=S or C=S groups. Thione (C=S) groups can thus be oxidized to keto groups (C=O) as occurs in the metabolic conversion of thiopentone to pentobarbitone.

Thiopental → Pentobarbitone

This reaction also occurs to some extent during the metabolism of certain organophosphorous insecticides containing P=S groups. For these compounds the reaction is as follows:

$$R'O-\underset{\underset{OR}{|}}{\overset{\overset{OR}{|}}{P}}=S \longrightarrow R'O-\underset{\underset{OR}{|}}{\overset{\overset{OR}{|}}{P}}=O$$

An example of this is the conversion of parathion ($R = C_2H_5$; $R' = C_6H_4NO_2$) to paraoxon. The conversion of P=S organophosphates to their P=O analogues greatly enhances anticholinesterase activity.

(g) *Epoxidation.* This metabolic reaction consists of the enzymic addition of oxygen across a double bond. It occurs during the course of metabolism of aromatic compounds such as naphthalene and various organo-chlorine insecticides such as aldrin, isodrin and heptachlor.

Epoxidation is probably the initial point of oxidative attack of an aromatic system as the epoxide so formed can give rise to a phenol, to a dihydrodiol by the enzymic addition of water and to a glutathione conjugate by reaction with glutathione (Jerina *et al.*, 1968). The latter conjugate can be transformed to a mercapturic acid.

2. Reductions

Reductive reactions are far less common than oxidative reactions. They can occur with compounds containing nitro, azo or ketone groups and can be summarized as follows:

(a) The reduction of nitro compounds which occurs in several stages:

$$RNO_2 \longrightarrow RNO \longrightarrow RNHOH \longrightarrow RNH_2$$

(b) The reduction of azo compounds to amines

$$RN=NR' \longrightarrow RNHNHR' \longrightarrow RNH_2 + R'NH_2$$

(c) The reduction of ketones to secondary alcohols

$$RCOR' \longrightarrow RCHOHR'$$

Examples of the reduction of aromatic nitro compounds are the reduction of nitrobenzene, p-nitrobenzoic acid and chloramphenicol to their respective arylamines.

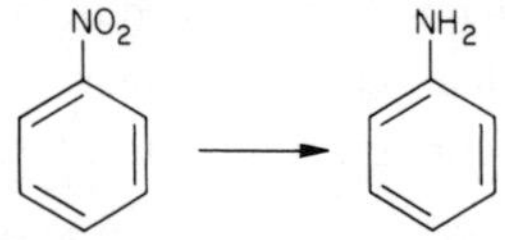

Nitrobenzene   Aniline

The nature of the processes involved in nitro reduction is controversial. There are probably at least four mechanisms in the liver whereby nitro compounds can be reduced to amines and some reactions are probably semi-enzymic. Activity is not confined to the liver but also occurs in the lungs, heart and brain. The gut flora can also effect nitro reduction and this is probably important in the metabolism of orally ingested nitro compounds or nitro compounds excreted into the intestine in the bile. Probably the formation of hydroxylamine intermediates during the metabolic reduction of nitro compounds accounts for the toxicity of the latter.

Splitting of the azo linkage is a common reaction of compounds containing such a group. It occurs for example with the two antibacterial drugs Prontosil and Neoprontosil which are reduced by azo splitting to sulphanilamide; the latter being responsible for the antibacterial activity of the parent drugs.

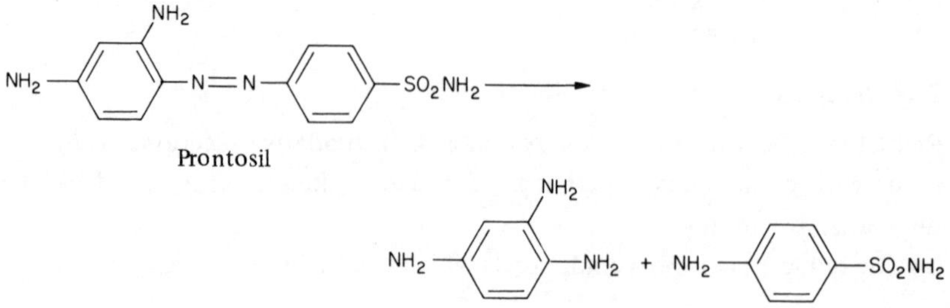

Prontosil

Sulphanilamide

Azo compounds can be split both by the liver and by the gut flora. Several azo compounds, particularly those containing sulphonic acid residues, are extensively excreted in the bile and as a consequence suffer azo reduction by enzymes of the gut flora.

Ketones can be extensively reduced in the body to their corresponding secondary alcohols. The drug acetohexamide is for example reduced to its corresponding secondary alcohol hydroxyacetohexamide.

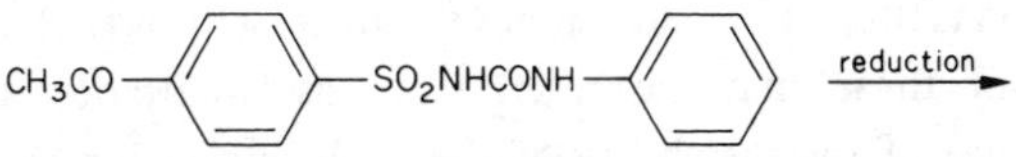

Acetohexamide

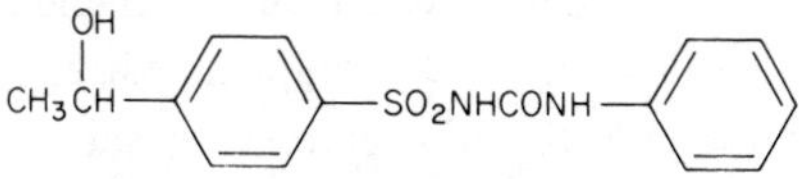

Hydroxyacetohexamide

In addition to these reductive reactions, a number of others are occasionally encountered. These include the reduction of aldehydes to primary alcohols, a well-known example being the metabolic conversion of chloral hydrate to trichloroethanol.

$$CCl_3 \cdot CHO \longrightarrow CCl_3 \cdot CH_2OH$$
Chloral   Trichloroethanol

Other occasional metabolic reductions are the saturation of double bonds, the reductive splitting of disulphide links and the reduction of pentavalent arsenical compounds to their trivalent forms.

3. Hydrolysis

Hydrolysis is a common metabolic reaction of drugs and chemicals containing ester or amide groups, the products being phenols, alcohols and carboxylic acids. The hydrolase enzymes which carry out these reactions are widely distributed and occur not only in the liver microsomes but also in the plasma and other tissues. An example of the hydrolysis of an ester is provided by the antihypercholesterolaemic drug ethyl p-chlorophenoxyisobutyrate which is hydrolysed to the corresponding carboxylic acid and ethanol.

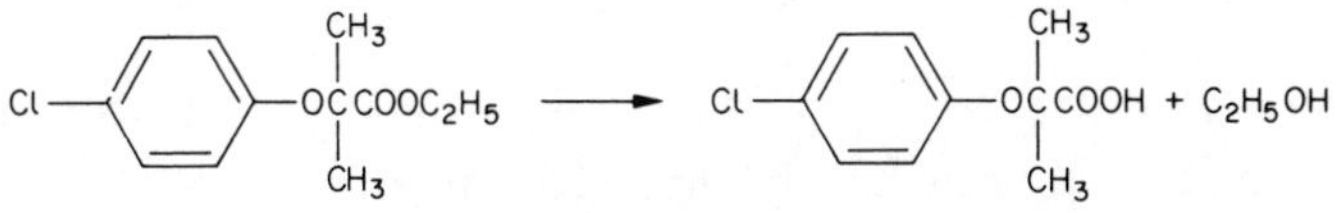

Other examples of drugs which undergo metabolic hydrolysis are aspirin, atropine, ethylbiscoumacetate and heroin (diacetylmorphine).

Generally amides are more stable metabolically than esters but they can be hydrolysed by enzymes termed amidases to their corresponding carboxylic acids:

$$RCONH_2 \longrightarrow R\,COOH$$

Some hydrolytic reactions may proceed spontaneously without the intervention of enzymes and these may be referred to as 'spontaneous reactions'. These occur because of the instability of the molecule under the physical conditions encountered in the body. A striking example of this phenomenon is provided by thalidomide which at body pH undergoes a spontaneous and complex pattern of hydrolysis to give twelve other compounds. This teratogenic substance contains in its molecular structure four substituted amide bonds all of which can be split above pH 6. Indeed it appears that the teratogenicity may be related to the reactivity of certain of these amide bonds.

Another example is seen with the molluscicide compound N-triphenyl-methylmorpholine (Frescon) which is used for the control of aquatic and semi-aquatic snails acting as intermediate hosts of schistosomes and liver flukes

In man and animals it undergoes spontaneous hydrolysis catalysed by the acid of the stomach to triphenylmethylcarbinol and morpholine.

The enzymes of the phase I reactions

The phase I oxidations, reductions and hydrolyses are carried out by enzymes which occur predominantly in the liver although they may also occur in other tissues such as the kidneys, lungs, adrenal glands, blood and tissues of the gastrointestinal tract. The enzymes are mainly located in the endoplasmic reticulum of the hepatic cells and can be isolated from disrupted liver preparations by high speed centrifugation to give the so called microsomal fraction. The endoplasmic reticulum probably consists of an ordered lipoprotein structure with lipid molecules arranged in a bimolecular layer within which the drug metabolizing enzymes are organized. The substrates for these enzymes of the reticulum have to be lipid-soluble and probably they are taken up by the membrane by a process akin to solubilization.

Microsomal oxidation reactions have a specific requirement for the reduced form of nicotinamide-adenine dinucleotide phosphate (NADPH) as co-factor and oxygen. In oxidation the enzymes catalyse the consumption of one molecule of oxygen per molecule of substrate with one atom of oxygen appearing in the product and the other undergoing reduction and appearing as water.

The oxidizing system contains at least two catalysts, namely, the NADPH-oxidizing flavoprotein called NADPH-cytochrome C reductase and a carbon monoxide binding haemoprotein known as cytochrome P-450. A scheme for electron transport in microsomal oxidative processes involving these two catalysts has been suggested by Holtzman *et al.*, 1968 as follows:

Fp = flavoprotein; ox = oxidized; red = reduced; substrate-OH = hydroxylated substrate; X = an unidentified carrier.

It is possible that the carrier X between NADPH-cytochrome C reductase and the P-450 is unnecessary in hepatic microsomal oxidations. In the adrenal mitochondrial P-450 system X appears to be a non-haem iron protein. The steps involved in the oxidation of a substrate are probably as follows: first, the substrate binds firmly with both the oxidized and reduced forms of

P-450. The substrate-reduced P-450 complex then reacts with oxygen to give the oxidized substrate and the oxidized form of P-450. The reduced form of cytochrome P-450 is then reformed via a reductive system involving flavoprotein and NADPH.

As regards reductive reactions, their enzymology has not been as thoroughly investigated as in the case of the oxidative mechanisms. There are at least four mechanisms for the reduction of nitro compounds in liver: cytochrome P-450 and NADPH-cytochrome C reductase in liver microsomes, xanthine oxidase and a fourth unidentified reductase (Gillette, 1971).

Extrahepatic metabolism

The principal organ involved in drug metabolism is the liver but other organs and tissues may also contribute to the metabolism of a compound. Drug metabolizing activity has been shown to be associated with, besides the liver, the tissues of the gastrointestinal tract, the kidneys, lungs, skin, nervous tissue, blood and the gut flora. The tissues of the gastrointestinal tract for example have a significant ability to conjugate a phenolic compound with sulphate and glucuronic acid and as a consequence an orally administered substance may be appreciably conjugated while being absorbed from the intestinal tract. Orally administered stilboestrol appears in the portal blood of rats about 50% in the conjugated form (Fischer and Millburn, 1970) and oral isoprenaline is extensively conjugated with sulphate by the gut wall (Davies *et al.*, 1969)

Lung tissue is able to O-methylate isoprenaline and isoetharine and to N-dealkylate and N-hydroxylate simple aromatic amines such as N-methylaniline. The kidney can effect reactions such as aromatic hydroxylation, N-dealkylation, glucuronide formation and glycine and glutamine conjugation. Generally the levels of drug-metabolizing activity found in extrahepatic tissues are less than those occurring in the liver so that the overall quantitative contribution of extrahepatic metabolism to the metabolism of a compound is less than that of the liver. Nevertheless, extrahepatic metabolism may assume particular importance in certain situations. Thus, the adrenal medullary and sympathetic nervous tissue can carry out the β-hydroxylation of phenylisopropylamines of the amphetamine type. The β-hydroxylated products of such reactions may be important for certain of the effects (e.g. tolerance) that occur with compounds of this type.

Amphetamine   →(dopamine β–hydroxylase)→   Norephedrine

Gut floral metabolism

The intestinal flora constitutes one of the more important extrahepatic sites of drug metabolism particularly in relation to biliary excretion since the elimination of a compound by this route is one of the two main ways whereby a compound is brought into contact with the gut flora. Incomplete absorption after oral ingestion is the other means. Metabolism by the gut flora, and particularly by the intestinal bacteria, can be important in relation to biliary excretion since it may be a factor in the enterohepatic circulation and therefore delayed excretion of a substance. Furthermore, enterobacterial metabolism may lead to the formation of toxic or pharmacologically active metabolites (Chapter 8).

The gut flora consists of four main groups of organisms, namely, bacteria, protozoans, fungi and on occasions parasitic nematodes and cestodes. The most important by far, of these groups, in gut floral metabolism, are the bacteria. The most common intestinal bacteria have been shown by Drasar *et al.* (1970) to be as follows: *Enterobacteria, Enterococci, Viridans Streptococci, Staphylococci, Lactobacilli, Bacteroides, Bifidobacteria, Clostridia* and *Veillonella.* There are important differences in the numbers and distribution of these organisms along the gastrointestinal tract and this can vary markedly with species and diet.

Some of the reactions carried out by the gut flora also occur in the tissues. A few examples are the hydrolysis of esters and amides, the reduction of nitro, azo and keto groups and *N*-dealkylation. In this situation the gut flora can contribute quantitatively to the overall metabolism of a drug. An example here is the metabolism of neoprontosil which undergoes azo cleavage to give sulphanilamide. This transformation is effected in part by the liver but in the main by the gut flora – following the elimination of the drug in the bile (Gingell *et al.*, 1971).

Neoprontosil

reduction in liver
and by gut flora
after excretion in bile

NH_2SO_2 —⟨ ⟩— NH_2

Sulphanilamide

Of greater interest perhaps is the fact that some metabolic reactions may be peculiar to the gut flora and have no counterpart in the host's tissue. In this situation metabolism by the gut flora may lead to the appearance of unusual or novel metabolites. Examples of such restricted reactions are dehydroxylation, aromatization, reductive dealkylation, splitting of sulphamic acids, the hydrolysis of β-glycosides and dechlorination. The splitting of β-glycosides, particularly β-glucuronides, by the gut flora, is an important factor in the enterohepatic circulation of drugs excreted in bile as glucuronic acid conjugates.

The synthetic or conjugation reactions

Drugs and their metabolites containing suitable chemical groups such as hydroxyl (OH), amino (NH_2) and carboxyl (COOH) can undergo in the body synthetic reactions in which the compound is combined through one of these groups to a substance provided by the body. The latter is derived from the body's carbohydrate and protein resources and is called the conjugating agent. The overall reaction which is a synthetic reaction involving the union of the drug with a substance of endogenous origin is called a conjugation mechanism. Most conjugation reactions result in a decrease in the toxicity of the compound so that they are therefore sometimes referred to as detoxication mechanisms, the term implying a lessening of toxicity.

There are about 10 major conjugation mechanisms of which 8 occur in man and most other mammalian species (Table 9). The two other major mechanisms are the glucoside conjugation which occurs in insects and the ornithine conjugation which is found in certain birds. There are also a number of other minor mechanisms (e.g., the serine and taurine conjugation) which are much more restricted in their occurrence.

All the reactions require activated nucleotides as intermediates in the conjugation process and ATP as a source of energy. The nucleotide intermediate however can contain in its molecule either the conjugating agent or the foreign compound. It has been suggested therefore (Williams, 1968) that mechanistically, two types of conjugation mechanism exist. The first one

Table 9
The common conjugation mechanisms

Mechanism	Conjugating agent
Glucuronide synthesis	Glucuronic acid
Ethereal sulphate synthesis	Sulphate
Hippuric acid synthesis	Glycine
Glutamine conjugation*	Glutamine
Glutathione conjugation (mercapturic acid synthesis)	Glutathione
Methylation	Methyl group
Acetylation	Acetyl group
Thiocyanate synthesis	Thio group

*Occurs only in man, apes and New and Old World monkeys

is where an 'activated' conjugating agent is involved and the second where the foreign compound or its metabolite is 'activated'.

(1) Conjugating agent $\xrightarrow{\text{energy (ATP)}}$ 'activated' conjugating agent $\xrightarrow{\text{foreign compound}}$ conjugate

(2) Foreign compound $\xrightarrow{\text{energy (ATP)}}$ 'activated' foreign compound $\xrightarrow{\text{conjugating agent}}$ conjugate

There are important differences in the tissue and subcellular location of the two types of mechanism. The amino acid conjugation mechanisms for example are mitochondrial reactions and are restricted in their tissue location to the liver and/or kidney. By contrast the first type of reaction in which the conjugating agent is in an activated form is found in the liver and several other tissues and is located in the microsomal fraction as in the case of glucuronic acid conjugation or the soluble fraction as in the case of the sulphate and acetylation conjugation mechanisms.

From the point of view of biliary excretion the most important conjugation mechanisms are the glucuronide and glutathione mechanisms followed by the sulphate and glycine mechanisms. The acetylation and methylation reactions do not appear to be of much significance in biliary excretion although a few examples of compounds appearing in bile as metabolites arising from acetylation and methylation are known. Glutamine conjugates have not so far been reported to occur in bile.

There is a large literature on the conjugation mechanisms and for more

Table 10
Tissue and sub-cellular location of the two types of conjugation mechanisms

	Intermediate nucleotide	Tissue location	Subcellular location
Activated conjugating agent			
Glucuronic acid conjugation	Uridinediphosphate glucuronic acid	Liver and most other tissues	Microsomal
Ethereal sulphate synthesis	Phosphoadenosinephosphosulphate	Liver, kidney, intestine	Supernatant
Methylation	S-adenosylmethionine	Liver and many tissues	Microsomes and soluble
Acetylation	Acetyl-CoA	Liver and other tissues	Soluble
Activated foreign compound			
Hippuric acid synthesis	Aroyl-CoA	Liver and/or kidney	Mitochondria
Glutamine synthesis	Phenacetyl-CoA	Liver and kidney	Mitochondria

detailed information the reader is referred to the review of Williams (1968) and the edited works of Fishman (1970) and Brodie and Gillette (1971).

Glucuronide formation

The glucuronic acid conjugation is one of the most important metabolic conjugation reactions from the point of view of biliary excretion, since many drugs and their metabolites appear in bile largely as glucuronic acid conjugates. A glucuronide conjugate may be formed providing the compound has, or has acquired during its metabolism, a group at which this conjugation reaction can occur and this can be: (*a*) a hydroxyl group which may be alcoholic (primary, secondary or tertiary), hydroxylaminic, phenolic or enolic (*b*) a carboxyl group which is usually aromatic but in some cases it can be aliphatic (*c*) an amino group which is usually aromatic and in some cases a substituted sulphonamide group and finally (*d*) a sulphydryl group (Smith and Williams, 1966). The structures of these groups which can act as receptors for glucuronic acid in transfer reactions are shown in Table 11.

Glucuronides are strong acids (pK_a 3–4) which are highly ionized (>99.9%) and very water-soluble at physiological pH. The effect of conjugation of a substance with glucuronic acid is therefore to produce a strongly acid compound which is more water-soluble at body pH than its precursor. Glucuronides of all types including those of alcohols, phenols, carboxylic acids and *N*-glucuronides can be excreted in the bile (Table 12). It might be thought that glucuronides have a particular affinity for excretion in the bile but whether or not this is so, or just a reflection of the restricted scope of other conjugation processes, compared to glucuronide synthesis, is not clear. Certainly, glucuronide formation is the most versatile of the conjugation mechanisms from the point of view of the variety of chemical groups to which the conjugating agent can be transferred, the facility with which the glucuronic acid can be produced from carbohydrate in the body and the large number of tissues that can effect glucuronide formation.

Glucuronide conjugation is important in biliary excretion from two points of view: firstly it makes a non-polar compound much more polar and secondly it increases the molecular weight by 176 units. Both factors, namely, polarity and molecular weight are important for biliary excretion. Glucuronide conjugates that are extensively excreted in the bile, although polar, tend to be more lipophilic than those that are not. This is probably a reflection of their higher molecular weight particularly in the sense that the proportion of the lipophilic non-polar portion of the molecule compared to that of the polar sugar portion would be greater than that in a simple low molecular weight conjugate and this would therefore determine somewhat greater lipophilic properties.

Table 11
Types of groups in foreign compounds to which glucuronic acid can be transferred

Type of group		Structure*	Example of compound forming glucuronide
Hydroxyl	Phenolic	Ar*OH*	Morphine
	Enolic	$-CH=CO$*H*	4-hydroxycoumarin
	Alcoholic (primary)	$-CH_2OH$	Chloramphenicol
	Alcoholic (secondary)	$\diagup CHO$*H*	—
	Alcoholic (tertiary)	$\diagup \overline{\underline{C}}O$*H*	*tert*-butanol
	Hydroxylaminic	$-NO$*H*	*N*-hydroxy-*N*-2-fluorenylacetamide
Carboxyl	Aromatic	Ar COO*H*	Salicylic acid
	Aliphatic	$-CH_2COO$*H*	Indomethacin
Amino and imino	Aromatic	Ar N*H*$_2$	4,4'-diaminodiphenylsulphone
	Carbamate	$-OCON$*H*$_2$	Meprobamate
	Sulphonimide	$-SO_2N$*H*$-$	Sulphadimethoxine
	Heterocyclic	$\diagup N$*H*	Sulphisoxazole
Sulphydryl	Thiol	$-S$*H*	2-mercaptobenzothiazole
	Carbodithioic	$-CSS$*H*	Diethyldithiocarbamic acid

* The hydrogen italicized is replaced by the glucuronyl residue $C_6H_9O_6$ to form the conjugated glucuronic acid. Based on Smith and Williams (1966).

Table 12

Examples of various types of glucuronic acid conjugates excreted in bile

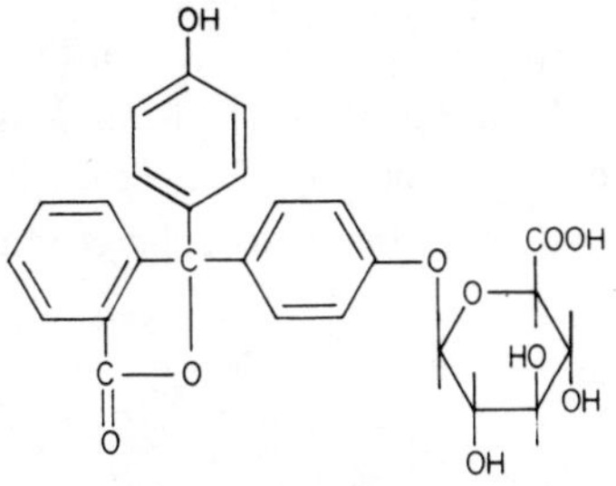

Phenolphthalein glucuronide
(phenolic ether type)

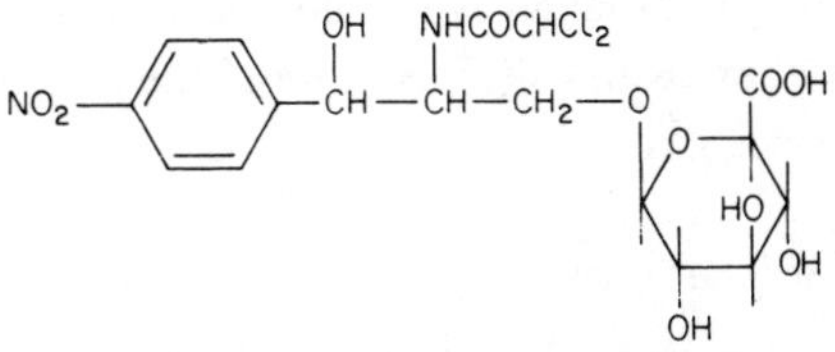

Chloramphenicol 3-glucuronide
(primary alcoholic ether type)

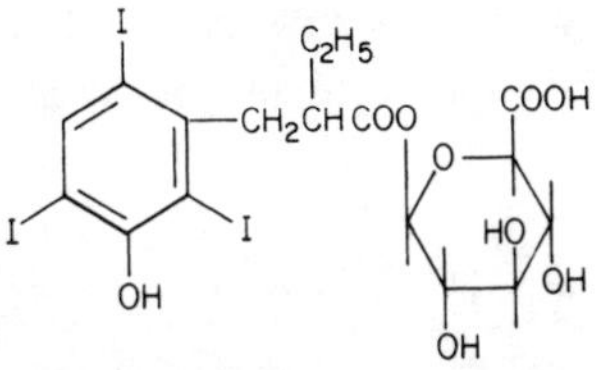

Iodopanoic acid ester glucuronide
(ester glucuronide)

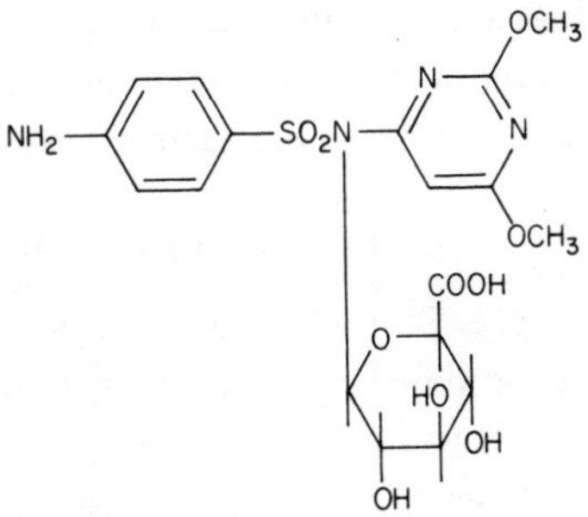

Sulphadimethoxine N'-glucuronide
(N-glucuronide)

The enzymic mechanism of glucuronide formation and its species and tissue occurrence are all now relatively well-known (see Dutton, 1966). The synthesis of the glucuronide proceeds by way of transfer of the glucuronic acid from a nucleotide, uridine diphosphate glucuronic acid (UDPGA) to an acceptor molecule; the reaction being catalysed by the enzyme glucuronyl transferase. The UDPGA is formed initially from uridine diphosphate glucose which is oxidized by a soluble enzyme, UDP glucose dehydrogenase. As pointed out earlier a remarkable variety of groups including phenols, alcohols,

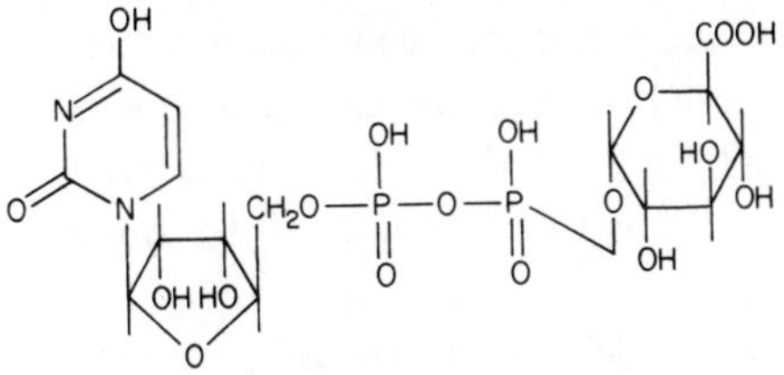

UDP-glucuronic acid

steroids, carboxylic acids and amines can act as receptors but whether or not a single glucuronyl transferase is involved in these transfers or there exists a family of such enzymes is not clear.

Glucuronide formation is widespread in its species occurrence except that the cat appears to have a defect in this particular mechanism. The formation of glucuronides is not limited to the liver and it can occur extrahepatically in other tissues such as those of the gastrointestinal tract, the kidneys, lungs and spleen.

Sulphate conjugation

From the point of view of biliary excretion, sulphate conjugation appears to be less important than glucuronide formation. This probably reflects the more limited scope of sulphate conjugation compared to the glucuronic acid conjugation. Compounds containing hydroxyl, amino, or sulphydryl groups are potentially capable of conjugating with sulphate in the body and the overall reaction may be depicted as follows:

$$R-X-H + HOSO_2-OH \longrightarrow R-X-SO_2OH + H_2O$$

where X is O or NH or possibly S.

The product of the conjugation, the sulphate conjugate, is a very strong acid which is almost entirely ionized at physiological pH. Phenols and alcohols undergo sulphate conjugation to give the so called ethereal sulphates while aromatic amines give N-sulphates or sulphamates. Ethereal sulphate formation shows a broad species distribution but is occasionally defective as in the pig. In this metabolic reaction an activated form of sulphate is transferred to an acceptor molecule under the influence of a transfering enzyme i.e. a sulphotransferase. The activated form of sulphate is the nucleotide 3′-phosphoadenosine-5′-phosphosulphate. A number of different sulphotransferases or sulphokinases exist. Thus, phenol sulphokinase catalyses the transfer of sulphate to phenols and a different kinase, arylamine sulphokinase, is involved in the formation of sulphamates of arylamines. Similarly, a number of sulphokinases are concerned in the sulphation of steroids.

A few sulphate conjugates have been shown to occur in bile and these include the ethereal sulphate of harmalol, a metabolite of the hallucinogen, harmine, and the sulphates of thyroxine and oestriol. Small amounts of indoxyl sulphate are excreted in the bile after the administration of indole to rats.

Sulphate conjugates of dehydroepiandrosterone and ethynyloestradiol are excreted in bile while the sulphate conjugates of 2-acetamido-6-naphthol, a metabolite of the carcinogen 2-naphthylamine, is eliminated in rat bile.

Examples of sulphate conjugates excreted in bile

Types of sulphate conjugate	Example

Simple ester sulphates

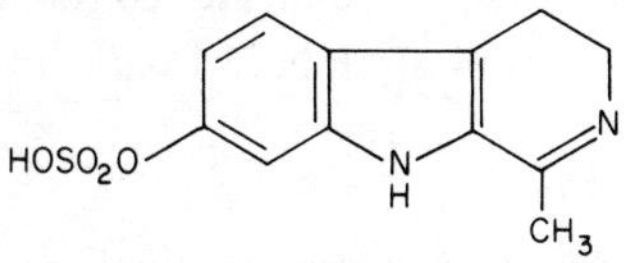

Harmalol sulphate

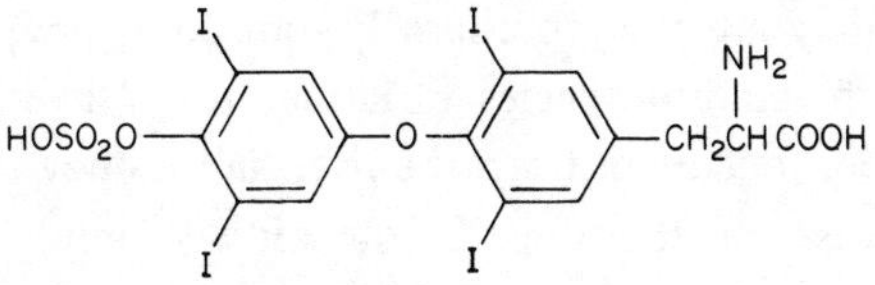

Thyroxine sulphate

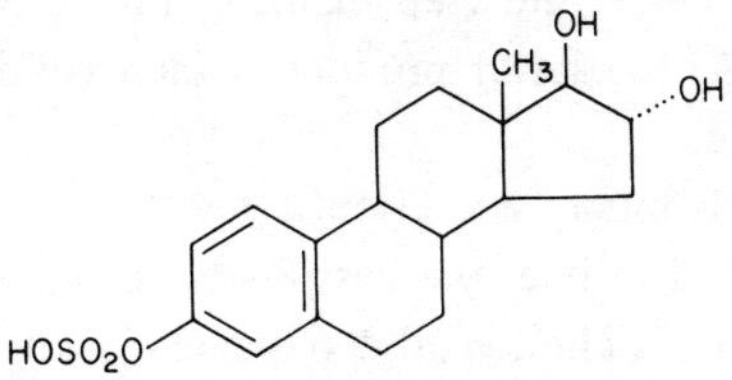

Oestriol 3-sulphate

Double conjugates

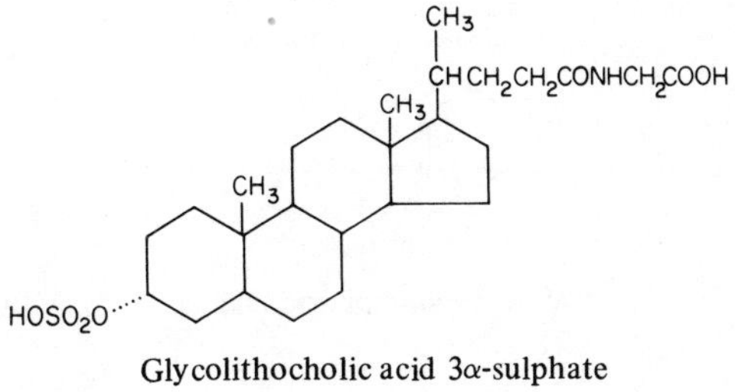

Glycolithocholic acid 3α-sulphate

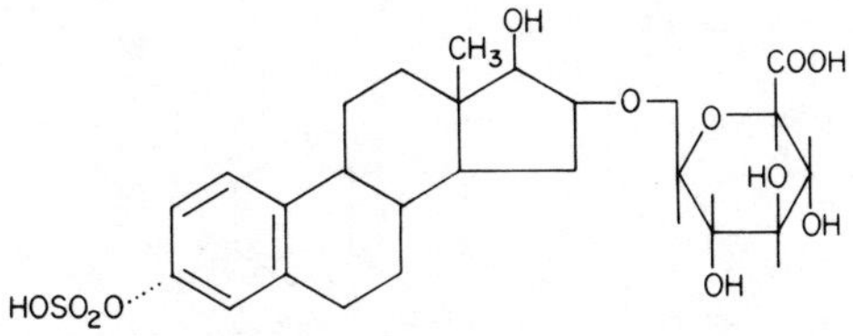

Oestriol 3-sulphate 16-glucuronide

Of interest is the appearance in bile of a number of double conjugates containing a sulphate group. Thus, glycolithocholic acid appears in human bile in part as its 3α-sulphate (Palmer 1967) while oestriol is excreted in human bile as a double conjugate containing both glucuronic acid and sulphate, namely oestriol 3-sulphate 16-glucuronide (Levitz *et al.*, 1965).

Glycine conjugation

Glycine conjugation is a common biochemical reaction of many types of carboxylic acids particularly those containing aromatic or heterocyclic groups. Glycine conjugates are typically strong acids having a pK_a of about 3 and they are therefore largely ionized at physiological pH. Its distribution is widespread but species variations occur in its tissue distribution. Thus the reaction occurs in both the liver and kidney of the rat, rabbit and ox but in the case of the dog, in the kidney only. The formation of the glycine conjugate is a mitochondrial reaction and proceeds in three steps: firstly, activation of the carboxyl group by forming an ATP derivative which is utilized in the second step, namely, the formation of an acyl derivative of coenzyme A; the latter product is then condensed with glycine to give the hippuric acid.

As regards biliary excretion, a few glycine conjugates have been reported to be excreted in bile, the best known examples being the glycine conjugates of the bile acids cholic and deoxycholic acids. 4-amino-3-iodohippuric acid is well excreted (25% of dose) in rat bile while 3,5-di-t-butyl-4-hydroxybenzoic acid, a metabolite of BHT, is extensively excreted in rat bile possibly as a glycine conjugate.

4-amino-3-iodohippuric acid

3,5-di-t-butyl-4-
hydroxybenzoylglycine

Glycocholic acid

Glutathione conjugation

The glutathione conjugation is a reaction of considerable interest from the point of view of biliary excretion since several types of compounds including urethane, aromatic hydrocarbons, aromatic amines and halogenated phthaleins such as sulphobromophthalein are excreted in bile as glutathione conjugates. In this reaction the compound or its metabolite is linked through a thio-ether linkage to a molecule of glutathione – a tripeptide consisting of cysteine, glycine and glutamic acid.

$$
\begin{array}{cc}
\text{COOH} & \text{CH}_2\text{SH} \\
| & | \\
\text{NH}_2\text{CH CH}_2\text{CH}_2\text{CONH} & \text{CH CO NH CH}_2\text{COOH}
\end{array}
$$

Glutathione (mol. wt. 307).

This conjugation reaction increases the molecular weight by 306 units and also introduces a centre of polarity into the molecule – changes that are favourable for biliary excretion to occur. In some cases degradation products of the glutathione conjugates are found in the bile, namely derivatives such as the cysteinylglycine and cysteine or N-acetylcysteine conjugates formed by step-wise removal of the amino acid residues from the tripeptide conjugate. So far glutathione conjugates have been found to occur only in bile and have not been detected in urine. The biliary pathway may therefore be the only channel for their elimination. Degradation products of glutathione conjugates, namely, the mercapturic acids are commonly found in urine as metabolites of several types of compound.

In glutathione conjugation the tripeptide is conjugated with the compound or a metabolite under the influence of an enzyme called glutathione S-transferase of which there are a number. One of these catalyses reactions of glutathione with aromatic and other cyclic compounds containing labile halogen or nitro groups. Thus 1,2-dichloro-4-nitrobenzene is conjugated with glutathione under the catalytic influence of glutathione S-aryltransferase.

The glutathione conjugation of sulphobromophthalein is catalysed by the same enzyme. Glutathione S-epoxide transferase catalyses the reaction of glutathione with epoxides. Epoxides are probably reactive metabolic

Table 13

Some examples of glutathione conjugates excreted in bile

Precursor	Biliary glutathione conjugate
$NH_2COOC_2H_5$ Urethane	$C_2H_5-S-CH_2R$ S-ethylglutathione
$CH_3SO_2OCH_3$ Methyl methanesulphonate	CH_3SCH_2-R S-methylglutathione

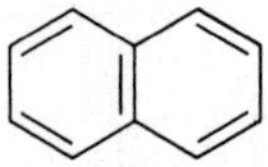

Naphthalene

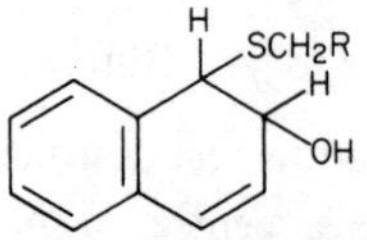

S-(1,2-dihydro-2-hydroxy-1-naphthyl) glutathione

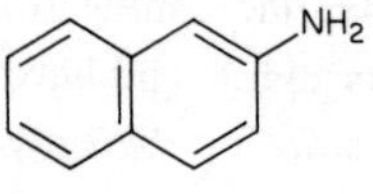

2-naphthylamine

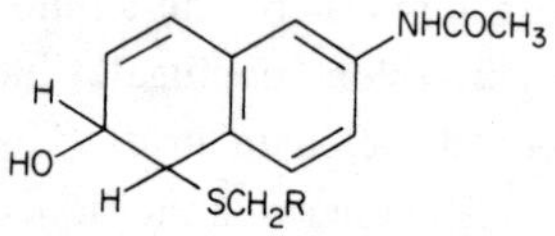

S-(2-acetamido-5,6-dihydro-6-hydroxy-5-naphthyl)glutathione

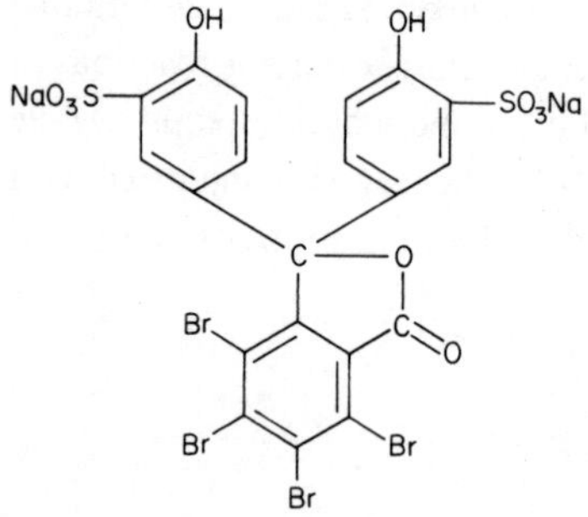

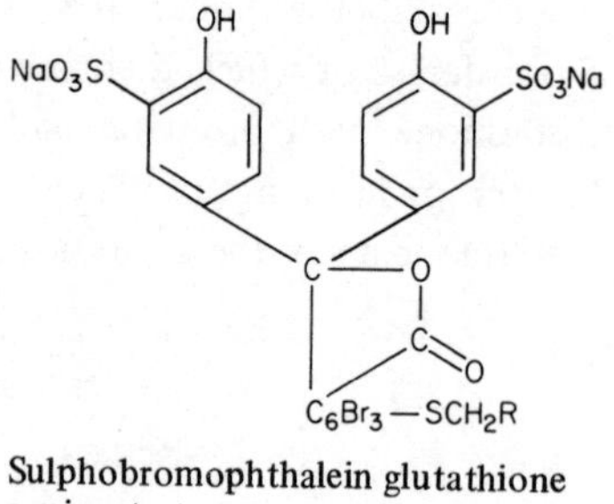

Sulphobromophthalein

Sulphobromophthalein glutathione conjugate

$$R = -CH \, CO \, NHCH_2 \, COOH$$
$$| $$
$$NHCOCH_2 \, CH_2 \, CHCOOH$$
$$| $$
$$NH_2$$

intermediates of polycyclic aromatic hydrocarbons and these can be conjugated with glutathione. Thus, naphthalene is converted via its epoxide to a glutathione conjugate which is excreted in the bile.

Naphthalene → 1,2-dihydronaphthalene-1,2-epoxide → S-(1,2-dihydro-2-hydroxy-1-naphthyl)glutathione

Glutathione S-alkyltransferase catalyses the S-alkylation of glutathione while several glutathione S-alkene-transferases catalyse the reaction of glutathione with αβ-unsaturated compounds such as unsaturated esters, ketones and nitriles.

S-(1,2-dihydro-2-hydroxy-1-naphthyl)glutathione

S-(1,2-dihydro-2-hydroxy-1-naphthyl)cysteinylglycine

S-(1,2-dihydro-2-hydroxy-1-naphthyl)cysteine

N-acetyl-S-(1,2-dihydro-2-hydroxy-1-naphthyl)cysteine

Glutathione conjugates, although having a marked affinity for excretion in the bile, are further metabolized in the body to various derivatives, particularly mercapturic acids. Thus, the glutamyl group of a glutathione conjugate can be removed by a process of transpeptidation to give a cysteinylglycine conjugate. This dipeptide conjugate can be hydrolysed by

Table 14

Some examples of compounds excreted in bile as acetyl conjugates

Precursor	Acetyl conjugates in bile
p-aminohippuric acid	p-acetamidohippuric acid
Procaineamide ethobromide	N-acetyl procaineamide ethobromide
Carbidium	N-acetylcarbidium
Sulphapyridine	N^4-acetylsulphapyridine

peptidases to give a cysteine conjugate and this can then be *N*-acetylated to give a mercapturic acid. As a consequence one may find in bile along with the glutathione conjugate these secondary products of metabolism. Thus, naphthalene is excreted in bile as its glutathione conjugate together with its secondary metabolites, namely, the cysteinylglycine, cysteine and *N*-acetyl-cysteinyl conjugates.

Acetylation

A number of compounds are excreted in bile as acetylated derivatives. Thus, procaineamide ethobromide and carbidium are extensively excreted in bile as acetyl conjugates while many simple aromatic amino compounds such as *p*-aminohippuric acid and various sulphonamides are excreted in bile to a small extent as their respective *N*-acetylated products (Table 14).

Probably acetylation is a metabolic reaction of little significance as far as biliary excretion is concerned since it has little influence on the molecular weight — it increases this by 42 units — and it has relatively little influence on polarity. In fact the acetylation of amino groups decreases their basicity.

Acetylation is a biochemical reaction of compounds containing amino groups and as far as drugs and other foreign compounds are concerned no other type of group undergoes this reaction. The process consists of the conversion of a primary amine into a monoacetyl compound thus:

$$RNH_2 \longrightarrow RNH-COCH_3$$

It can occur with aromatic amines ($ArNH_2$), hydrazine derivatives ($RNHNH_2$) sulphonamides ($Ar\,SO_2\,NH_2$) and certain aliphatic amino groups in compounds such as marfanil. The immediate source of the acetyl groups in biological acetylation is acetyl-CoA. The acetyl group of this coenzyme can, under the influence of the appropriate enzymes, the transacetylases, be transferred to a variety of acceptor amino groups.

In mammals acetylation of amino compounds appears to be a general metabolic reaction except that the dog is unable to acetylate aromatic amines and hydrazine groups.

Methylation

Methylation is a potential metabolic reaction of compounds containing amino, hydroxyl or sulphydryl groups. As in the case of acetylation, methylation does not appear to be a metabolic reaction of great significance as far as biliary excretion is concerned. It has little effect upon molecular weight (increased by 14 units) and has little influence upon polarity. Nevertheless a few compounds appear in bile as methylated metabolites.

Thus, both adrenaline and isoprenaline are extensively excreted in rat bile as glucuronic acid conjugates of their *O*-methylated derivatives. Similarly, protocatechuic acid is excreted in rat bile in the form of the glucuronide of its 3-methoxy derivative.

Methylation of phenolic compounds, particularly catechol derivatives and polyhydric phenols containing two vicinal hydroxyl groups is a fairly common metabolic reaction. Methylation of isolated phenolic hydroxyl groups is relatively uncommon but a few examples are known e.g. the *O*-methylation of 4-hydroxy-3,5-di-iodobenzoic acid to its 4-methoxy derivative. In the case of polyhydric phenols methylation is orientated. For catechols methylation can occur at both the *m*- and *p*-hydroxyl group but not

Table 15

Examples of compounds excreted in bile as methylated derivatives

Compound	Methylated metabolite in bile
Protocatechuic acid	4-carboxy-2-methoxyphenylglucuronide
Adrenaline	Metanephrine*
Isoprenaline	3-methoxyisoprenaline*

*Both are excreted in bile as glucuronide conjugates

at both simultaneously:

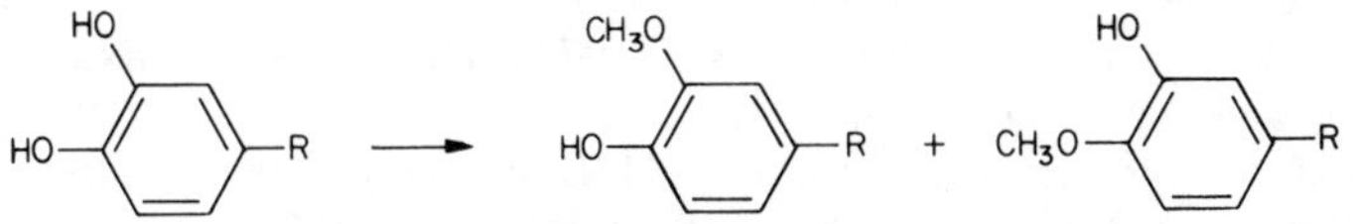

The proportion of *meta* to *para* methylation depends upon the nature of the group R. When the side chain R is unsaturated, there is nearly as much *meta* as *para*-methylation but when R is saturated *p*-methylation is much less than *m*-methylation. Thus, there occurs little if any *p*-methylation of adrenaline in the body and only the *m*-methylated compound, metanephrine is formed.

Besides the phenolic hydroxyl group methylation of aromatic amines and of the tertiary nitrogen of aromatic systems as in pyridine can occur – but these pathways seem to be of minor significance. The methylation of *N*-heterocycles such as pyridine and quinoline results in the formation of strongly basic quaternary ammonium compounds.

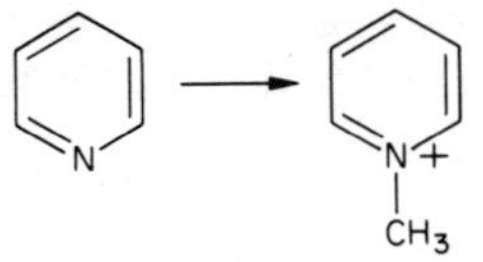

Pyridine   *N*–methylpyridine

The source of the methyl group in biological methylation is methionine which is utilised in an active form, namely, *S*-adenosylmethionine, formed from the amino acid and ATP.

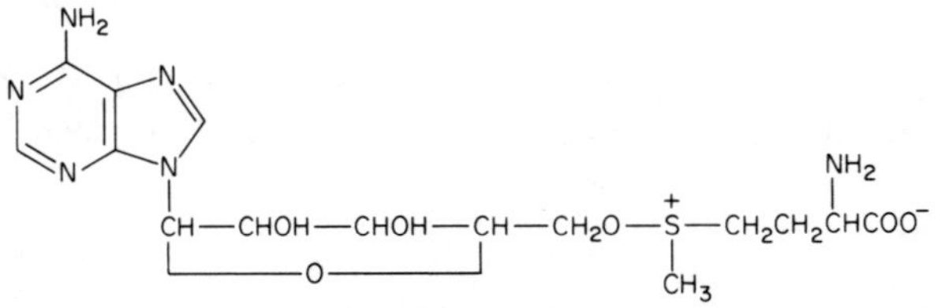

S–adenosylmethionine

Under the influence of a methyltransferase enzyme, the methyl group of *S*-adenosylmethionine is transferred to the appropriate receptor. Several transferases are known which catalyse various *O*-, *N*- and *S*-methylations.

REFERENCES

Bickel, M. H. (1969) *Pharmacol. Rev.*, **21**, 325.

Brodie, B. B. and Gillette, J. R. (1971) *Handbook of Experimental Pharmacology*, **28**, I and II.

Davies, D. S., Morgan, C. D., Conolly, M. E., Paterson, J. W., Sandler, M. and Dollery, C. T. (1969) *Fed. Proc.*, **28**, 797.

Drasar, B. S., Hill, M. J. and Williams, R. E. O. (1970) In *Metabolic Aspects of Food Safety*, p. 245, Edited by F. J. C. Roe, Blackwell, Oxford.

Dutton, G. J. (1966) In *Glucuronic Acid, Free and Combined*, p. 185, Edited by G. J. Dutton, Academic Press, New York and London.

Fischer, L. J. and Millburn, P. (1970) *J. Pharmacol. exp. Ther.*, **175**, 267.

Fishman, W. H. (1970) *Metabolic Conjugation and Metabolic Hydrolysis*, Volumes I and II, Academic Press, New York and London.

Gillette, J. R. (1971) *Handbook of Experimental Pharmacology*, **28**, II, 349.

Gingell, R., Bridges, J. W. and Williams, R. T. (1971) *Xenobiotica*, **1**, 143.

Holtzman, J. L., Gram, T. E., Gigon, P. L. and Gillette, J. R. (1968) *Biochem. J.*, **10**, 407.

Irving, C. C., Wiseman, R. Jr. and Hill, J. T. (1967) *Cancer. Res.*, **27**, 2309.

Jerina, D. M., Daly, J. W., Witkop, B., Zaltzman-Nirenberg, P. and Udenfriend, S. (1958) *J. Amer. chem. Soc.*, **90**, 6525.

Levine, W. G., Millburn, P., Smith, R. L. and Williams, R. T. (1970) *Biochem. Pharmacol.*, **19**, 235.

Levine, W. G. (1971) *Life Sci.*, **10**, Part II, 727

Levitz, M., Katz, J. and Twombly, G. H. (1965) *Steroids*, **6**, 553.

Palmer, R. H. (1967) *Proc. nat. Acad. Sci. (Wash.)*, **58**, 1047.

Parke, D. V. (1968) *The Biochemistry of Foreign Compounds*, Pergamon Press, London.

Smith, R. L. and Williams, R. T. (1966) In *Glucuronic Acid, Free and Combined*, p. 457, Edited by G. J. Dutton, Academic Press, New York and London.

Williams, R. T. (1959) *Detoxication Mechanisms*, 2nd ed., Chapman and Hall, London.

Williams, R. T. (1968) In *Biogenesis of Natural Compounds*, p. 590, Edited by P. Bernfeld, 2nd ed., Pergamon Press, Oxford and New York.

CHAPTER FIVE

Influence of Binding to Plasma Proteins and Renal Excretion on Biliary Elimination

Binding to plasma proteins

Early studies suggested that there may be a correlation between affinity for interaction with plasma proteins and excretion in the bile. Thus, Sandberg and Slaunwhite (1956) found that for a series of steroids, those that are highly excreted in human bile appear to be more highly bound to plasma proteins than those that are not. Brauer (1959) also suggested that organic carboxylic acids which are extensively eliminated in bile also tend to complex strongly with plasma proteins. There are two reasons why binding to plasma proteins was thought to be of significance in biliary excretion. Firstly, binding to the plasma albumin appeared to provide a mechanism for transport of the substance to the liver since substances such as bromsulphthalein and bilirubin both of which are highly excreted in the bile, are highly bound to plasma proteins prior to being taken up by the liver. Secondly, it was thought that there may be analogies between the processes involved in binding to plasma proteins and the mechanism of hepatic uptake.

It is true that many substances such as bilirubin, steroids, bromsulphthalein and glycyrrhetic acid, which are highly excreted in bile, are extensively bound to plasma albumin, but nevertheless there appears to be no direct relationship between the two phenomena. This is because the above compounds, although they are strongly bound to and are transported by the plasma proteins, appear in bile as metabolic transformation products which are more water-soluble and considerably less protein bound. Thus, bilirubin occurs in plasma predominantly bound to plasma albumin (Klatskin and Bungard, 1956; Ostrow and Schmid, 1963) but its glucuronide which appears in bile is less well bound (Billing *et al.*, 1963). Similarly, bromsulphthalein is strongly bound to plasma proteins (Baker and Bradley, 1966) but the form found in bile, namely, the glutathione conjugate, has an affinity for binding to plasma proteins 100 times less than BSP itself. The two sulphonamide drugs, sulphamethomidine and sulphadimethoxine are highly bound (90 and about 100% respectively) to plasma proteins in rat plasma and both are excreted in rat bile as their respective N^1-glucuronides. These conjugates however, are bound to plasma proteins to a much smaller extent, i.e. 28 and 33% respectively.

The hepatic uptake of the compound, which may be a prerequisite for its excretion in bile does not appear to be markedly affected by strong binding to plasma proteins. This is probably because the rate of association or dissociation of the compound — albumin complex occurs so rapidly that it is unlikely to be a limiting factor for hepatic uptake. The rate of dissociation of the albumin complex of the acid azo dye, 1-naphthol-4-[4-(4'azobenzeneazo)]-

Table 16
Plasma binding and biliary excretion of some sulphathiazole derivatives

Compound	R	Mol. wt.	% Bound to plasma	% dose excreted in bile in 3 h
Succinylsulphathiazole	CH$_2$CO— ǀ CH$_2$COOH	355	82	36
Phthalylsulphathiazole		403	88	22
Hexahydrophthalyl-sulphathiazole		409	88	80
Tetrachlorophthalyl-sulphathiazole		541	>97	63

Data from Hirom (1970)

phenylarsonic acid, occurs with a half time of 20 milliseconds (Froese *et al.*, 1962). Thus, although bilirubin is strongly bound to plasma albumin the latter does not participate in the transfer of bilirubin across the liver parenchymal cell membrane indicating that some dissociation occurs on or prior to uptake (Brown *et al.*, 1965). Similarly, bromsulphthalein although strongly protein bound is rapidly taken up by rat liver slices whether or not protein is present in the medium (Brauer and Pessotti, 1949), though albumin does reduce its rate of uptake in perfused livers (Andrews and del Rio Lozano, 1961).

Hirom (1970) has investigated the plasma binding and biliary excretion of four sulphonamide derivatives in the rat and found no direct relationship between the two. In this case all four compounds are excreted unchanged so that the binding phenomena investigated are concerned with the actual molecular form excreted. As can be seen from Table 16 three of the sulphonamides are moderately bound (82–88%) but they vary widely in the extent of biliary excretion (22–80%). Also, one compound, tetrachlorophthalylsulphathiazole is more strongly bound (>97%) than hexahydrophthalyl-sulphathiazole but its excretion in bile (63% of dose) is less than that of the latter (80%).

Inter-relationship between urinary and biliary excretion

Drugs and their metabolites are usually cleared from the body by elimination in the urine or bile or both. Occasionally, depending upon the compound, other channels of excretion such as the expired air, sweat and saliva may be of significance. Extra-hepatic excretion will clearly reduce the amounts of compound available for elimination in the bile. The most important of the extrahepatic excretion channels is of course the urine, and urinary elimination can in some cases have an important bearing on the biliary excretion of a compound.

The small biliary excretion of substances of relatively low molecular weight has at various times been attributed to their rapid and effective removal from the body by urinary excretion. This is not the case however, since the biliary excretion of such compounds remains small even when loss by urinary excretion is prevented. This can be seen from the data in Table 17 which shows the extent of biliary excretion of four simple aromatic compounds in bile fistula rats with and without functioning kidneys. The biliary excretion of these compounds is low in both groups of animals. Blocking the renal route by ligation of the kidneys slightly increases the biliary excretion but even so at 3 h after injection of the compounds, 90–99% of the compound still remains in the body.

Table 17

Effect of stopping urinary excretion on the biliary elimination of some low molecular weight aromatic compounds in the rat

		% dose in bile of rats in 3 h	
Compound	Mol. wt.	Control	Renal ligated
Benzoic acid	122	1	5
4-aminophenylglucuronide	285	0.1	0.2
4-acetamidohippuric acid	236	1.3	9
3-aminophenylsulphate	189	0.2	1

Data from Abou-El-Makarem *et al.* (1967)

Complementary relationship of urinary and biliary excretion

Some evidence favours the view that the urinary and biliary pathways for the elimination of foreign compounds and their metabolites may be complementary to each other. There are three main patterns of excretion of foreign compounds and their metabolites from the body. They may be eliminated almost entirely in either the urine or the bile or they may appear in varying proportions in both. Table 18 shows some examples of the excretion patterns of various conjugates in the rat.

Simple conjugates of relatively low molecular weight such as phenylsulphate, 4-acetamidohippuric acid and benzoylglucuronide are excreted almost entirely in the urine. Conjugates of relatively high molecular weight

Table 18

Patterns of excretion of various conjugates in the rat

Main route of excretion		
Urine	Phenylsulphate	(174)
	4-acetamidohippuric acid	(236)
	Benzoylglucuronide	(298)
Urine and Bile	α-tetralylglucuronide	(324)
	Vanilloyl glucuronide	(344)
	Sulphadimethoxine N^1-glucuronide	(487)
Bile	Stilboestrol glucuronide	(445)
	Phenolphthalein disulphate	(479)
	Glycyrrhetic acid glucuronide	(647)

Molecular weights are shown in parentheses.

Table 19

Urinary excretion of drugs in the rat: influence of molecular weight

Compound	Mol. wt. range (approx)	% dose eliminated in urine
Phenylsulphate; indoxylsulphate; hippuric acid; phenacetylglycine cyclamate; sulphacetamide	<250	90–100
Methylenedisalicylic acid; succinyl-sulphathiazole; morphine glucuronide; tartrazine	250–450	20–60
Phenolphthalein disulphate; bromochlorophenol blue; bromocresol green; indocyanine green	500–800	<5

such as the glucuronides of stilboestrol and glycyrrhetic acid and phenolphthalein disulphate are eliminated almost entirely in the bile. Conjugates of intermediate molecular weight are excreted to varying proportions in both urine and bile.

It thus appears that as in the case of biliary elimination, an important factor influencing the urinary excretion of a compound is its molecular weight. Table 19 indicates the significance of molecular weight in influencing the extent of urinary excretion in the rat of a number of compounds drawn at random from the literature. Urinary excretion in the rat accounts for 90–100% of the dose of several simple compounds having molecular weights less than about 250. Conversely, urinary excretion in the rat of several high molecular weight compounds (500–800) accounts for less than 5% of the dose. For several substances of intermediate molecular weight (250–450), urinary elimination is also intermediate (20–60% of dose).

The view that molecular weight has an important bearing on the extent of urinary excretion of a compound is also supported by the results found by Hirom *et al.* (1972) for a series of sulphonamides. For a series of sulphonamides, most of which are excreted unchanged when injected into rats, the amount recovered in urine dropped as the molecular weight increased (Table 20).

Three processes may be involved in the excretion of a substance by the kidneys: glomerular filtration, tubular secretion and tubular reabsorption. The most effective combination consists of clearance by filtration and tubular

Table 20

Urinary excretion of sulphonamides in the rat: influence of molecular weight

Compound	Mol. weight range	% dose in urine
Sulphathiazole Acetylsulphathiazole Succinylsulphanilamide	250—300	80—90
Succinylsulphacetamide Phthalylsulphanilamide Oxalylsulphathiazole	300—350	60—80
Succinylsulphathiazole Glutarylsulphathiazole Adipylsulphathiazole	350—400	40—60
Hexahydrophthalylsulphathiazole Carboxynaphthoylsulphathiazole Tetrachlorophthalylsulphathiazole	400—550	10—35

secretion with little or no reabsorption occurring. It is striking that many of the compounds which have been shown to undergo clearance in the urine by filtration and tubular secretion are organic anions of relatively low molecular weight particularly the polar glycine, sulphate and glucuronide conjugates. Weiner and Mudge (1964) quote many such examples in their review and three of these may be quoted here namely phenylsulphate (mol. wt. 142), 4-aminohippurate (194) and resorcinol glucuronide (254). By contrast there are several examples of glucuronide conjugates of relatively high molecular weight which appear to be excreted in the urine by a process of filtration without tubular secretion. Thus, in man the glucuronides of both andros-terone and aetiocholanolone are excreted in the urine by glomerular filtration (Kellie and Smith, 1957). Similarly, pregnanediol glucuronide is probably excreted in the urine of the chicken solely by glomerular filtration, since the conjugate is not actively secreted by the kidneys (Sperber, 1948). Though much more data is required on this point it is provocative that while active tubular secretion of low molecular weight conjugates occurs, the hepatic secretion of such compounds is poor while the converse seems to be true for higher molecular weight conjugates. In this sense the two excretory pathways seem to be complementary to each other.

Many compounds are excreted in quantity in both urine and bile, the proportions appearing in the two excreta depending upon the nature of the substance and species. Such chemicals or their metabolites have characteristics favourable for both hepatic and renal elimination. Thus, about 40% of an injected dose of tartrazine is excreted in the bile of the female rat and about 45% in the urine (Gregson *et al*., 1972). Clearly this substance, which is excreted unchanged, has properties suitable for both renal and hepatic elimination to occur. The biliary excretion of substances of this type is usually markedly increased if loss in the urine is prevented. The enhanced biliary excretion of such compounds can be attributed to increased availability to the liver.

REFERENCES

Abou-El-Makarem, M. M., Millburn, P., Smith, R. L. and Williams, R. T. (1967) *Biochem, J.,* **105**, 1269.

Andrews, W. H. H. and del Rio Lozano, I. (1961) *Quart. J. exp. Physiol.,* **46**, 238.

Baker, K. J. and Bradley, S. E. (1966) *J. clin. Invest.,* **45**, 281.

Billing, B. H., Maggiore, Q. and Carter, M. A. (1963) *Ann. N. Y. Acad. Sci.,* **111**, 319.

Brauer, R. W. and Pessotti, R. L. (1949) *J. Pharmacol. exp. Ther.,* **97**, 358.

Brauer, R. W. (1959) *J. Amer. med. Ass.,* **169**, 1462.

Brown, W. R., Grodsky, G. M., Carbone, J. V. (1964) *Amer. J. Physiol.,* **207**, 1237.

Froese, A., Sehon, A. H. and Eigen, M. (1962) *Can. J. Chem.,* **40**, 1786.

Gregson, R. H. S., Hirom, P. C., Millburn, P. Smith, R. L. Turbert, H. B. and Williams, R. T. (1972) *J. Pharm. Pharmacol.,* **24**, 20.

Hirom, P. C. (1970) Ph.D., Thesis, University of London.

Hirom, P. C., Millburn, P., Smith, R. L. and Williams, R. T. (1972) In press.

Kellie, A. E. and Smith, E. R. (1957) *Biochem. J.,* **66**, 490.

Klatskin, G. and Bungards, L. (1956). *J. clin. Invest.,* **35**, 537.

Ostrow, J. D. and Schmid, R. (1963) *J. clin. Invest.,* **42**, 1286.

Sandberg, A. A. and Slaunwhite, W. R. (1956) *J. clin. Endocr.,* **16**, 923.

Sperber, I. (1948) *K. LantbrHögsk. Annlr.,* **15**, 317.

Weiner, I. M. and Mudge, G. H. (1964) *Amer. J. Med.,* **36**, 743.

CHAPTER SIX

Species Variations in Biliary Excretion

The biliary excretion of foreign compounds and their metabolites has been studied in but a few species – probably not more than twenty or so. Nevertheless it appears that all the species studied which include rodents, carnivores, avians, fish and man and some sub-human primates have the ability to eliminate foreign compounds and their metabolites in the bile. The extent, however, to which such compounds are eliminated in the bile can vary widely with species for reasons that are still largely obscure. One of the earliest observations on a species difference in biliary excretion is probably that of Bradley and Ivy (1940) who found that the drug cinchophen is highly excreted (up to 70% of dose) in the bile of dogs but not of rabbits (Berman and Ivy, 1940).

That animal species vary in the extent to which they use the biliary route for the elimination of drugs and their metabolites is a fact not only of academic interest but also of considerable practical significance (Smith, 1970). It is of importance, for example, when selecting animal species for the evaluation of drugs and veterinary materials which require for their proper function to be localized within the hepatobiliary system. Thus, one may be misled unless a careful choice of species is made, and particularly if the results are to be extrapolated to man or domestic species. This may apply, for example in the development of compounds for use as radio-contrast media for visualization of the gall-bladder and biliary tract, as choleretics and as chemotherapeutic agents for treating bile duct infections and parasitic infestations such as those due to *Fasciola*.

The occurrence of extensive biliary elimination of certain compounds in some species but not in others may have important toxicological implications and this may be a factor in determining inter-species variations in response to a toxic agent. Some drugs for example may tend to persist in certain species in which extensive biliary excretion occurs, because of enterohepatic circulation.

Interspecies variation in biliary excretion are almost certainly the basis of many old observations in the literature that the faecal excretion of various injected compounds often tends to be higher in species such as the rat and dog which are 'good' biliary excretors compared to the rabbit and monkey which relatively speaking are 'poor' biliary excretors. The rat for example excretes 75% of an injected dose of stilboestrol in the faeces whereas the rabbit eliminates the drug mainly in the urine. The high faecal excretion of stilboestrol in the rat is related to its extensive biliary excretion in this species (Fischer et al., 1966). Similarly, the faecal excretion of injected 5,5'-methylenedisalicylic acid is less than one per cent of the dose in the rabbit, guinea pig and monkey – in which little biliary excretion of this drug occurs, whereas faecal excretion in the rat accounts for 30% of the dose – due to extensive biliary excretion (Davison and Williams, 1968).

Biliary excretion of low molecular weight compounds ($<$ about 300)

Experience has shown that with the exception of certain quaternary ammonium compounds, the extent of biliary excretion of foreign compounds and their metabolites having molecular weights less than about 300 or so is uniformly low ($<5-10\%$ of dose) in all species so far studied. This applies to compounds of endogenous as well as exogenous origin since many metabolites of intermediary metabolism having low molecular weights e.g. the amino acids, glucose and urea are not extensively excreted in bile. Low molecular weight compounds are usually eliminated in the urine, or if volatile, in the expired air.

Table 21 shows that the extent of biliary excretion of three low molecular weight aromatic compounds, benzoic acid, aniline and 4-acetamidohippuric acid is small ($1-6\%$ of dose) in some eight species. While these species resemble each other in that they excrete relatively small amounts of these compounds and their metabolites in the bile, there is a species variation in the nature of the transformation products eliminated. Thus, hippuric acid is the main biliary metabolite of benzoic acid in the guinea pig and rabbit while ornithuric acid is the major biliary metabolite in the hen. Cats excrete in the bile free 2-aminophenol whereas the other species eliminate conjugates of either 2-or 4-aminophenol or both (Abou-El-Makarem et al., 1967a). This species difference is not surprising since the ortho -hydroxylation of aniline is higher than para-hydroxylation in the cat (Parke and Williams, 1956) in which glucuronic acid conjugation is at a low level (Capel et al., 1972).

Table 21
Biliary excretion of low molecular weight benzene derivatives in various species

	% dose in bile in 3 h							
	Rat	Guinea pig	Rabbit	Dog	Cat	Sheep	Rhesus monkey	Hen
⬡—COOH Benzoic acid	1	2	1	1	1	—	—	1
⬡—NH$_2$ Aniline	6	6	3	1	2	—	—	3
CH$_3$CONH—⬡—CONHCH$_2$COOH 4-acetamidohippuric acid	1	1	2	4	1	4	1	1

Data from Abou-El-Makarem (1967a)

Biliary excretion in various species of polar compounds of molecular weights in the range of 300–500

Marked species variations in the extent of biliary excretion of anions having molecular weights in the approximate range of 300–600 can occur. For anions of higher molecular weight, it seems that interspecies variations are less since all species so far studied excrete such compounds extensively in the bile.

Some examples of interspecies variations in the biliary excretion of foreign compounds are shown in Table 22. Three of the compounds are conjugates, namely, the glucuronides of stilboestrol, sulphadimethoxine and phenolph-thalein having molecular weights of 445, 487 and 495 respectively and all are excreted in the bile unchanged. The other two compounds, methylene-disalicylic acid (mol. wt. 288) and succinylsulphathiazole (mol. wt. 355) are also polar compounds and also appear in the bile unchanged.

The most extensive comparative data is for succinylsulphathiazole and it is quite clear that there are marked species differences in the pattern of its biliary excretion. Its biliary excretion is relatively high (20–30% of the dose in 3 h) in the rat, fruit bat, hen and dog but very low in the rabbit, guinea pig and rhesus monkey (0.2–1% of the dose). The cat and sheep are intermediate, and excrete about 7% of the dose in the bile. The species covering for 5,5'-methylenedisalicylic acid is less extensive but nevertheless the same marked species variation in biliary excretion is clear. Thus, the rat and dog excrete about 50–60% of the dose in the bile in 6 h while the corresponding values for the rabbit and guinea pig are 5% and 4% respectively. Similar but less dramatic species differences in biliary excretion occur with the other compounds of higher molecular weight (445–495). The biliary excretion of stilboestrol glucuronide for example accounts for 70–90% of the dose in the rat, hen, dog and cat and only 20–30% in the guinea pig and rabbit. Parallel species differences occur with both sulphadimethoxine N^1-glucuronide and phenolphthalein glucuronide whose biliary excretion is high in the rat, hen and dog but low in the rabbit, guinea pig and rhesus monkey. The cat and sheep once again appear to be intermediate.

These species differences arise from the fact that the value for the threshold molecular weight for appreciable biliary excretion to occur, varies from species to species. From studies on the biliary excretion of aromatic compounds for example, it has been proposed that the threshold molecular weights for the rat, guinea pig and rabbit are of the order 325 ± 50, 400± ± 50 and 475 ± 50 respectively (Millburn et al., 1967; Abdel Aziz et al., 1971). The threshold values for the other species have not been ascertained but they almost certainly lie in the range of 300–500 or so.

Table 22

Interspecies variations in the biliary excretion of compounds of molecular weight in the range 300–500

Species	% dose excreted in bile in 3 or 6 h				
	Methylene disalicylic acid (288)	Succinyl-sulphathiazole (355)	Stilboestrol glucuronide (445)	Sulphadimethoxine N^1-glucuronide (487)	Phenolphthalein glucuronide (495)
Rat	54	29	95	43	54
Dog	65	20	65	43	81
Hen	–	25	93	–	71
Fruit bat	–	25	–	–	–
Cat	–	7	77	–	34
Sheep	–	7	–	–	38
Rabbit	5	1	32	10	13
Guinea pig	4	1	20	12	6
Pig	–	<1	–	–	–
Rhesus monkey	–	<1	–	–	9

For details of dosing and period of bile collection see Abou-El-Makarem *et al.* (1967a); Davison and Williams (1968) and Aziz *et al.* (1971). Molecular weights are shown in parentheses.

These interspecies variations give rise to important differences in the ways in which different species excrete drugs and their metabolites. Thus, a species such as the rat with a low molecular weight threshold may largely excrete a compound by the biliary route and ultimately in the faeces, whereas a species having a high threshold molecular weight requirement may eliminate the compound and its metabolites in the urine.

Structures of compounds of molecular weights in the range 300–500 approx. used in comparative biliary excretion studies.

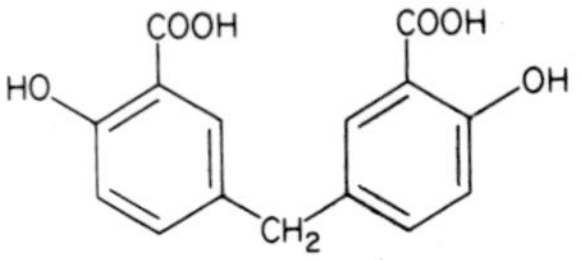

5,5′-Methylenedisalicylic acid

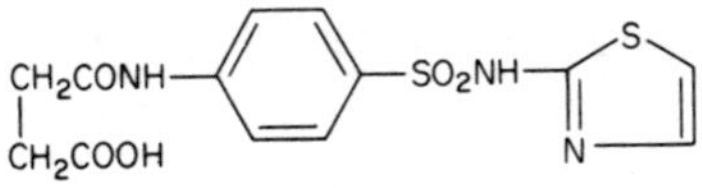

Succinylsulphathiazole

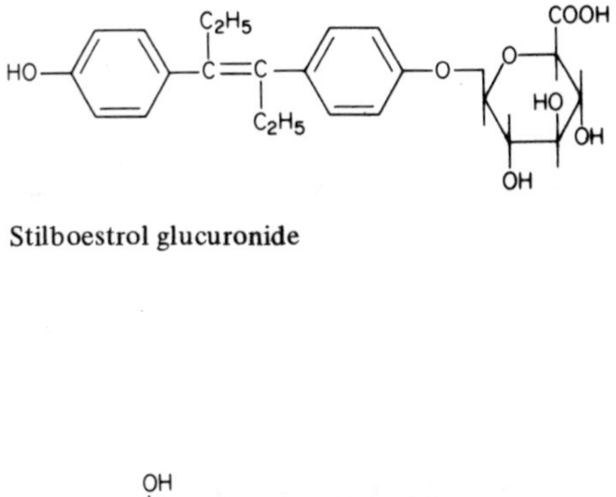

Stilboestrol glucuronide

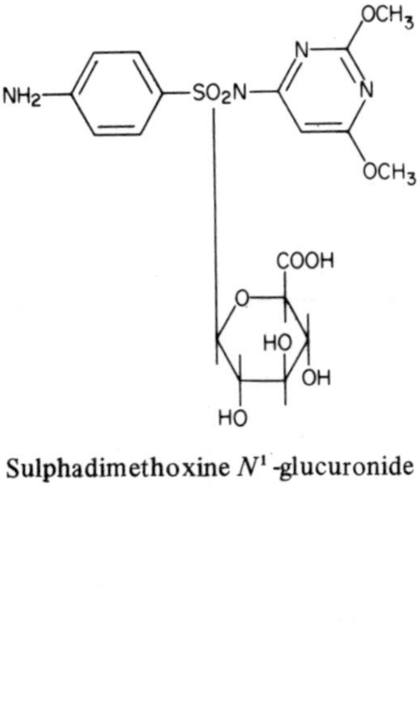

Sulphadimethoxine N^1-glucuronide

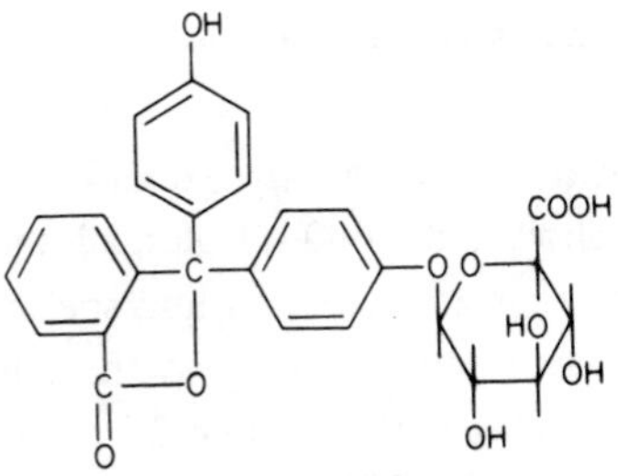

Phenolphthalein glucuronide

Further examples of interspecies variations in biliary excretion of compounds

Some further examples of interspecies variations in biliary excretion are shown in Table 23. Morphine (mol. wt. 285) for example is largely transformed *in vivo* to its 3-glucuronide which has a molecular weight of 461. The biliary excretion of this compound as might be expected, is high in the rat, guinea pig and dog but relatively low in the rabbit, rhesus monkey and man. Similarly, the biliary excretion of chloramphenicol (mol. wt. 323) which is largely eliminated as its 3-glucuronide (mol. wt. 499) is high in the good biliary excretors, the rat and dog, but low in the rhesus monkey and man. Griseofulvin (mol. wt. 353) is extensively eliminated as metabolites in the bile of rats but not of rabbits and tartrazine (mol. wt. 468) is highly excreted in the bile of the rat and guinea pig but not the rabbit.

Table 23
Further examples of interspecies variations in biliary excretion

| Species | % dose eliminated in the bile | | | |
	Morphine[a]	Chloramphenicol[b]	Griseofulvin[c]	Tartrazine[d]
Rat	63	80	80	49
Guinea pig	50	—	—	39
Dog	35–50	60	—	—
Rabbit	8	—	11	6
Rhesus monkey	5–20	15	—	—
Man	<1–7	3	—	—

[a]March and Elliott (1954); Woods (1954); Mellett and Woods (1956); Elliott *et al.* (1954); Hirom, P. C., Millburn, P and Smith, R. L. Unpublished data
[b]Glazko (1967)
[c]Symchowicz *et al.* (1967)
[d]Gregson *et al.* (1972)

Biliary excretion of organic anions with molecular weights above about 500–600

Experience and systematic studies have shown that the biliary excretion of organic anions with molecular weights above about 500–600 is high in all the animal species so far studied. Differences in the rates at which various species excrete such compounds in the bile may occur but nevertheless the bile appears to be the dominant channel for their elimination. Table 24 shows seven examples of anionic compounds (mol. wt. > 500) which are highly excreted (50–100% of dose) in the bile of some five species, including man.

Table 24
The biliary excretion of some organic anions of mol. wt. >500–600 in various species

% dose excreted in bile

Species	Dichloromethotrexate[a] (524)	Bromochlorophenol Blue[b] (580)	Bromophenol Blue[b] (669)	Bromocresol green[b] (697)	Indocyanine green[c] (753)	Sulphobromophthalein[d] (794)	Rose Bengal[e] (793)
Rat	80	89	69	73	82	82	56
Guinea pig	–	98	99	100	97	92	–
Dog	80	–	–	–	97	56–97	–
Rabbit	38	75	82	85	94	–	50–70
Man	60	–	–	–	70	61	high

[a]Oliverio and Davidson (1962); Davidson (1965).
[b]Aziz et al. (1971).
[c]Wheeler et al. (1958); Caesar et al. (1961); Cherrick et al. (1960); Levine, Millburn, Smith and Williams – unpublished results.
[d]Schenker et al. (1965); Krebs (1959); Monroe and Kittinger (1961); Cantarow et al. (1948); Brauer and Pessotti (1950).
[e]Taplin et al. (1955); Nosslin and Morgan (1965); Meurman (1960).

Four of these, namely, bromochlorophenol blue, bromophenol blue, bromo-cresol green and indocyanine green are excreted unchanged. Sulphobromoph-thalein is excreted conjugated with glutathione, and this conjugate has a molecular weight in excess of 1000.

Biliary excretion of drugs in man

The biliary excretion of drugs and their metabolites, has not, for obvious ethical and practical reasons, been systematically studied in man. Never-theless, studies with certain groups of compounds particularly the steroids, antibiotics and X-ray contrast media clearly show that the biliary pathway can be an important channel of drug elimination in man.

Studies on the biliary excretion of drugs in man is also hampered by the lack of suitable techniques for complete bile collection. Most studies have been carried out on patients with T-tube drainage following operation and this probably rarely allows a total collection of bile to be made. Frequently, bile collected in this manner may be only 30–70% of the total output, assuming a daily output of hepatic bile in man of 800–1200 ml. There are further objections to the significance of such studies, namely, the effect of surgery on the hepato-biliary system and the influence of the original disease condition.

Some studies on drug excretion in bile have been made using a duodenal tube to withdraw aspirations composed of bile, gastric and pancreatic juice. The main problem here is that the aspirate is obviously composite and also one has to await the intermittent release of bile from the gall-bladder.

Because of differences in the modes of bile collection used by various investigators, different dose levels and routes of administration employed, it is difficult to make comparisons for the different compounds. Nevertheless certain useful generalizations can be made about biliary elimination of drugs in man. Firstly, although only a few compounds have been examined, it appears that drugs of relatively low molecular weight are poorly or not excreted in human bile. Thus, Beckett and Rowland (1965) found no amphetamine in the bile of a patient with a bile duct fistula following an oral dose of 10 mg (+)-amphetamine. Biliary excretion of the low molecular weight salicylate drugs is also at a low level in man as only small amounts of these compounds have been recovered in human bile at autopsy following the ingestion, either accidentally or for suicidal purposes, of large amounts of salicylates (Gross and Greenberg, 1948). Similarly, the biliary excretion of sulphanilamide is at a low level in man (Bettman and Spier, 1939).

Tables 25 and 26 show a compilation of various compounds, including steroids, antibiotics, diagnostic agents and various drugs which have been

Table 25
Drugs excreted in human bile

Drug	Mol. wt.	Dose and route	Method and duration (h) of bile collection	% dose in bile	Nature of material in bile	Reference
Taloximine	248	150 mg	T-tube drainage (48 h)	31	glucuronide conjugates	Griffin and Turner (1970)
Benzomethamine	356	50 mg i.m.	bile duct fistula (8h)	14	not identified	Levine and Clark (1955)
Indomethacin	358	not given	bile duct fistula (24h)	15	indomethacin glucuronide	Hucker et al. (1966)
Dichloromethotrexate	523	1.5 mg/kg i.v.	bile fistula	65	partly as 7-hydroxy derivative	Adamson (1971)
Carbenoxolone	571	100 or 200 mg orally	T-tube drainage	50–70	carbenoxolone 30-glucuronide	Downer et al. (1970)
Rifomycin SV	698	250 mg i.m.	bile fistula	60	not identified	Füresz and Scotti (1961)
Erythromycin	734	250 mg i.v.	bile fistula	30	not identified	Piller and Bernstein (1955)
Indocyanine green	775	0.7 mg/kg i.v.	T-tube drainage	70	unchanged	Hirom et al. (1972)
Bromsulphthalein	794	5 mg/kg i.v.	T-tube drainage	61	glutathione conjugates	Monroe and Kittinger (1961)
Rifamide	811	150 mg i.m.	T-tube drainage	56	unchanged	Acocella et al. (1966)

Table 26
Steroids excreted in human bile

Steroid	Mol. wt.	Dose and route	Method and duration of bile collection	% dose in bile	Nature of excreted material	Reference
Oestradiol	272	0.37–0.74 mg i.v.	bile fistula (12h)	52	conjugated	Sandberg and Slaunwhite (1957)
Oestriol	288	0.05–0.25 mg i.v.	bile fistula (72h)	23	not identified	Sandberg and Slaunwhite (1965)
Testosterone	288	0.2–1 mg i.v.	bile fistula (48h)	13	conjugated	Sandberg and Slaunwhite (1956)
Progesterone	314	0.36 mg i.v.	T-tube drainage	42	conjugated pregnanediol and pregnanolone	Wiest et al. (1958)
Deoxycorticosterone	330	4.7–9.4 μg i.v.	bile fistula (72h)	43	unidentified	Harris et al. (1967)
Corticosterone	346	i.v.	T-tube drainage (48h)	20–30	conjugated	Migeon et al. (1956)
Cortisone	360	i.v.	bile fistula	4	not identified	Peterson et al. (1957)
Hydrocortisone	362	50–500 mg i.v.	bile fistula (24h)	4	not identified	Peterson et al. (1955)

86

reported to undergo biliary excretion in man, and for which quantitative information is available. It should however be pointed out that many other drugs e.g. penicillins, tetracyclines, phenolphthalein, digitoxin and morphine have been reported to be excreted in human bile but in most of these cases adequate quantitative information is lacking. It can be seen that a number of drugs are extensively eliminated in human bile. Thus, for the following drugs, taloximine, dichloromethotrexate, carbenoxolone, rifomycin SV, erythromycin, indocyanine green, bromsulphthalein and rifamide, biliary excretion accounts for some 30–70% of the dose and probably more. It will be noted that these are all relatively high molecular weight polar compounds or they give rise to polar metabolites of high molecular weight (500–1000). It thus appears that the same two factors, namely, molecular weight and polarity which have been shown to have a bearing on biliary excretion in experimental animals, are also important for this process in man. These results may be taken to imply that biliary excretion of polar compounds or polar metabolites having a molecular weight in the region of 500–1000 or so may be expected to be appreciable in man. This view is supported by the extensive biliary excretion in man of the various high molecular weight cholecystographic media e.g. pheniodol, iopanoic acid, iophenoxic acid, iodophthalein and iodipamide which are polar compounds having molecular weights in the range 500–1200.

Further information about the significance of biliary excretion in man can be gained from studies on the elimination of steroids in the bile. Table 26 shows that extensive excretion (30–50% of dose) of certain steroids, namely, oestradiol, progesterone, deoxycorticosterone and corticosterone occurs in man. They appear in bile largely as anionic conjugates which would be expected to have molecular weights in the region of 500 or so. Other endogenous metabolites that are highly excreted in human bile e.g. conjugates of the bile acids and bilirubin have molecular weights in the approximate range 500–1000.

The result with benzomethamine (14% of dose in bile) shown in Table 25 is of interest since this is a quaternary ammonium compound of mol. wt. 356 and animal studies have suggested that the molecular weight criteria for the biliary excretion of cations may be lower than those for anions.

Species differences in the biliary excretion of organic cations

The biliary excretion of organic cations has been much less studied than for organic anions. Nevertheless sufficient information is available to indicate that the position is quite different and that the species variation found to exist for anions may not apply to cations. Thus, in one systematic study it

Table 27

Biliary excretion of some organic cations in the rat, guinea pig and rabbit

Compound		% dose in bile in 3 h		
	Mol. wt.	Rat	Guinea pig	Rabbit
$C_6H_5 \overset{+}{N}(CH_3)_3$ Trimethylphenylammonium	136	0.5	0.1	0.3
$(C_6H_5CH_2)_2 \overset{+}{N}(CH_3)_2$ Dibenzyldimethylammonium	226	27	41	29
$(C_6H_5CH_2)_3 \overset{+}{N}.CH_3$ Tribenzylmethylammonium	302	39	38	41

Hughes *et al.* (1972)

was found that the extent of biliary excretion of two simple mono-onium compounds having molecular weights of 226 and 302 respectively was relatively high in the rat, guinea pig and rabbit (Table 27). Both compounds are excreted in the bile unchanged. It is to be noted that the molecular weight of one of these, namely dibenzyldimethylammonium is a good deal less than that of the molecular weight requirement found to apply for anion excretion in the rat, guinea pig and rabbit. Similarly, the molecular weight of tribenzylmethylammonium (302) is well below the minimum proposed for anion excretion in bile in the guinea pig and rabbit. It thus appears that not only do different molecular weight criteria apply for hepatic excretion of cations but also the species patterns are quite different from those found for anions. Such views appear to be corroborated by other findings in the literature. Thus, the quaternary amine benzomethamine (mol. wt. 356) is excreted in rat, rabbit, and human bile to the extent of 31, 32 and 14% respectively (Levine and Clarke, 1955).

Because of the lower molecular weight requirements it appears probable that biliary excretion could be a more significant process for their elimination than is the case for many anions.

Factors determining interspecies variation in biliary excretion

It has been seen that marked variations occur in the extent to which various species excrete in the bile organic anions of molecular weight in the approximate range 300–500. Below this range biliary excretion appears to be uniformly low while above this it is high. Thus, any theory must explain why the minimum molecular weight threshold for biliary excretion varies with species. At the present time it appears that the species variations are related to differences in the excretion process and not to anatomical or physiological factors (see Abou-El-Makarem, 1967). Thus, although there are small anatomical differences (Elias, 1949 a,b) and differences, sometimes quite marked, in hepatic blood flow rates and bile production (see Table 28) these do not seem to be related to the question of species difference in biliary excretion.

That the species difference in biliary excretion may arise from differences in the nature of the excretion process is suggested from comparative studies on the biliary elimination of succinylsulphathiazole in the rat and rabbit. This compound is highly excreted in the bile of the rat but not of the latter species. In the rat an injected dose of $[^{14}C]$ succinylsulphathiazole is taken up by the liver and concentrated and concentratively transferred unchanged to the bile. Its excretion is depressed by the concomittant administration of other organic anions, such as bile salts and phenolphthalein glucuronide which are also excreted in the bile. Furthermore, the excretion process can be saturated by the administration of large doses of the compound. In the rabbit however there is little concentration of the drug in the liver and there is no concentrative transfer to the bile. Furthermore, its low biliary excretion in the rabbit is not influenced by giving other organic anions nor is it saturable.

Table 28
Bile flow and hepatic blood flow rates in various species

Species	Liver wt as % of total body weight	Hepatic blood flow rate* ml blood/ 100 g liver/min.	Bile flow rate ml bile/kg body wt/day
Rat	3.36	79	28.6–47.1
Guinea pig	3.86	–	228
Rabbit	3.2	74†	118
Cat	3.59	35–48	14
Dog	2.94	82	12
Hen	1.53	–	14
Sheep	2.97	–	12
Monkey	2.09	–	28

* Hepatic arterial and portal. The above values have been mainly taken from or calculated from data given in *Handbook of Biological Data* (editor, W. S. Spector, W. B. Saunders Company Philadelphia) and from *Blood and Other Body Fluids* (editor D. S. Dittmer, Federation of American Societies for Experimental Biology Washington D.C.)
† Dobson and Jones (1952)

(Abou-El-Makarem *et al.*, 1967b). This difference could be related to differences in the uptake, the secretion of the compound or its reabsorption from the biliary ductule system. Some preliminary studies suggest that the latter could be a factor in explaining the marked difference in biliary excretion of succinylsulphathiazole in the rat and rabbit. When this compound is given by retrograde infusion into the biliary system of the rabbit the compound is apparently readily absorbed and rapidly excreted in the urine whereas the converse occurs in the rat (Clark, Hirom, Millburn and Smith — unpublished findings). If a reabsorption process is important in biliary excretion it is possible that there are species variations in the size of organic anions that can be absorbed from the biliary canaliculi system.

Sex factors in biliary excretion

While marked interspecies variations in the extent of biliary excretion of foreign compounds can occur, little is known about the influence of other biological factors such as sex and strain. Sex differences in the extent of biliary excretion of several compounds have been described to occur in the rat but not so far in other species. The pattern appears to be haphazard, for with some compounds biliary excretion in the female is greater than in the male while the reverse may be true for other compounds, and with some compounds there may be no sex difference.

In some cases sex differences in biliary excretion may be due to sex differences in metabolism, particularly in those cases where a compound acquires by metabolism the appropriate properties of adequate molecular weight and polarity for biliary excretion. The rate of glucuronide formation for example is faster in male rats than in females and this could therefore influence the biliary excretion of a compound which undergoes metabolic conjugation prior to elimination in the bile.

In other cases the sex difference is seen with compounds that are excreted unchanged and therefore the difference is due to other reasons, perhaps the excretion process itself.

The phenomenon may be best illustrated by considering a number of examples but particularly tartrazine which is the best studied case. Tartrazine is the sodium salt of a tribasic acid whose trianion has a molecular weight of 465. When injected intravenously, cannulated male rats eliminate about 17% of the dose in the bile unchanged and about 70% in the urine whereas cannulated female rats excrete 40% in the bile and 45% in the urine (Gregson *et al.*, 1972). This sex difference in the pattern of excretion of tartrazine is also seen in intact rats for intact males excrete 85% of an injected dose in the urine while females eliminate only 51% by this route. This difference in excretion pattern is conditioned by the sex hormones since pretreatment of males with oestradiol markedly enhances their ability to excrete tartrazine in the bile while the opposite effect is seen in females treated with testosterone (Bertagni *et al.*, 1972). The sex difference in respect of tartrazine which is excreted unchanged seems to be peculiar to the rat as it does not occur in the guinea pig or rabbit.

A sex difference in the biliary excretion in the rat of indocyanine green, which is also eliminated unchanged, has been observed. Thus, female rats excrete 87% of an injected dose of the dye in the bile in 1.5 h whereas the value for males is only 41% (Hart *et al.*, 1969). The reverse situation however appears to hold for chlorothiazide which is more highly excreted in the bile of males than of females. Daniel and Gage (1965) found that in experiments with single animals, there occurred a much greater biliary excretion of ^{14}C after the oral administration of $[^{14}C]$butylated hydroxytoluene to a male than after administration to a female rat.

Whether or not sex differences in biliary excretion occur in man are not known but clearly this could be important particularly in respect of the enterohepatic circulation of drug metabolites.

Table 29
Sex differences in the biliary excretion of tartrazine

Species	Sex	% dose in 3 h in	
		Bile	Urine
Rat	F	40	45
	M	17	72
Guinea pig	F	39	38
	M	33	47
Rabbit	F	6	67
	M	5	61

REFERENCES

Abou-El-Makarem, M. M. (1967) Ph.D. Thesis University of London.
Abou-El-Makarem, M. M., Millburn, P., Smith, R. L. and Williams, R. T. (1967a) *Biochem. J.*, **105**, 1289.
Abou-El-Makarem, M. M., Millburn, P. and Smith, R. L. (1967b) *Biochem. J.*, **105**, 1295.

Acocella, G., Lamarina, F., Tenconi, L. T. and Nicolis, F. B. (1966) *Gut*, 7, 380.

Adamson, R. H. (1971) *Ann. N.Y. Acad. Sci.*, 179, 432.

Aziz, F. T. A., Hirom, P. C., Millburn, P., Smith, R. L. and Williams, R. T. (1971) *Biochem. J.*, 125, 25P.

Beckett, A. H. and Rowland, M. (1965) *J. Pharm. Pharmacol.*, 17, 628.

Berman, A. L. and Ivy, J. H. (1940) *Proc. Soc. exp. Biol. (N.Y.)*, 45, 853.

Bertagni, P., Hirom, P. C., Millburn, P., Osiyemi, F. A., Smith, R. L., Turbert, H. B. and Williams, R. T. (1972) *J. Pharm. Pharmacol.*, 24, 620.

Bettman, R. and Spier, E. (1939) *Proc. Soc. exp. Biol. (N.Y.)*, 41, 463.

Bradley, W. B. and Ivy, A. C. (1940) *Proc. Soc. exp. Biol. (N.Y.)*, 45, 143.

Brauer, R. W. and Pessotti, R. L. (1950) *Amer. J. Physiol.*, 162, 565.

Caesar, J., Shaldon, S., Chinadussi, L., Guevara, L. and Sherlock, S. (1961) *Clin. Sci.*, 21, 43.

Cantarow, A., Wirts, C. W., Snape, W. J. and Miller, L. L. (1948) *Amer. J. Physiol.*, 154, 211.

Capel, I. D., French, M. R., Millburn, P., Smith, R. L. and Williams, R. T. (1972) *Xenobiotica*, 2, 25.

Cherrick, G. R., Stein, S. W., Leevy, C. M. and Davidson, C. S. (1960) *J. clin. Invest.*, 39, 592.

Daniel, J. W. and Gage, J. C. (1965) *Food Cosmet. Toxicol.*, 3, 405.

Davidson, J. D. (1965) In discussion of 'The influence of enterohepatic circulation on toxicity of drugs' by Williams, R. T., Millburn, P. and Smith, R. L. p. 110, *Ann. N.Y. Acad. Sci.*, 123, 124.

Davison, C. and Williams, R. T. (1968) *J. Pharm. Pharmacol.*, 20, 12.

Dobson, E. L. and Jones, H. B. (1952) *Acta med. Scand. Suppl.*, 273, 1.

Downer, H. D., Galloway, R. W., Horwich, L. and Parke, D. V. (1970) *J. Pharm. Pharmacol.*, 22, 479.

Elias, H. (1949a) *Amer. J. Anat.*, 84, 311.

Elias, H. (1949b) *Amer. J. Anat.*, 85, 379.

Elliott, H. W., Tolbert, B. M., Adler, T. K. and Anderson, H. H. (1954) *Proc. Soc. exp. Biol. (N.Y.)*, 85, 77.

Fischer, L. J., Millburn, P., Smith, R. L. and Williams, R. T. (1966) *Biochem. J.*, 100, 69P.

Füresz, S. and Scotti, R. (1961) *Farmaco. Ed. sci.*, 16, 262.

Glazko, A. J. (1967) Antimicrobial Agents and Chemotherapy – 1966, p. 655.

Gregson, R. H. S., Hirom, P. C., Millburn, P., Smith, R. L., Turbert, H. B. and Williams, R. T. (1972) *J. Pharm. Pharmacol.*, 24, 20.

Griffin, J. P. and Turner, P. (1970) *Brit. J. Pharmacol.*, 39, 249P.

Gross, M. and Greenberg, L. A. (1948) *The Salicylates*, p. 49, Hillhouse Press, New Haven.

Harris, J. J., Hoegel, C. and Crane, M. G. (1967) *J. clin. Endocr.*, 27, 106.

Hart, L. G., Guarino, A. M. and Adamson, R. H. (1969) *Amer. J. Physiol.*, 217, 46.

Hirom, P. C., Millburn, P., Smith, R. L. and Williams, R. T. (1972) *Biochem. J.*, 129, 1071.

Hucker, H. B., Zacchei, A. G., Cox, S. V., Brodie, D. A. and Cantwell, N. H. R. (1966) *J. Pharmacol. exp. Ther.,* **153**, 237.

Hughes, R., Millburn, P., Smith, R. L. and Williams, R. T. (1972) *Biochem. J.,* **128**, 144P.

Krebs, J. S. (1959) *Amer. J. Physiol.,* **197**, 292.

Levine, R. M. and Clark, B. B. (1955) *J. Pharmacol. exp. Ther.,* **114**, 63.

March, C. H. and Elliott, H. W. (1954) *Proc. Soc. exp. Biol. (N.Y.),* **86**, 494.

Mellett, L. B. and Woods, L. A. (1956) *J. Pharmacol. exp. Ther.,* **116**, 77.

Meurman, L. (1960) *Acta med. scand.,* Suppl. 354.

Migeon, C. J., Sandberg, A. A., Paul, A. C. and Samuels, L. T. (1956) *J. clin. Endocr.,* **16**, 1291.

Millburn, P., Smith, R. L. and Williams, R. T. (1967) *Biochem. J.,* **105**, 1275.

Monroe, L. S. and Kittinger, A. L. (1961) *J. Lab. clin. Med.,* **58**, 468.

Nosslin, B. and Morgan, E. H. (1965) *J. Lab. clin. Med.,* **65**, 891.

Oliverio, V. T. and Davidson, J. D. (1962) *J. Pharmacol. exp. Ther.,* **137**, 76.

Parke, D. V. and Williams, R. T. (1956) *Biochem. J.,* **63**, 12P.

Peterson, R. E., Wyngaarden, J. B., Guerra, S. L., Brodie, B. B. and Bunim, J. J. (1955) *J. clin Invest.,* **34**, 1779.

Peterson, R. E., Pierce, C. E., Wyngaarden, J. B., Bunim, J. J. and Brodie, B. B. (1957) *J. clin. Invest.,* **36**, 1301.

Piller, M. and Bernstein, A. (1955) *Schweiz. med. Wschr.,* **85**, 104.

Sandberg, A. A. and Slaunwhite, W. R. (1956) *J. clin. Invest.,* **35**, 1331.

Sandberg, A. A. and Slaunwhite, W. R. (1957) *J. clin. Invest.,* **36**, 1266.

Sandberg, A. A. and Slaunwhite, W. R. (1965) *J. clin. Invest.,* **44**, 694.

Schenker, S., Goldstein, J. and Combes, B. (1965) *Amer. J. Physiol.,* **208**, 563.

Smith, R. L. (1970) *Proc. Europ. Soc. Study Drug Toxicity,* **11**, 19.

Symchowicz, S., Staub, M. S. and Wong, K. K. (1967) *Biochem. Pharmacol.,* **16**, 2405.

Taplin, G. V., Meredith, O. M. and Kade, H. (1955) *J. Lab. clin. Med.,* **45**, 665.

Wheeler, H. O., Cranston, W. I. and Meltzer, J. I. (1958) *Proc. Soc. exp. Biol. (N.Y.),* **99**, 11.

Wiest, W. G., Fujimoto, G. I. and Sandberg, A. A. (1958) *J. clin. Endocr.,* **18**, 972.

Woods, L. A. (1954) *J. Pharmacol. exp. Ther.,* **112**, 158.

CHAPTER SEVEN

Mechanisms Involved in Biliary Excretion

The processes whereby compounds and their metabolites are concentratively transferred from blood into the bile remain obscure and little definite information can be given about them at the present time. This is largely due to our ignorance of the mechanisms involved in bile formation itself. The subject has been reviewed at various times and for more detailed information the reader is referred to the reviews of Brauer (1959), Sperber (1959), Schanker (1968) and Millburn (1970).

The transfer of a compound from blood to bile may usefully be considered to occur in a number of stages: (*a*) passage across the sinusoid wall, (*b*) uptake by the parenchymal cell, (*c*) metabolism, (*d*) concentrative transfer from the liver cell into the bile and (*e*) possible modification of the final bile composition by reabsorption processes.

Passage across the sinusoid wall

The lining of the sinusoid appears to have in its structure large pores which allow large molecules and even colloidal particles to pass through. Plasma proteins but not blood cells seem to pass through freely. Passage, even for large particles, appears to be rapid since 30 seconds after injection of colloidal thorium dioxide, electron micrographs have shown the presence of thorium particles on both surfaces of the endothelium as well as on the surface of the underlying hepatic cells. It would seem therefore that the sinusoid lining would be freely permeable to most drugs and other foreign chemicals and they would therefore readily have access to the liver parenchymal cells.

Passage into hepatic parenchymal cells

Biliary excretion is in the main a function of the hepatic parenchymal cells. The question of the uptake of drugs and other foreign chemicals into these cells therefore becomes important. Compounds which are excreted in bile in quantity in general show a marked tendency to localize initially in hepatic parenchymal tissue. This has been shown to occur for bromsulphthalein (Brauer and Pessotti, 1950) which is stored in high concentrations in the liver of dogs following its infusion; and both fluorescein (Hanzon, 1952) and digitoxin (Bine *et al.*, 1951) localize rapidly in the hepatic tissue of rats before they are excreted in the bile. According to some studies by Kurz (1961) the hepatic uptake of drugs is influenced by their lipid solubility; penetration into the liver being favoured by high lipid solubility. The significance of this factor is however probably limited since even very polar compounds such as succinylsulphathiazole and the glucuronide conjugates of stilboestrol, sulphadimethoxine and phenolphthalein are taken up by the liver and excreted in the bile.

Whether or not there are mechanisms within the parenchymal membrane by which the uptake of compounds into liver cells is facilitated is not known. Recently, two proteins designated Y and Z, which occur in rat liver cell cytoplasm and which bind anions such as bilirubin and bromsulphthalein, have been proposed as intracellular acceptors that, by binding, facilitate the transfer of organic anions from the plasma to the liver cell (Levi *et al.*, 1969). A number of points support this theory; the two proteins selectively bind various organic anions (Levi *et al.*, 1969). Y, the major hepatic anion-binding protein, is present exclusively in the liver. Its concentration increases after the administration of phenobarbitone and a concomitant increase in the uptake of organic anions by the liver occurs (Reyes *et al.*, 1969).

Most compounds taken up by the liver undergo metabolic transformation prior to excretion in the bile and often these changes are crucial for extensive biliary excretion to occur. The compound may undergo an initial oxidative, reductive or hydrolytic reaction and the product so formed may then undergo a conjugation reaction in which it is combined with a substance provided by the body from its carbohydrate or amino acid resources (p. 52). Whether or not compounds can be metabolized while attached to hepatic uptake proteins is not known but it seems unlikely. Probably only the unbound drug is metabolized; extensive binding probably does not impede metabolism because of the rapidity of dissociation of the protein-drug complex (p. 70).

The time required for metabolism, which is usually a prerequisite for biliary excretion to occur, may explain the delay which is found between the time of uptake of a compound into the liver and its subsequent appearance in bile. Thus, both sulphobromophthalein and fluorescein are taken up by the liver as soon as they appear in the blood stream, but secretion in bile is delayed, possibly because of metabolism which is slower initially than is uptake (Hanzon, 1952; Brauer and Pessotti, 1950).

Transfer of drugs and their metabolites from hepatic cells to bile

Substances which appear in bile following their administration have been divided by Brauer (1959) into three groups A, B and C according to their concentration in the bile compared with that of blood. Substances of Class A include those whose concentration in the bile is close to that of plasma i.e. the ratio bile concentration/blood concentration is close to unity. Such compounds include glucose and the ions Na^+, K^+ and Cl^-. Class B includes substances for which the bile/blood ratio is greater than 1, usually from 10 to 1000 as occurs for the bile salts, bilirubin diglucuronide and the conjugates of many drugs and hormones. This group of compounds show a marked tendency to be excreted in the bile. Class C comprises compounds for which the bile/blood ratio is less than 1 and includes substances such as proteins, inulin, sucrose and phosphates..

Compounds of Class B, which are the most interesting from the point of view of biliary excretion are in the main polar, water-soluble substances having molecular weights of about 300–400 and upwards. They appear to be amphipathic in character i.e. they possess both non-polar and hydrophilic groups. They are frequently conjugates such as glucuronides or conjugates with glutathione. A number of theories have been proposed to explain their movement from plasma to bile often against large concentration gradients.

The first suggestion is that they are transferred by an energy-dependent process of active transport (see Schanker 1968). This is suggested by the fact that movement of organic anions from liver cells to bile occurs against a concentration and an electro-chemical potential gradient. Furthermore, a number of compounds show a maximal rate of excretion (transport maximum; T_M value). The transfer mechanism is also saturable and certain compounds can compete with one another forexcretion in the bile. It is possible that the transfer of foreign organic anions into bile is accomplished by the same mechanism as that responsible for the transfer of the bile salts and bilirubin conjugates into bile since bile salts compete with certain foreign compounds for elimination in the bile.

In addition to an anion secreting mechanism the liver appears to possess a mechanism for the concentrative transfer of certain organic cations from liver to bile (Schanker and Solomon, 1963). The mechanism appears to be an active one since it is saturable and the excretion of one cation can be influenced by another but not by an anion. The natural substrates, if any, for this hepatic cation mechanism are unknown.

An alternative suggestion, which takes into account molecular size, an important factor in biliary excretion, is that biliary elimination may be, at least in part, a consequence of selective reabsorption (Clark *et al.*, 1971). It has been noted that compounds of relatively low molecular weight (< about 300) which are poorly excreted in the bile by the rat, are rapidly absorbed into the circulation and excreted in the urine if given by a technique of retrograde injection into the common bile duct. However, with compounds of higher molecular weight (>300) it was found that when given by the same route their absorption was impeded and they rapidly appeared in bile once flow was allowed to commence. This might suggest that during bile production there occurs the formation of a 'primary bile' whose composition is subsequently modified in the biliary tree by absorption of smaller molecules and ions leaving the larger ones behind.

A third mechanism suggested by Hirom (1970) depends upon the fact that bile salts and phospholipids can exist in the form of mixed micelles (see Hofmann and Small, 1967). It is suggested that many compounds that are excreted in bile in quantity are amphipathic in character and therefore they might be incorporated into the bile salt/phospholipid/cholesterol micelles occurring in bile. If this occurred it could constitute a concentration gradient from the hepatic cells to the bile thus allowing the transfer of the compound.

The processes whereby compounds of Classes A and C of Brauer's classification get into bile are even less well understood than those concerned in the secretion of organic anions of Class B. It is a common finding that when compounds of relatively low molecular weight e.g. benzoic acid, phenol and aniline are given to animals, small amounts (up to a few % of the dose) appear in the bile. It is possible that such compounds and their metabolites find their way into bile by diffusion from the parenchymal cells or through the intercellular spaces between hepatic parenchymal cells. Schanker (1968) has suggested that such diffusion processes may account for the appearance in bile of small amounts of the lipid-insoluble saccharides, inulin, sucrose and mannitol. Alternatively, substances of the above types may appear in bile as a consequence of diffusion and equilibration processes. The primary bile in passing down the biliary tree comes into restricted contact with the blood plasma and this affords an opportunity for the equilibration of various ions and compounds to occur. This equilibration process may be a function of the peribiliary plexus derived from the hepatic artery.

A third view is that certain compounds of relatively low molecular weight may appear in quantity in the initial or 'primary bile' and these then suffer more or less complete absorption as the bile passes down the biliary tree (Clark *et al.*, 1971). The acceptance of such a view however would require, among other things, the demonstration of the existence of such a 'primary bile' and its analysis.

REFERENCES

Bine, R. Jr., Friedman, M., Byers, S. O. and Bland, C. (1951) *Circulation*, 4, 105.

Brauer, R. W. and Pessotti, R. L. (1950) *Amer. J. Physiol.*, 162, 565.

Brauer, R. W. (1959) *J. Amer. med. Ass.*, 169, 1462.

Clark, A. G., Hirom, P. C. Millburn, P. and Smith, R. L. (1971) *J. Pharm. Pharmacol.*, 23, 150.

Hanzon, V. (1952) *Acta physiol. scand.*, 28, Suppl. 101.

Hirom, P. C. (1970) Ph.D. Thesis University of London.

Hofmann, A. F. and Small D. M. (1967) *Ann. Rev. Med.*, 18, 333.

Kurz, H. (1961) *Biochem. Pharmacol.*, 8, 20.

Levi, A. J., Gatmaitan, Z. and Arias, I. M. (1969) *J. clin. Invest.*, 48, 2156.

Millburn, P. M. (1970) In *Metabolic Conjugation and Metabolic Hydrolysis*, Vol 2. p. 1, Edited by W. H. Fishman, Academic Press, New York and London.

Reyes, H., Levi, A. J., Gatmaitan, Z. and Arias, I. M. (1969) *Proc. nat. Acad. Sci (Wash)*, 64, 168.

Schanker, L. S. and Solomon, H. M. (1963) *Amer. J. Physiol.*, 204, 829.

Schanker, L. S. (1968) In *Handbook of Physiology*, Section 6: Alimentary Canal, Vol 5, p. 2433, American Physiological Society, Washington D.C., USA.

Sperber, I. (1959) *Pharmacol. Rev.*, 11, 109.

CHAPTER EIGHT

Implications of Biliary Excretion

A wide variety of foreign chemicals, including drugs, food additives, pesticides and toxic chemicals are excreted in the bile either as such or more frequently as transformation products. In principle the elimination of a compound in the bile serves to clear it from the blood and tissues thereby enabling the body to rid itself of the substance. In this way any biological effects the compound may have are curtailed and the body is protected against its accumulation and intoxication. As an example of this one might consider the case of the cardioactive glycoside, oubain which is highly excreted in bile in the unchanged state. Protection against oubain poisoning therefore depends upon its removal by biliary excretion. The toxicity of the glycoside in rats in fact increases about five-fold if the biliary channel of elimination is removed by partial hepatectomy. However as the liver regenerates, over a period of two weeks the toxicity of the compound rapidly declines to that found in normal animals (Farah, 1946).

Although biliary excretion may be seen at its simplest as a route for the elimination of potentially toxic compounds there are nevertheless considerations that are peculiar to this excretion pathway. Thus, as a consequence of biliary excretion a compound may be taken up into an enterohepatic circulation which may markedly delay its eventual elimination from the body thus causing it to persist. The excretion of a compound in the bile brings it into contact with the gut flora which may metabolize it. The enterobacterial transformation of drugs excreted with the bile may have an important bearing upon their pharmacological and toxicological properties by the formation of active metabolites.

Finally, the excretion of a compound in the bile can mean that high concentrations may be localized within the hepatobiliary system and the intestine and this could be important in relation to the production of localized toxic effects. Weisburger *et al.*, (1967), for example, suggested that carcinogens of large molecular structure, which one would expect to be excreted mainly by the liver in the bile, tend to give rise to tumours of the liver in preference to other sites. Similarly, the ability of certain azo compounds and aminobiphenyls to cause tumours of the gall-bladder and intestine respectively is probably associated with the elimination of these substances in the bile.

Enterohepatic circulation

In enterohepatic circulation a compound, following excretion in the bile, is absorbed from the intestine and returned in the portal circulation to the liver from where it is recycled once more through the bile. A substance may be gradually lost from an enterohepatic circulation through excretion with the faeces or if it escapes to the peripheral circulation it may be excreted in the urine. The classical example of enterohepatic circulation is seen with the bile salts. For the rat it has been calculated that the bile acid pool undergoes daily 10 complete enterohepatic circulations (Norman and Sjövall, 1958) while in man two enterohepatic circulations of the bile acid pool occur with each meal (Borgström *et al.*, 1957). Enterohepatic circulation may be regarded as a mechanism for the conservation and reutilization of the physiologically important bile acids. Other endogenous compounds including the oestrogenic hormones, progesterone, the thyroid hormones and vitamin A and its metabolites undergo extensive enterohepatic circulation in some species and this may also be of physiological importance.

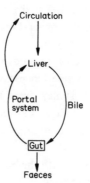

Fig. 4.
Diagram of the enterohepatic circulation of a drug. (Reproduced with permission from *Progress in Drug Research, 9*, (1966))

Table 30
Endogenous compounds that undergo enterohepatic circulation

Compound	Form excreted in bile	Species	Reference
Cholic acid	taurocholate and glycocholate	rat and guinea pig	Weiner and Lack (1968)
Oestrone	conjugates	guinea pig and man	Sandberg and Slaunwhite (1957; 1965) Sandberg et al. (1967)
Testosterone	conjugates	rat and man	Ashmore et al. (1953); Sandberg and Slaunwhite (1956)
Hydrocortisone	polar metabolites	rat	Hyde and Williams (1957)
Isoprenaline	3-methoxy isoprenaline glucuronide	rat	Herrting (1964)
Thyroxine	thyroxine glucuronide	rat	
Vitamin A	conjugates	rat	Zachman and Olson (1964)
Cyanocobalamin	–	man	Grasbeck et al. (1958)
Urobilinogen	mainly urobilinogen	rat	Lester and Schmid (1964)

At the same time many foreign compounds and their metabolites may become involved in an enterohepatic circulation as a consequence of their excretion in the bile.

Factors affecting the enterohepatic circulation of a compound

The enterohepatic circulation of a compound will be influenced by a number of factors as follows: (1) the extent and rate of excretion of the compound in the bile (2) the activity of the gall-bladder (3) the fate of the substance in the intestine and (4) the fate of the compound after reabsorption from the gut.

The extent and rate of excretion in the bile

This will be influenced by physico-chemical factors such as molecular weight, structural factors and polarity as previously described (p. 16) as well as by biological factors such as metabolism and species.

The activity of the gall-bladder

Bile is normally stored in the gall-bladder in which it undergoes concentration by absorption of water. It is released as a response to the sight of, or the eating of a meal, by contraction of the gall-bladder and by relaxation of the sphincter of Oddi. Bile may be expelled at fairly frequent intervals into the duodenum following the ingestion of a meal. In the absence of the latter, bile can be stored and concentrated in the gall-bladder for many hours and probably several days. A few animal species e.g. the rat, deer and whale do not have gall-bladders.

There have been no studies on the role of the gall-bladder in the enterohepatic circulation of drugs and their metabolites. Studies with the cholecystographic media however have clearly established that drugs can be stored in the gall-bladder for varying periods of time following their excretion in the bile. From the point of view of the persistence of drugs it is of considerable interest that drugs and their metabolites could be released intermittently into an enterohepatic circulation following storage in the gall-bladder. Misra *et al.* (1961) found that the plasma levels of conjugated normorphine 24 h after injection of the alkaloid into dogs were very high; they were several times greater than those at 3 and 8 h after drug administration and this was attributed to storage in and release from the gall-bladder of the drug following its elimination in the bile.

Fate of the compound in the intestine

Following elimination in the bile a compound may be excreted with the faeces or absorbed in the intestine at least in part, into an enterohepatic

Table 31
Examples of drugs that undergo enterohepatic circulation

Drug	Form excreted in bile	Species	Reference
Ampicillin	—	rat	Stewart and Harrison (1961)
Nafcillin	—	dog	Glassman et al. (1964)
Chloramphenicol	chloramphenicol glucuronide	rat	Glazko et al. (1952)
Erythromycin	erythromycin	dog	Lee et al. (1953); Welles et al. (1953)
Rifomycin SV	rifomycin SV	dog	Maffii et al. (1961)
Stilboestrol	stilboestrol glucuronide	rat	Fischer et al. (1966)
Quinestrol	conjugates	rat	Meli et al. (1968)
Norethynodrel	glucuronide of 17α-ethynyl-3β, 17β-dihydroxy-5(10)-oestrene	rabbit	Arai et al. (1962)
Digitoxin	polar conjugates	dog, man	Katzung and Meyers (1965); Okita et al. (1955)
Indomethacin	indomethacin glucuronide	dog	Hucker et al. (1966)
Glutethimide	glucuronides of hydroxyglutethimide	rat	Keberle et al. (1962)
Morphine	morphine 3-glucuronide	dog	Woods (1954)
Methylamphetamine	glucuronide of 4-hydroxynorephedrine	rat	Caldwell et al. (1971)
Diphenylhydantoin	polar metabolites	rat	Noach et al. (1958)
Dipyridamole	glucuronides of dipyridamole	dog, rabbit	Beisenherz et al. (1960); Zak et al. (1963)
Imipramine	glucuronides of 2-hydroxy- and 2-hydroxydesmethyl-imipramine	rat	Bickel and Weder (1968)
Pentaerythritol trinitrate	glucuronides of pentaerythritol mono-, di- and tri-nitrate	rat	Crew et al. (1971)
Iophenoxic acid	glucuronides of iophenoxic acid	rat	Wade et al. (1971)
Butylated hydroxytoluene	conjugates	rat	Ladomery et al. (1967a, b)

circulation; in both situations extensive metabolism of the compound by the gut flora may occur. Indeed, in most cases of enterohepatic circulation of drugs, the enterobacterial deconjugation of conjugates excreted in the bile is crucial for the recycling process.

Several examples are known of compounds which undergo biliary-faecal excretion directly without being absorbed and involved in enterohepatic circulation. Thus, indocyanine green is excreted in dog bile and is voided with the faeces without reabsorption occurring. Similarly, the anti-asthmatic drug, cromoglycate, is excreted in the bile in several species and is passed out with the faeces without being involved in enterohepatic circulation. Strong bases such as benzomethamine (Levine and Clark, 1955) and oxyphenonium (Levine and Clark, 1957), which are excreted to a moderate extent in rat bile, are also not absorbed into an enterohepatic circulation. Compounds that do not enter into an enterohepatic recycle are generally strongly polar compounds of relatively high molecular weight which are excreted in the bile unchanged, i.e. they already have in their molecular structures those physico-chemical features that are decisive for biliary excretion to occur. It is probable that the strongly polar properties of such compounds precludes extensive reabsorption from the intestinal tract occurring since strong acids and bases are in general poorly absorbed from the gastrointestinal tract (Schanker, 1963).

Most drugs and other foreign compounds are excreted in bile in the form of polar conjugates, particularly as conjugates with glucuronic acid or glutathione and occasionally with sulphate or glycine. In general, it is this group of substances which is likely to become involved in enterohepatic circulation (see Table 31), since the enteric tract contains conjugate splitting hydrolases, probably of bacterial origin, which hydrolyse conjugates. The products, because of their greater lipophilicity can then be absorbed from the gut. Enterobacterial metabolism in this context may be seen as the reverse of the general pattern of metabolism that occurs in the tissues of the body. Bacterial metabolism of the compound tends to reduce molecular weight and increase lipophilic properties, the latter favouring absorption, whereas in general tissue metabolism increases both molecular weight and polarity by the processes of metabolic conjugation.

Delayed excretion and persistence of compounds as a consequence of enterohepatic circulation

One important consequence of enterohepatic circulation is that it retards the ultimate elimination of a compound from the body in the urine and faeces and thereby promotes its persistence. One may therefore find marked differences in the rate of elimination of a compound from the body if its enterohepatic circulation is interrupted. Thus, in normal rats the excretion half-life (time required for excretion of 50% of compound) of [^{14}C] glutethimide is 24 h compared to 6.5 h in animals with biliary fistulae, in which enterohepatic circulation is prevented by channelling off the bile containing the metabolites of the drug. Similarly in the case of digitoxin its half-life in sham-operated dogs is 14 h compared with only 6 h in animals with biliary fistulas which prevent recycling (Katzung and Meyers, 1965). As a consequence of enterohepatic circulation, a large proportion of the dose of a drug can be localized within the hepatobiliary system and the intestine from which it is slowly lost either by excretion in the urine or by being voided with the faeces, or both.

The elimination of a compound in the urine may be delayed by the enterohepatic process. This delaying effect is seen to occur for compounds of both endogenous and exogenous origin. The urinary excretion of steroids that undergo enterohepatic circulation in man is retarded compared to steroids which undergo only limited recycling. Thus, with oestrone and oestradiol, which both undergo enterohepatic circulation in man, their eventual elimination in urine is slower compared to cortisol, testosterone and corticosterone which undergo only limited recycling. Following the administration of ^{14}C-labelled cortisol, testosterone or corticosterone about one-third of the radioactivity is excreted in the urine in the first 4 h and over 60—70% in the first 12 h. On the other hand, following the administration of [^{14}C] oestrone or [^{14}C] oestradiol only 12% of the radioactivity is excreted in the first 4 h and about one-third after 12 h. Furthermore, significant amounts of radioactivity are excreted in the urine as late as 4—5 days after the administration whereas the elimination of ^{14}C in the urine from the other labelled steroids is essentially complete within 48 h. (Sandberg and Slaunwhite, 1957).

This pattern of retarded urinary excretion due to enterohepatic circulation is also seen to occur with many drugs and their metabolites (Table 32). With such compounds small amounts of the substance and its metabolites may be detected in the urine for days, weeks and even months following administration. With some compounds, much of the dose may eventually be lost with the faeces and the factors that determine this, i.e. the relative dominance of the urinary and faecal pathways as ultimate channels of excretion, are not as yet understood.

Enterohepatic circulation can obviously be an important factor contributing to the persistence of compounds in the body. In the case of the bile salts and probably other compounds of intermediary metabolism this is of

Table 32
Delayed urinary excretion attributable to enterohepatic circulation

Compound	Excretion in urine continues for
Stilboestrol	>4–7 days
Morphine	>5 days
Butylated hydroxytoluene	>7 days
Digitoxin	>50 days
1:2:5:6-dibenzanthracene	>85 days
Iophenoxic acid	>25 days

physiological interest. Some foreign compounds show a remarkable persistence as a consequence of enterohepatic circulation. The formerly used radio-opaque medium iophenoxic acid persists in man for an unduly long period; its plasma half-life has been estimated to be 2½ years. A major factor in this persistence is the enterohepatic circulation of conjugates of iophenoxic acid (Mudge *et al.*, 1971). Similarly, recycling contributes to the persistence of stilboestrol (see Smith, 1971) butylated hydroxytoluene (Ladomery *et al.*, 1967a; 1967b) and antibiotics such as rifomycin SV (Maffii *et al.*, 1961). Enterohepatic circulation probably contributes to the persistence of many other compounds such as the chlorinated hydrocarbon pesticides, carcinogenic hydrocarbons and the anti-trypanosome compounds prothidium and ethidium which show a remarkable persistence in the body.

It should also be borne in mind that there can occur marked species differences in enterohepatic circulation and that this should be considered when making interspecies comparisons. The main source of these differences is the species variations in the extent of biliary excretion of anions having molecular weights in the range 300–500 or so. Chloramphenicol, for example, undergoes a marked enterohepatic circulation in the rat but not in man in which its biliary excretion is very limited. Similarly, morphine undergoes recycling in the rat but not in man where once again its biliary elimination is limited compared to the rodent species.

Influence of enterohepatic circulation upon plasma levels of drugs

The influence of enterohepatic cycling upon plasma and tissue levels of drugs and their metabolites and its implication for their biological activity has not been systematically studied. With some drugs it appears that, although extensive enterohepatic circulation occurs, little of the drug escapes to the peripheral circulation and most of the compound is eventually lost with the faeces. Thus, although stilboestrol undergoes marked enterohepatic cycling in the rat, most of the drug whether given orally or by injection, is excreted with the faeces and the recycling has little effect upon the peripheral plasma levels of the compound. On the other hand enterohepatic circulation may influence blood levels of some drugs. Thus, the plasma levels in intact rats of the antibiotic rifamycin AMP can be, due to enterohepatic cycling, 2—5 times greater than those found in animals with biliary fistulae (Curci and Loscalzo, 1966). Glazko (1965) has also found that for several drugs known to be involved in enterohepatic circulation, establishment of a biliary fistula results in lower blood levels and decreased biological half-life.

Whether or not the enterohepatic circulation of drugs occurs in man has not been established but there is one observation with the steroids, oestrone and oestradiol, suggesting that it can occur. Thus, the levels of conjugated oestrone and oestradiol have been found to be lower in patients with biliary fistulae than in those without. Patients without biliary fistulae showed significant levels of conjugated oestradiol in the plasma two days after its intravenous injection but in fistula patients the plasma levels were much lower. The levels of the free steroids were however the same in normal and fistula subjects (Sandberg and Slaunwhite, 1957).

Formation by enterobacterial metabolism of active metabolites from compounds excreted in the bile

The excretion of a compound in the bile brings it into contact with the gut flora. The latter can effect a wide variety of metabolic reactions and it may therefore metabolically transform the compound once it reaches the intestine in the bile. Such transformations may have an important bearing on any pharmacological and toxic properties that the drug may possess. The enterobacterial hydrolysis of glucuronide conjugates excreted in the bile appears to be important for the enterohepatic process. This has been seen to occur for example in the case of the enterohepatic cycling of stilboestrol and N-2-fluorenylacetamide both of which are excreted as conjugates with glucuronic acid.

The gut flora can however accomplish a wide variety of other metabolic reactions in addition to splitting conjugates. Thus, in the rat neoprontosil is readily excreted in the bile and is split by reductive enzymes of the gut flora to the active drug sulphanilamide (Gingell et al., 1971).

Neoprontosil   Sulphanilamide

Neoprontosil or 'soluble prontosil' was originally developed as a soluble form of the original drug 'prontosil rubrum' so that it could be given by injection. It seems very likely that in man its activity depended upon its excretion in the bile followed by enterobacterial conversion to the active drug, sulphanilamide.

The gut flora can effect N- and O-dealkylation reactions and enterobacterial dealkylation of drugs excreted in the bile may be an important aspect of their overall fate. Thus, L-3-methoxy-4-hydroxyphenylalanine is excreted in the bile (20% of dose) in rats and in the gut it is converted by O-dealkylation to L-dopa (Chalmers et al., 1971).

$$CH_3O-,\ HO-\underset{}{}-CH_2CHCOOH\ (NH_2) \xrightarrow[\text{dealkylated by gut flora}]{\text{excreted in bile}} HO-,\ HO-\underset{}{}-CH_2CHCOOH\ (NH_2)$$

3-methoxy-4-hydroxyphenylalanine   3,4-dihydroxyphenylalanine

The latter is absorbed and in the body is converted to dopamine thereby causing an increase in brain levels of this neurotransmitter. The tissues are unable to effect the O-dealkylation of this compound so that the activity of the injected drug depends upon its elimination in the bile followed by enterobacterial dealkylation. Similarly, the N-dealkylation of imipramine and its metabolites is in part due to the demethylation by the gut flora of metabolites excreted in the bile (Minder et al., 1971).

Biliary excretion coupled with enterobacterial metabolism may result in the formation of toxic metabolites. A good example of this is seen with chloramphenicol which is excreted in rat bile as its glucuronide conjugate. In the gut the conjugate is split and the aglycone converted by reduction to arylamines (Glazko et al., 1952) which have a toxic action on the thyroid (Thompson et al., 1954). Glycosides besides β-glucuronides can also undergo hydrolysis in the gut and this may be important in toxic metabolite formation. Several of the cardioactive glycosides undergo extensive excretion in the bile and can be split by the gut bacteria to more toxic substances by removal of sugar residues.

Biliary excretion and carcinogenesis

A number of compounds cause cancer of the hepatobiliary system and the gut and this may be related to their extensive elimination into the enteric tract with the bile. Thus, o-aminoazotoluene induces tumours of the gall-bladder while derivatives of phenanthrene, aminobiphenyl and fluorene, all of which are compounds of relatively high molecular weight and could be expected to be excreted in bile, are known to cause intestinal tumours in the rat.

It might be postulated that a metabolite, perhaps the active carcinogen, may be excreted in the bile in the form of a polar and inactive conjugate. In the gut the latter may be hydrolyzed so releasing the active carcinogen which may then act locally on intestinal tissues.

N-2-acetamidofluorene

4-aminobiphenyl

Benzidine

Structures of some aromatic amines which induce intestine carcinomas in rats

An example of this is seen with the carcinogen *N*-2-fluorenylacetamide which induces tumours in a number of organs including the intestine of rats. The compound is extensively excreted in the bile mainly as the glucuronide conjugate of the carcinogenic metabolite *N*-hydroxy-*N*-2-fluorenylacetamide (Irving *et al.*, 1967). In the gut the conjugate is split to release the active carcinogen which itself undergoes enterobacterial *N*-dehydroxylation to regenerate *N*-2-fluorenylacetamide. (Williams *et al.*, 1970). The latter is excreted in the faeces although this may be preceded by some enterohepatic circulation.

A similar sequence of events could explain the ability of 4-aminobiphenyl to cause intestinal tumours in rats when given by subcutaneous injection (Walpole *et al.*, 1952). Biphenyl derivatives are extensively excreted in the bile of rats particularly as glucuronide conjugates (Millburn *et al.*, 1967). In the rat it is probable that 4-aminobiphenyl behaves like other aromatic amines and undergoes both aromatic and *N*-hydroxylation, the products appearing in the bile as their glucuronides. In the gut the conjugates would be split by bacterial β-glucuronidase thereby releasing the active carcinogens. It would appear that the location of the tumours in the enteric tract would depend upon a number of factors: (*a*) the intrinsic carcinogenicity of the hydroxyamine (*b*) the rate of hydrolysis of the conjugates in the intestinal contents and (c) the rate of absorption from the gut and rate of loss in the faeces. Hydrolysis might be expected to be greater the further the conjugate moves along the intestine. Variation in these factors for different compounds may explain why 4-aminobiphenyl produces tumours of the large intestine only relatively slowly, whereas 3,2′-dimethyl-4-aminobiphenyl produces earlier tumours in both the large and small intestine.

It has been suggested that bile acids may under certain conditions be converted to carcinogenic metabolites by the intestinal flora and that these could produce cancer of the large bowel. There occur marked geographical variations in the incidence of bowel cancer and this might be due to differences in the nature of the gut flora brought about by differences in diet (Hill *et al.*, 1971).

Some clinical implications of the biliary excretion of drugs

The elimination of a drug in the bile serves to clear the substance from the circulation and thereby to limit its effects. A number of drugs e.g. rifamycin, dichloromethotrexate and glycyrrhetic acid undergo extensive excretion in human bile and for some, enterohepatic circulation probably occurs.

The ability of the liver to concentrate and to excrete certain compounds in the bile has been utilized in the development of diagnostic agents for the evaluation of hepatobiliary function. Abel and Rowntree (1909) first showed that phenolphthalein and its halogenated derivatives are highly excreted in bile. Subsequently, halogenated phthaleins were developed both for the measurement of liver function and also for the X-ray visualization of the gall-bladder and biliary tract. Phenoltetrabromophthalein was introduced for use in a test of liver function by Rosenthal and White in 1925 and it is still in use today. When testing hepatic function it is assumed that following injection, the dye is taken up almost exclusively by the liver and eliminated in the bile. The functional efficiency of the liver is then assessed by the rate at which the dye disappears from the blood. In people with normal liver function, the dye should disappear from the blood within 30 min of an injection of 2 mg/kg or in about 45 min after a 5 mg/kg dose. In liver disease the rate of uptake of the dye by the liver and its excretion in bile may be impaired and therefore the rate of its disappearance from the plasma is also slower.

Another halogenated phthalein derivative, namely, tetraiodophthalein was introduced as a medium for the X-ray visualization of the gall-bladder and biliary tract (Graham and Cole, 1924). Its efficiency in this respect depended upon its extensive excretion in bile and consequent concentration within the hepatobiliary system and the iodine groups which are relatively opaque to X-rays.

The elimination of drugs in bile may also be of importance for their therapeutic effects. Thus, the effective therapy of bacterial infections of the hepatobiliary system by certain antibiotics may be related to their extensive excretion in the bile. It is noteworthy that antibiotics such as the rifamycins and erythromycin are extensively excreted in the bile whereas others such as the penicillins and streptomycin are not. Similarly, the extensive excretion and concentration within the hepatobiliary system of the anti-tumour drug, dichloromethotrexate, may indicate the type of drug which might be tried in the treatment of tumours of the hepatobiliary system.

The hepatobiliary system is also liable to infestation by parasitic agents which cause diseases such as Weil's disease, bilharzia and tropical abscesses of the liver caused by *Entamoeba histolytica*. In the development of drugs for treating these conditions it is possible that consideration of some of the principles which appear to influence the biliary excretion of drugs may prove useful. Similarly, it may be possible to develop compounds which are highly excreted in bile and which have the property of promoting the dissolution of cholesterol gall-stones. It seems possible that the excretion of drugs in bile may have a bearing on the pathogenesis of cholestatic liver disease. Thus, certain amines can form insoluble salts with the bile acids thereby precipitating them from bile and giving rise to plugs which might block the finer biliary ductules. A number of amines are known to cause cholestatic liver disease including 4,4'-diaminodiphenylmethane (Kopelman *et al.*, 1966) and a number of phenothiazines such as chlorpromazine (Popper, 1968). Chlorpromazine has been shown to precipitate both the glycoprotein and protein components of human bile and this precipitation may be responsible, at least in part, for the cholestatic jaundice seen in some patients taking this drug (Clarke and Denborough, 1971).

REFERENCES

Abel, J. J. and Rowntree, L. G. (1909) *J. Pharmacol. exp. Ther.*, 1, 231.

Arai, K., Golab, T., Layne, D. S. and Pincus, G. (1962) *Endocrinology*, 71, 639.

Ashmore, J., Elliott, W. H., Doisy, E. A. Jr. and Doisy, E. A. (1953) *J. biol. Chem.*, 200, 661.

Beisenherz, G., Koss, F. W., Schüle, A., Gebauer, I., Bärisch, R. and Fröde, R. (1960) *Arzneimittel-Forsch.*, 10, 307.

Bickel, M. H. and Weder, H. J. (1968) *Arch int. Pharmacodyn.*, 173, 433.

Borgström, B., Dahlqvist, A., Lundh, G. and Sjövall, J. (1957) *J. clin. Invest.*, 36, 1521.

Caldwell, J., Dring, L. G. and Williams, R. T. (1971) *Biochem. J.*, 124, 16P.

Chalmers, J. P., Davies, D. S., Draffan, G. H., Reid, J. L. and Thorgeirsson, S. S. (1971) *Brit. J. Pharmacol.*, 43, 455P.

Clarke, A. E. and Denborough, M. A. (1971) *Clin. Chem.*, **17**, 998.

Crew, M. C., Gala, R. L., Haynes, L. J. and Di Carlo, F. J. (1971) *Biochem. Pharmacol.*, **20**, 3077.

Curci, G. and Loscalzo, B. (1966) Extracts from the Acts of the XVIII Italian Phthisiology Congress, Milan, Nov. 4-6, Riv. 1st Vacc. Conserzi antituberc., supplementary Ed., **2**, 2.

Farah, A. (1946) *J. Pharmacol. exp. Ther.*, **86**, 248.

Fischer, L. J., Millburn, P., Smith, R. L. and Williams, R. T. (1966) *Biochem. J.*, **100**, 69P.

Gingell, R., Bridges, J. W. and Williams, R. T. (1971) *Xenobiotica*, **1**, 143.

Glassman, J. M., Warren, G. H., Rosenman, S. G. and Agersborg, H. P. K. (1964) *Toxicol. appl. Pharmacol.*, **6**, 220.

Glazko, A. J., Dill, W. A. and Wolf, L. M. (1952) *J. Pharmacol. exp. Ther.*, **104**, 452.

Glazko, A. J. (1965) In discussion of 'The influence of enterohepatic circulation on toxicity of drugs' by Williams, R. T., Millburn, P. and Smith, R. L. p. 110, *Ann. N.Y. Acad. Sci.*, **123**, 123.

Graham, E. A. and Cole, W. H. (1924) *J. Amer. med. Ass.*, **82**, 613.

Grasbeck, R., Nyberg, W. and Reizenstein, P. (1958) *Proc. Soc. Exp. Biol. (N.Y.)*, **97**, 780.

Hertting, G. (1964) *Biochem. Pharmacol.*, **13**, 1119.

Hill, M. J., Drasar, B. S., Aries, V., Crowther, J. S., Hawksworth, G. and Williams, R. E. O. (1971) *Lancet*, **1**, 95.

Hucker, H. B., Zacchei, A. G., Cox, S. V., Brodie, D. A. and Cantwell, N. H. R. (1966) *J. Pharmacol. exp. Ther.*, **153**, 237.

Hyde, P. M. and Williams, R. H. (1957) *J. biol. Chem.*, **227**, 1063.

Irving, C. C., Wiseman, R. Jr., and Hill, J. T. (1967) *Cancer Res.*, **27**, 2309.

Katzung, B. G. and Meyers, F. H. (1965) *J. Pharmacol. exp. Ther.*, **149**, 257.

Keberle, H., Hoffmann, K. and Bernhard, K. (1962) *Experientia (Basel)*, **18**, 105.

Kopelman, H., Robertson, M. H., Sanders, P. G. and Ash, I. (1966) *Brit. med. J.*, **1**, 514.

Ladomery, L. G., Ryan, A. J. and Wright, S. E. (1967a) *J. Pharm. Pharmacol.*, **19**, 383.

Ladomery, L. G., Ryan, A. J. and Wright, S. E. (1967b) *J. Pharm. Pharmacol.*, **19**, 388.

Lee, C.-C., Anderson, R. C., and Chen, K. K. (1953) *Antibiot. Ann.*, (1953-1954) p. 485.

Lee, C.-C., Anderson, R. C., Bird, H. L. Jr. and Chen, K. K. (1953) *Antibiot. Ann.*, (1953-54) p. 493.

Lester, R. and Schmid, R. (1964) *Nature (Lond.)*, **201**, 711.

Levine, R. M. and Clark, B. B. (1955) *J. Pharmacol. exp. Ther.*, **114**, 63.

Levine, R. M. and Clark, B. B. (1957) *J. Pharmacol. exp. Ther.*, **121**, 63.

Maffii, G., Bianchi, G., Schiatti, P. and Gallo, G. G. (1961) *Farmaco, Ed. sci.*, **16**, 246.

Meli, A., Steinetz, B. G., Giannina, T., Cargill, D. I. and Manning, J. P. (1968) *Proc. Soc. Exp. Biol. (N.Y.)*, **127**, 1042.

Millburn, P., Smith, R. L. and Williams, R. T. (1967) *Biochem. J.*, **105**, 1275.

Minder, R., Schnetzer, F. and Bickel, M. H. (1971) *Navnyn-Schmiedeberg's Arch. Pharmak. exp. Path.*, **268**, 334.

Misra, A. L., Jacoby, H. I. and Woods, L. A. (1961) *J. Pharmacol. exp. Ther.*, **132**, 311.

Mudge, G. H., Strewler, G. J. Jr., Desbiens, N., Berndt, W. O. and Wade, D. N. (1971) *J. Pharmacol. exp. Ther.*, **178**, 159.

Noach, E. L., Woodbury, D. M. and Goodman, L. S. (1958) *J. Pharmacol. exp. Ther.*, **122**, 301.

Norman, A. and Sjövall, J. (1958) *J. biol. Chem.*, **233**, 872.

Okita, G. T., Talso, P. J., Curry, J. H. Jr., Smith, F. D. Jr and Geiling, E. M. K. (1955) *J. Pharmacol. exp. Ther.*, **115**, 371.

Popper, H. (1968) *Ann. Rev. Med.*, **19**, 39.

Rosenthal, S. M. and White, E. C. (1925) *J. Amer. med. Ass.*, **84**, 1112.

Sandberg, A. A. and Slaunwhite, W. R. Jr. (1956) *J. clin. Invest.*, **35**, 1331.

Sandberg, A. A. and Slaunwhite, W. R. Jr. (1957) *J. clin. Invest.*, **36**, 1266.

Sandberg, A. A. and Slaunwhite, W. R. Jr. (1965) *J. clin. Invest.*, **44**, 694.

Sandberg, A. A., Kirdani, R. Y., Back, N., Weyman, P. and Slaunwhite, W. R. Jr. (1967) *Amer. J. Physiol.*, **213**, 1138.

Schanker, L. S. (1963) In *Proceedings of the First International Pharmacological Meeting* August 22-25, 1961. Vol. 4, p. 121. 'Drugs and Membranes' edited by C. A. M. Hogben, Pergamon Press, Oxford.

Smith, R. L. (1971) In *Mechanisms of Toxicity*, p. 229, edited by W. N. Aldridge, Macmillan, London.

Stewart, G. T. and Harrison, P. M. (1961) *Brit. J. Pharmacol.*, **17**, 414.

Thompson, R., Sturtevant, M., Bird, O. D. and Glazko, A. J. (1954) *Endocrinology*, **55**, 665.

Wade, D. N., Desbiens, N., Strewler, G. J. Jr., Berndt, W. O. and Mudge, G. H. (1971) *J. Pharmacol. exp. Ther.*, **178**, 173.

Walpole, A. L., Williams, M. H. C. and Roberts, D. C. (1952) *Brit. J. industr. Med.*, **9**, 255.

Weiner, I. M. and Lack, L. (1968) In *Handbook of Physiology* Section 6: Alimentary Canal, vol. 3. p. 1439, American Physiological Society, Washington D.C.

Weisburger, J. H., Hadidian, Z., Fredrickson, T. N. and Weisburger, E. K. (1967) In *Bladder Cancer* p. 45, edited by K. E. Lampe, Aesculapius Publ. Co., Florida.

Welles, J. S., Anderson, R. C. and Chen, K. K. (1955) *Antibiot. Ann.*, (1954-1955) p. 291.

Williams, J. P. Jr., Grantham, P. H., Marsh, H. H., Weisburger, J. H. and Weisburger, E. K. (1970) *Biochem. Pharmacol.*, **19**, 173.

Woods, L. A. (1954) *J. Pharmacol. exp. Ther.*, **112**, 158.

Zachman, R. D. and Olson, J. A. (1964) *Nature (Lond).*, **201**, 1222.

Zak, S. B., Tallen, H. H., Quinn, G. P., Fratta, I. and Greengard, P. (1963) *J. Pharmacol. exp. Ther.*, **141**, 392.

PART TWO

Elimination of Drugs and Toxic Substances in Bile

CHAPTER NINE

Simple Aliphatic Derivatives

It appears that simple aliphatic derivatives e.g. alcohols, ketones, amines and carboxylic acids are not extensively excreted in the bile and the main channel for their elimination is the urine and, for certain volatile compounds, the expired air. The biliary excretion of such compounds has not been systematically studied but there are a few examples in the literature of where the biliary excretion of a simple aliphatic derivative has been examined and the results suggest that this is low. Extensive biliary elimination for simple aliphatic compounds would not be anticipated in view of their low molecular weight (see p. 17).

Oxalic acid (mol. wt. 126) occurs in the bile of dogs when given orally or by subcutaneous injection (Borgström, 1938) and *methyl chloride* (mol. wt. 50) appears in bile after its intravenous injection (Sperling *et al.*, 1950). The amounts eliminated by this route are probably small. Ketone bodies also appear in the bile of rats; their biliary excretion is enhanced in chronic alloxan diabetes (Linder and Rudas, 1965).

Dimethylsulphoxide (mol. wt. 78)

Dimethylsulphoxide is widely used as an industrial material and solvent. It is rapidly absorbed when administered either orally or dermally. When administered dermally to rabbits small amounts of the unchanged compound and an oxidation product, dimethylsulphone, appear in the bile (Hucker *et al.*, 1966).

Urethane (mol. wt. 89)

Urethane and its metabolite *N*-hydroxy-urethane (mol. wt. 105) are of interest since they are both carcinogenic. When administered to rats urethane is largely transformed to carbon dioxide and excreted as such in the expired air (Boyland and Rhoden, 1949; Skipper *et al.*, 1948). However, rats injected with urethane eliminate in the bile a metabolite which appears to be *S*-ethylglutathione. Rats dosed with *N*-hydroxyurethane excrete in the bile a metabolite which may be *S*-ethylglutathione sulphoxide (Boyland and Nery, 1965).

$$NH_2 COOC_2H_5$$
Urethane

$$HONHCOOC_2H_5$$
N-hydroxyurethane

$$C_2H_5-SCH_2-R$$
S-ethylglutathione

$$C_2H_5-S\,CH_2-R$$
$$\downarrow$$
$$O$$
S-ethylglutathione sulphoxide

$$R = -CH\begin{array}{c} NH-Glu \\ \diagup \\ \diagdown \\ CO-Gly \end{array}$$

Urethane and its biliary metabolites.

Methyl methanesulphonate (mol. wt. 110)

Methyl methanesulphonate is a simple biological alkylating agent. In rats it can produce reversible sterility and will suppress the growth of certain types of tumours. When [^{14}C]methyl methanesulphonate is injected into rats about 16% of the radioactivity is eliminated in the bile in 24 h and in the same time about 30% is excreted in the urine and expired air. The bile contains six radioactive metabolites two of which have been identified as *S*-methyl-glutathione and *S*-methylcysteine respectively. The urinary metabolites are *N*-acetyl-*S*-methylcysteine, *S*-methylthioacetic acid and *S*-methylcysteine. The urinary cysteine and *N*-acetyl conjugates are probably at least in part, derived from enterobacterial degradation of the glutathione conjugate excreted in the bile (Pillinger *et al.*, 1965).

$$CH_3SO_2OCH_3$$
Methyl methanesulphonate

$$CH_3SCH_2-\underset{\underset{CONHCH_2COOH}{|}}{\overset{\overset{NH_2}{|}}{\underset{|}{\overset{|}{CH}}}}$$
NHCOCH$_2$CH$_2$CHCOOH
S-methylglutathione

$$\underset{\underset{COOH}{|}}{\overset{\overset{CH_2-S-CH_3}{|}}{CH\cdot NH_2}}$$
S-methylcysteine

Carbon tetrachloride (mol. wt. 154)

Carbon tetrachloride is a compound of considerable importance since it is widely used as an industrial solvent and for treating liver-fluke infestation in sheep. Although it has been used for the latter purpose for many years its mode of action is still obscure. It can cause fatty liver and hepatic necrosis and it has therefore been an important tool in the investigation of these phenomena. It is a volatile compound (b.p. 77°C) and is mainly eliminated in the expired air (Robbins, 1929; McCollister *et al.*, 1951) but small amounts are eliminated in the form of metabolites in the bile. Using a sensitive gas-chromatographic method Fowler (1969) found small amounts of chloroform, hexachloroethane as well as the unchanged compound and two unidentified metabolites in the gall-bladder bile of rabbits dosed orally with carbon tetrachloride.

$$
\begin{array}{ccc}
\overset{\displaystyle Cl}{\underset{\displaystyle Cl}{Cl-\overset{|}{\underset{|}{C}}-Cl}} &
\overset{\displaystyle Cl}{\underset{\displaystyle Cl}{Cl-\overset{|}{\underset{|}{C}}-H}} &
\overset{\displaystyle Cl\ \ \ Cl}{\underset{\displaystyle Cl\ \ \ Cl}{Cl-\overset{|}{\underset{|}{C}}-\overset{|}{\underset{|}{C}}-Cl}}
\end{array}
$$

Carbon tetrachloride   Chloroform   Hexachloroethane

The hexachloroethane is probably derived from dimerization of two trichloromethyl radicals. Although hexachloroethane has anthelmintic and hepatotoxic properties it is unlikely that it is responsible for the particular effects of carbon tetrachloride.

Khalidi and Zaki (1969) have also found that carbon tetrachloride is eliminated in the bile of sheep. Most of the radioactivity that appears in the bile of sheep dosed orally with $[^{14}C]$ carbon tetrachloride is in the form of non-volatile water-soluble derivatives. An interesting finding is that bile collected from sheep dosed with carbon tetrachloride has flukicidal activity against the liver fluke *in vitro*.

Methylglyoxal-bis-guanylhydrazone (methyl-GAG; mol. wt. 184)

Methylglyoxal-bis-guanylhydrazone is a synthetic drug used for treatment of acute myeloblastic leukaemia. The biliary excretion of this polar compound is low since rats eliminate less than 0.5% of injected dose of $[^{14}C]$ methyl-GAG in the bile in 4–6 h. and about 70% of the radioactivity is found in the urine unchanged (Oliverio *et al.*, 1963).

$$
\begin{array}{l}
\overset{\displaystyle NH}{\overset{\|}{}} \\
CH_3-C=N-NH\cdot C\cdot NH_2 \\
| \\
CH=N-NH\cdot C\cdot NH_2 \\
\underset{\displaystyle NH}{\underset{\|}{}}
\end{array}
$$

Pentaerythritol trinitrate (mol. wt. 271)

Pentaerythritol trinitrate is a hypotensive agent with a prolonged action. It is an interesting example of a relatively simple aliphatic compound which is highly excreted in bile. When given orally or by intravenous injection to rats about 60% of a dose of $[^{14}C]$ pentaerythritol trinitrate is excreted in the bile. The drug undergoes extensive enterohepatic circulation and this could account for its prolonged action. The bile contains three glucuronides, namely, the glucuronic acid conjugates of pentaerythritol mononitrate (mol. wt. 357), the dinitrate (mol. wt. 402) and of the trinitrate (mol. wt. 447) and they occur in the relative proportions 4:79:17 (Crew et al., 1971).

$$O_2NOCH_2 - \underset{\underset{CH_2ONO_2}{|}}{\overset{\overset{CH_2OH}{|}}{C}} - CH_2ONO_2 \longrightarrow O_2NOCH_2 - \underset{\underset{CH_2ONO_2}{|}}{\overset{\overset{CH_2OC_6H_9O_6}{|}}{C}} - CH_2ONO_2$$

Pentaerythritol trinitrate   Pentaerythritol trinitrate
                                                      glucuronide

$$HOCH_2 - \underset{\underset{CH_2ONO_2}{|}}{\overset{\overset{CH_2OH}{|}}{C}} - CH_2ONO_2 \longrightarrow HOCH_2 - \underset{\underset{CH_2OH}{|}}{\overset{\overset{CH_2OH}{|}}{C}} - CH_2ONO_2$$

Pentaerythritol dinitrate   Pentaerythritol mononitrate

(Both excreted as glucuronide conjugates)

By contrast $[^{14}C]$ pentaerythritol itself is poorly excreted in bile for when injected intravenously into biliary cannulated rats less than 1% of the dose appears in the bile. The bile-blood ratio for the compound is about 2 suggesting that transfer is mainly due to passive diffusion whereas with pentaerythritol trinitrate the ratio is about 100–150 indicating that the glucuronide conjugates are being concentratively transferred.

REFERENCES

Borgström, S. (1938) Skand. Arch. Physiol., **79**, 1.

Boyland, E. and Nery, R. (1965) Biochem. J., **94**, 198.

Boyland, E. and Rhoden, E. (1949) Biochem. J., **44**, 528.

Crew, M. C., Gala, R. L., Haynes, L. J. and DiCarlo, F. J. (1971) Biochem. Pharmacol., **20**, 3077.

Fowler, J. S. L. (1969) Brit. J. Pharmacol., **37**, 733.

Hucker, H. B., Ahmad, P. M. and Miller, E. A. (1966) J. Pharmacol. exp. Ther., **154**, 176.

Khalidi, A. and Zaki, S. A. (1969) *Brit. J. Pharmacol.,* 36, 253.

Lindner, A. and Rudas, B. (1965) *Med. Pharmacol. exp.,* 12, 309.

McCollister, D. D., Beamer, W. H., Atchison, G. J. and Spencer, H. C. (1951) *J. Pharmacol. exp. Ther.,* 102, 112.

Oliverio, V. T., Adamson, R. H., Henderson, E. S. and Davidson, J. D. (1963) *J. Pharmacol. exp. Ther.,* 141, 149.

Pillinger, D. J., Fox, B. W. and Craig, A. W. (1965) In *Isotopes in Experimental Pharmacology* p. 415. Ed. L. J. Roth, Univ. Chicago Press, Chicago.

Robbins, B. H. (1929) *J. Pharmacol. exp. Ther.,* 37, 203.

Skipper, H. E., Bryan, C. E., White, L. Jr. and Hutchison, O. S. (1948) *J. biol. Chem.,* 173, 371.

Sperling, F., Macri, F. J. and Von Oettingen, W. F. (1950) *Arch. industr. Hyg.,* 1, 215.

CHAPTER TEN

Simple Aromatic Compounds

In general benzene and its simple derivatives of relatively low molecular weight (approx. <150) are poorly excreted in the bile irrespective of species (Abou-El-Makarem *et al.*, 1967; Millburn, 1970; Smith, 1970). For such compounds e.g. phenol, aniline and benzoic acid, urinary excretion is the dominant pathway of elimination.

Biliary excretion however becomes more significant, as might be expected, for aromatic compounds of higher molecular weight or which give rise to metabolites of relatively high molecular weight. Thus both isoprenaline (mol. wt. 211) and butylated hydroxytoluene (mol. wt. 220) are extensively excreted in rat bile as glucuronides having molecular weights in excess of 300. Iodinated benzene derivatives are extensively eliminated in the bile and this finds practical application since several of the cholecystographic media used for X-ray visualization of the hepatobiliary system, such as iodopanoic acid and iophenoxic acid, are relatively simple, high molecular weight iodinated compounds.

Hepatic elimination in the rat also becomes more important for compounds containing two aromatic rings in their structure such as diphenylamine (mol. wt. 169) and diphenylacetic acid (mol. wt. 212). Similarly, certain naphthalene derivatives are more extensively excreted in bile than their corresponding benzene derivatives and this may be associated with their greater molecular weight.

Aniline (mol. wt.93; pK_a 4.7)

This compound is eliminated largely in the urine as conjugates of oxidation products (Parke, 1960) and biliary excretion is relatively limited. The rat, guinea pig, rabbit and hen excrete only about 3–6% of an injected dose

(20 mg/kg) of $[^{14}C]$ aniline in the bile while in the cat (1.6%) and the dog (0.3%) the excretion is even lower (Abou-El-Makarem *et al.*, 1967).

4-aminophenol; R = H
4-aminophenylglucuronide R = $-C_6H_9O_6$

2-aminophenol; R = H
2-aminophenylglucuronide R = $-C_6H_9O_6$

Biliary metabolites of aniline

The bile contains mainly 4-aminophenol and its glucuronide and smaller amounts of 2-aminophenol and its glucuronic acid conjugate. Cat bile, however, contains only 2-aminophenol. This species difference may be attributed to the fact that in the cat aromatic hydroxylation of monosubstituted benzenes occurs predominantly in the *ortho* position (Parke, 1960) and that the glucuronide conjugation of some compounds in this species is defective (Robinson and Williams, 1958).

Phenol (mol. wt. 94; pK_a 9.7)

Phenol is excreted in the urine largely as phenylglucuronide and phenylsulphate and as conjugates of its oxidation product quinol (Capel *et al.*, 1972). The relative proportions of the metabolites excreted depend upon the species. Biliary excretion is limited since rats excrete only 5% of an injected dose of $[^{14}C]$ phenol in the bile mainly in the form of four metabolites, one of which, phenylglucuronide, predominates. The remaining three have not been identified. Phenylsulphate which is the major urinary metabolite of phenol in the rat does not appear in the bile. (Abou-El-Makarem *et al.*, 1967).

Phenylglucuronide   Phenylsulphate

Benzoic acid (mol. wt. 122; pK_a 4.2)

Biliary excretion is relatively unimportant in the elimination of this compound since most of an injected dose of benzoic acid is eliminated in the urine'as conjugates, the nature and relative proportions of which vary with species (Bridges *et al.*, 1970). Less than 2% of an injected dose of [^{14}C] benzoic acid is excreted in the bile of the rat, guinea pig, rabbit, dog, cat and hen (Abou-El-Makarem *et al.*, 1967). The nature of the biliary metabolites varies with species reflecting inter-species variations in the patterns of metabolic conjugation.

Benzoic acid   Hippuric acid   Benzoylglucuronide   Ornithuric acid

In the guinea pig and rabbit the main biliary metabolite is hippuric acid, while rat, cat and dog bile contain in addition to this compound, benzoylglucuronide. Hen bile contains largely ornithuric acid and some unchanged benzoic acid. The low biliary excretion of benzoic acid is not a consequence of its very effective elimination by the kidneys since if this channel of removal is blocked by renal ligation, its biliary excretion still remains low (Williams *et al.*, 1965).

2-aminobenzoic acid (mol. wt. 137)

The biliary excretion of this compound is also low since rats eliminate only about 5% of an injected dose (10 mg/kg) in the bile, partly unchanged and partly in the form of a number of metabolites, two of which appear to be the glycine and glucuronide conjugates (Abou-El-Makarem *et al.*, 1967). Both the rat and rabbit eliminate the compound in the urine largely as conjugates with glucuronic acid and glycine (Mitsuba and Ichihara, 1927; Quick 1932; Charconnet-Harding *et al.*, 1953).

2-aminobenzoic acid   2-aminohippuric acid   2-aminobenzoylglucuronide

4-aminobenzoic acid (mol. wt. 137; pK_a 4.9)

Like the 2-isomer, 4-aminobenzoic acid is mainly eliminated in the urine as conjugates and excretion in the bile appears to be of little significance. It undergoes *N*-acetylation and the carboxyl group can be conjugated with glucuronic acid and glycine. Rats excrete in the bile only about 3% of an injected dose of 4-aminobenzoic acid, partly unchanged and as 4-amino- and 4-acetamido-hippuric acid together with some unidentified metabolites (Abou-El-Makarem *et al.*, 1967).

4-aminobenzoic   4-aminohippuric   4-acetamidohippuric
acid   acid   acid

4-aminohippuric acid (mol. wt. 194; pK_a 4.0)

This compound is a metabolite of 4-aminobenzoic acid and like the parent compound is mainly eliminated in the urine with only small amounts appearing in the bile. The rat, guinea pig, rabbit and dog excrete 3–6% of an injected dose in the bile while the cat and hen eliminate less than 1% by this pathway. Dog bile contains only unchanged 4-aminohippuric acid while the other species eliminate mainly the acetyl conjugate, namely, 4-acetamido-hippuric acid (Abou-El-Makarem *et al.*, 1967). This species difference reflects the well known inability of the dog to acetylate aromatic primary amino groups.

4-acetamidohippuric acid (mol. wt. 236)

Only 2–4% of an injected dose of 4-acetamidohippuric acid is eliminated unchanged in the bile of the dog, sheep and rabbit while the rat, hen, cat, guinea pig and rhesus monkey excrete 1% or less by this pathway (Abou-El-Makarem *et al.*, 1967).

Salicylic acid (mol. wt. 138; pK_a 3.2)

Salicylic acid and its derivatives have been extensively used in medicine since the beginning of the century. Their metabolism and excretion has been extensively investigated so that there is a large literature on the subject (see Gross and Greenberg, 1948). The main channel of elimination is the urine in which the drug appears unchanged and as conjugates with glycine and glucuronic acid and as oxidation products (see Williams, 1959). Biliary excretion is of limited significance since rats eliminate only 1.5% of an injected dose by this pathway (Abou-El-Makarem *et al.*, 1967). Biliary elimination of salicylate also appears to be small in man since only small amounts of the drug have been recovered in human bile at autopsy following the ingestion, either accidentally or for suicidal purposes, of large amounts of salicylate (see Gross and Greenberg, 1948).

5,5'-methylenedisalicylic acid (mol. wt. 288; pK_a 3.5)

5,5'-methylenedisalicylic acid is used in the synthesis of triarylmethane dyes and in pharmaceutical formulation because of its ability to form complexes with drugs such as phenacetin and prednisolone and salts with organic bases. The salt formed with the antibiotic bacitracin is widely used as an animal feed supplement. Its physiological disposition differs from that of the parent compound salicylic acid since it is metabolically inert and is therefore excreted unchanged, and also in both the rat and dog, extensive biliary excretion occurs. This is a reflection of its greater molecular weight associated with the presence of two aromatic rings in its structure. The compound is eliminated unchanged by the rat, mouse, hamster, rabbit, guinea pig, chicken and rhesus monkey. There is however, a marked species difference in the excretion pattern. Thus, in the rat and dog extensive biliary excretion occurs (50–60% of dose) but in the rabbit and guinea pig this is much lower (5%) and much more of the drug appears in the urine (Davison and Williams, 1968).

p-nitrobenzoic acid (mol. wt. 167; pK_a 3.4)

p-nitrobenzoic acid is a strong acid which is excreted in the urine largely unchanged. It is not excreted in rat bile (Abou-El-Makarem *et al.*, 1967).

Phenylacetic acid (mol. wt. 136; pK_a 4.25)

Phenylacetic acid is eliminated in the urine mainly in the form of conjugates, the nature and relative proportions of which vary with species (see Williams, 1959; James *et al.*, 1972). Its biliary excretion in rats is low; only 3% of an injected dose is eliminated by this pathway. By contrast more than 40% of an injected dose of **diphenylacetic acid** (mol. wt. 212) is excreted in the bile of both Wistar and homozygous Gunn rats in the form of its ester glucuronide (mol. wt. 388) (Javitt, 1966).

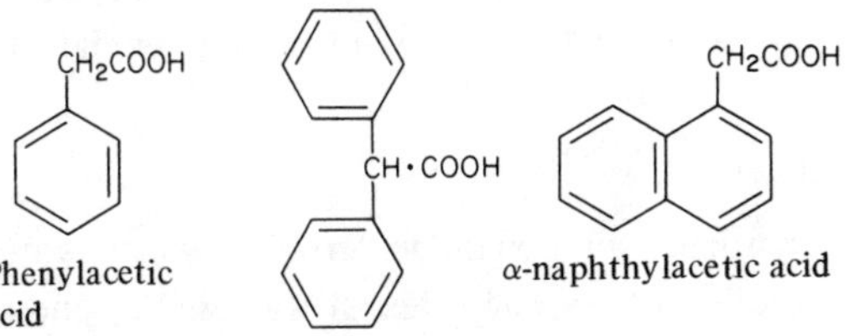

Phenylacetic acid

Diphenylacetic acid

α-naphthylacetic acid

Similarly, the biliary excretion in the rat of α-naphthylacetic acid (mol. wt. 186) is somewhat greater than that of phenylacetic acid and accounts for 5–12% of the dose (Lethco and Brouwer, 1966). The biliary metabolites may be the same as those occurring in the urine, namely, the glycine and glucuronic acid conjugates of α-naphthylacetic acid.

Protocatechuic acid (mol. wt. 154)

Protocatechuic acid is excreted in both the urine and bile of rats, the former being the main pathway of elimination. Rats eliminate about 72% of an oral dose of $[^{14}C]$ protocatechuic acid in the urine while animals injected intraperitoneally with the compound excrete about 13% in the bile (Dacre and Williams, 1968). The bile contains mainly a non-reducing glucuronide of the 3-methyl ether of protocatechuic acid, namely, vanillic acid, which is probably 4-carboxy-2-methoxyphenylglucuronide. By contrast the urine

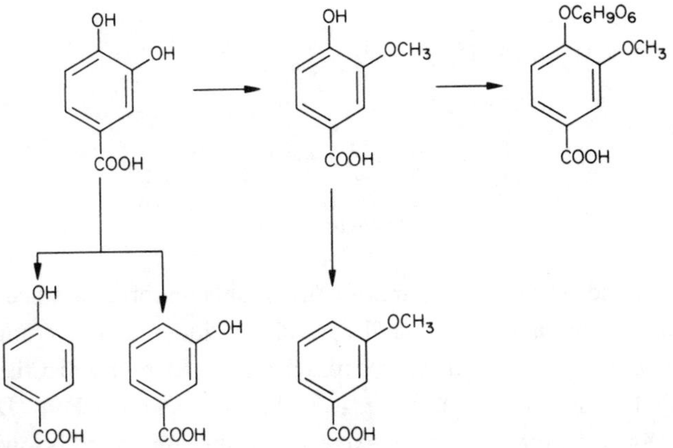

Some urinary and biliary metabolites of protocatechuic acid in the rat

contains the free and conjugated forms of the following compounds: protocatechuic acid, vanillic acid, 3- and 4-hydroxybenzoic acids and 3-methoxybenzoic acid. The 3- and 4-hydroxybenzoic acids probably arise by bacterial degradation of the 4-carboxy-2-methoxyphenylglucuronide excreted in the bile.

Probenecid (mol. wt. 285)

Probenecid is a synthetic sulphonamide derivative which is an inhibitor of the renal tubular secretion of organic acids. It was used at one time to enhance blood levels of penicillin by decreasing its secretion by the renal tubules. It is now used in the treatment of gout.

In rats with ligated renal pedicles, to prevent excretion in the urine, 80–90% of an injected dose is eliminated in the bile mainly as a glucuronide conjugate together with some unchanged drug (Guarino and Schanker, 1968). The biliary excretion of both probenecid and its glucuronide is reduced by the administration of phenolphthalein. The glucuronide conjugate has not been identified but it is probably the ester glucuronide (mol. wt. 461). The extent of its biliary excretion in the cannulated rat with intact renal function and in other species does not appear to have been determined. Renal excretion of the unchanged drug and a conjugate however, is important for the elimination of the drug in the dog (Earle and Brodie, 1947) and in man (Beyer *et al.*, 1951).

Phenylthiourea (mol. wt. 152)

Phenylthiourea

Thiourea and its derivatives are of considerable importance since they find application as preservatives and drugs. Phenylthiourea is a compound of considerable interest since it is very toxic to rats (Richter and Clisby, 1942) but much less so to the guinea pig, rabbit, cat and chicken (Dieke and Richter, 1946). In the rat, biliary excretion of the compound is low (1.5% of dose) (Abou-El-Makarem *et al.*, 1967) and about 80% appears in the urine largely as transformation products (Scheline *et al.*, 1961).

Thiambutosine (mol. wt. 343.5)

In contrast to phenylthiourea biliary excretion of the antileprotic thiourea derivative, thiambutosine is extensive. About a third of an oral dose (50 mg/kg) of this drug is excreted in rat bile in the form of two glucuronide conjugates, the aglycones of which probably are the two carboxylic acid metabolites derived from terminal and β-oxidation of the butyl side chain (Williams, *et al.*, 1965). Some biliary excretion of the drug and its metabolites also occurs in the rabbit (Schmid and Tripod, 1959).

$$(CH_3)_2N-\bigcirc-NHCSNH-\bigcirc-O(CH_2)_3CH_3$$

Thiambutosine

Diphenylamine (mol. wt. 169)

Diphenylamine is used in dye manufacture and for stabilizing nitrocellulose explosives and celluloid and also in veterinary medicine for treating screw worm infestation. Rats eliminate a significant proportion (25% of an intravenous dose in 6 h) in the bile but the greatest part (75% of dose) appears in the urine when the compound is given by the intraperitoneal route (Alexander *et al.*, 1965).

$$\bigcirc-NH-\bigcirc \qquad HO-\bigcirc-NH-\bigcirc$$

Diphenylamine   4-hydroxydiphenylamine

$$HO-\bigcirc-NH-\bigcirc-OH$$

4,4'-dihydroxydiphenylamine

No unchanged diphenylamine appears in the urine or bile and the compound occurs in these excreta largely as conjugates of two oxidation products, namely, 4-hydroxy- and 4,4'-dihydroxydiphenylamine.

Propham (isopropyl *N*-phenylcarbamate; mol. wt. 179)

Propham is a synthetic carbamate herbicide. Rats excrete about 74% of an injected dose in the urine in 4 days and about 4% in the faeces (Bend *et al.*, 1971). When injected intravenously however into biliary cannulated rats about 31% of a dose of $[^{14}C]$ propham is excreted in the bile.

$$\bigcirc-NHCOOCH(CH_3)_2$$

Propham

The low faecal excretion in intact animals however indicates that most of the biliary material is reabsorbed and eventually excreted in the urine. The biliary material consists mainly of a glucuronide conjugate possibly of isopropyl *N*-(4-hydroxyphenyl)carbamate. The urine however, contains mainly the sulphate conjugate of this metabolite.

The catecholamines

Significant biliary excretion of the metabolites of the catecholamines occurs in rats and this is particularly extensive for isoprenaline. In each case the amines appear in the bile mainly as the glucuronide conjugates of the metabolites formed by methylation of the 3-phenolic hydroxyl group. About 15% of a dose of [^{3}H]noradrenaline injected intravenously (1.74 mμ mole/kg) into rats appears in the bile and 85% in the urine (Hertting, 1964).

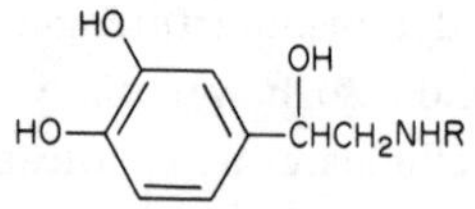

Compound	R	Mol. wt.	$pK_a{}^1$	$pK_a{}^2$
Noradrenaline	H	169	8.9, 8.7	9.8
Adrenaline	CH$_3$	183	8.9, 8.7	9.9
Isoprenaline	CH(CH$_3$)$_2$	211	–	–

(pK_a values refer to phenolic and basic groups)

Similarly, rats excrete in the bile about 10% of a dose of [^{3}H]adrenaline given by intrajugular infusion and about 70% in the urine. However, if the amine is given by intraportal infusion the biliary excretion increases to over 30%. The biliary material consists almost entirely of metanephrine glucuronide together with a small amount of 3-methoxy-4-hydroxyphenylglycol sulphate (Hertting and La Brosse, 1962).

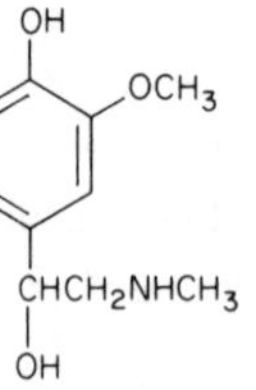

Metanephrine

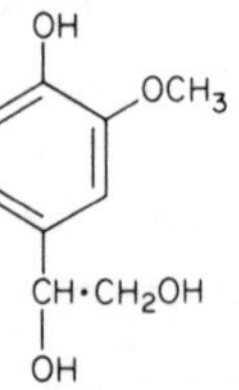

3-methoxy-4-hydroxy-phenylglycol

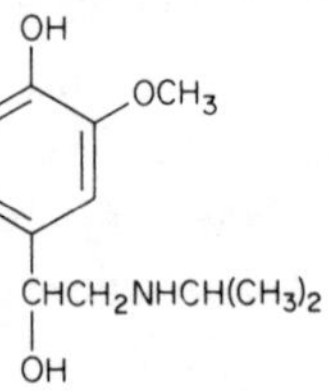

3-methoxy isoprenaline

The adrenaline metabolites secreted into the gut in the bile are partly absorbed into an enterohepatic circulation.

Isoprenaline is excreted more extensively in the bile than both adrenaline and noradrenaline. Thus, rats excrete 30–40% of a dose of [^{3}H]isoprenaline in the bile in 8 h and about 60% in the urine. The biliary material is almost entirely 3-methoxyisoprenaline glucuronide. The latter undergoes some enterohepatic circulation for when bile containing the labelled glucuronide is administered intraduodenally to rats, radioactivity appears in both the urine and bile after a delay of several hours (Hertting, 1964). The biliary excretion and enterohepatic circulation of the amine probably explains its slow rate of elimination from the body compared to noradrenaline, which is less extensively excreted in the bile.

AMPHETAMINE AND RELATED COMPOUNDS

This group of substances includes the drugs, amphetamine, p-hydroxy-amphetamine, N-methylamphetamine, ephedrine and fenfluramine. Because of their importance in clinical medicine and the problem of their abuse their metabolism has been extensively studied.

Amphetamine (mol. wt. 135, pK_a 9.9)

Amphetamine is eliminated mainly in the urine, partly unchanged and as transformation products, the nature and relative proportions of which being species dependent (Dring et al., 1970). Appreciable biliary excretion of amphetamine metabolites occurs in the rat and these undergo enterohepatic circulation (Caldwell et al., 1971a). Thus, the rat excretes 16% of an injected dose of [^{14}C]amphetamine in the bile in 24 h and 69% in the urine. The faecal excretion of radioactivity by intact rats given [^{14}C]amphetamine is low (4–5% of dose) showing that the greater part of the material excreted in

Amphetamine

the bile is absorbed and then excreted in the urine. The amounts (% dose) of the metabolites found in rat bile and urine are as follows: amphetamine 1 and 24%; total 4-hydroxyamphetamine, 15 and 38%; hippuric acid, 0.1 and 6%. The main metabolite of amphetamine in bile is 4-hydroxyamphetamine glucuronide (12% of dose; mol. wt. 327).

Some biliary excretion of amphetamine also occurs in the dog (Axelrod, 1954). In the case of man however, very little, if any biliary excretion of amphetamine occurs, since Beckett and Rowland (1965) using a gas-chromatographic method found no amphetamine in the bile of a patient who had taken a dose (10 mg) of the drug.

N-methylamphetamine (mol. wt. 149; pK_a 10.1)

As in the case of amphetamine, appreciable biliary excretion and entero-hepatic circulation of methylamphetamine occurs in the rat. Biliary can-nulated rats eliminate 18% and 54% of an injected dose of $[^{14}C]$ methyl-amphetamine in the bile and urine respectively in 24 h (Caldwell et al., 1971b). Nearly all the material eliminated in the bile is absorbed and eventually excreted in the urine since intact rats excrete 80% of an oral dose of the drug in the urine in 3 days and only 3% in the faeces. The bile, unlike the urine, contains little unchanged methylamphetamine and amphetamine and the main biliary metabolite is the glucuronide of 4-hydroxynorephedrine (mol. wt. 343). The amounts (% dose) of the metabolites occurring in rat bile and urine are as follows: methylamphetamine, 1 and 16; amphetamine 2 and 22; total 4-hydroxymethamphetamine, 1 and 6; total 4-hydroxyamphet-amine, 1 and 4; total 4-hydroxynorephedrine, 13 and 2. Appreciable biliary excretion of d-methylamphetamine also occurs in the mouse (Vree and van Rossum, 1970).

Biliary metabolites of methylamphetamine in the rat.

Butylated hydroxytoluene (BHT; 3,5-di-t-butyl-4-hydroxytoluene; mol. wt. 220)

Butylated hydroxytoluene is a synthetic antioxidant widely used in foods. It is relatively slowly excreted from the body and its retention has been attributed to its extensive biliary excretion and enterohepatic circulation and storage in the body fat (Daniel and Gage, 1965; Ladomery et al., 1967a). When given orally or by intraperitoneal injection to rats, 70–90% of the dose is recovered in the urine and faeces in 4 days. Faecal excretion may account for as much as 40% of the injected dose and this arises from biliary excretion since after intraperitoneal injection over 50% of a dose of BHT is found in the bile in 6 h. If injected intravenously over 90% of the dose appears in the bile. Most of the biliary material consists of conjugates of the following metabolites of BHT: 3,5-di-t-butyl-4-hydroxybenzoic acid (40% of dose), 3,5-di-t-butyl-4-hydroxybenzaldehyde (6%), 3,5-di-t-butyl-4-hydroxybenzyl alcohol (2%), 1,2-bis(3,5-di-t-butyl-4-hydroxyphenyl)ethane (0.4%), unchanged BHT (0.5%) together with three other unidentified metabolites (Ladomery et al., 1967b).

Biliary metabolites of BHT in the rat.

At 2 and 4 days after dosing about 15 and 4% respectively of the dose remains in the body and this is largely associated with the liver, bile and small intestine (Daniel and Gage, 1965). Some BHT is stored in the body fat. Fat storage of BHT is more marked in the female rat than in the male.

NAPHTHALENE DERIVATIVES

α-naphthylacetic acid (mol. wt. 186)

α-naphthylacetic acid is used to promote rooting of plant cuttings. The rat excretes the compound mainly in the urine as its glycine and glucuronide conjugates and only about 5–12% of the dose appears in the bile (Lethco and Brouwer, 1966).

β-naphthylamine

β-naphthylamine is a well known bladder carcinogen and has been the subject of many metabolic investigations. Nearly all the studies have centred upon the nature of the urinary metabolites of the compound formed by various species. Boyland and Manson (1966) however, have shown that metabolites of β-naphthylamine are also eliminated in the bile of the rat and furthermore some of these are peculiar to the bile and are not found in the urine. Bile of rats dosed with β-naphthylamine contains besides some unchanged compound, metabolic products arising from its hydroxylation and conjugation with glucuronic acid, sulphate and glutathione. These have been identified by Boyland and Manson (1966) using paper chromatography to be as follows: 2-acetamido-6-naphthol,   2-acetamido-5,6-dihydro-5,6-dihydroxy-naphthalene, 2-acetamido-6-naphthyl hydrogen sulphate (2-acetamido-6-naphthyl-glucosid)uronic acid, (2-naphthylamine N-glucosid(uronic acid, N-acetyl-S-(2-acetamido-5,6-dihydro-6-hydroxy-5-naphthyl)cysteine. In addition the bile contains two further conjugates which appear to be S-(2 acetamido-5,6-dihydro-6-hydroxy-5-naphthyl)glutathione and the corresponding cysteinyl-glycine conjugate. The latter are not found in the urine.

β-naphthylamine   2-acetamidonaphthalene   2-naphthylhydroxylamine

2-acetamidonaphthalene

Rats dosed with 2-acetamidonaphthalene excrete in the urine and bile the same metabolites as are seen with β-naphthylamine (Boyland and Manson, 1966).

2-naphthylhydroxylamine

2-naphthylhydroxylamine is also a bladder carcinogen and its metabolic formation from 2-naphthylamine may be at least partly responsible for the carcinogenic properties of the latter. Rats excrete the same metabolites in the bile as those seen with 2-naphthylamine and 2-acetamidonaphthalene (Boyland and Manson, 1966).

N-acetyl-2-naphthylhydroxylamine

The bile of rats dosed with this compound contains (N-acetyl-2-naphthyl-hydroxylamine O-glucosid)uronic acid and a trace of 2-naphthylamine. (Boyland and Manson, 1966).

Propanolol (mol. wt. 259)

Propanolol is an adrenergic blocking agent used in the treatment of cardiac arrhythmias. The rat and guinea pig excrete part of an injected dose of [^{14}C] propanolol in the bile in the form of glucuronides of propanolol and 4-hydroxypropanolol (Bond, 1967).

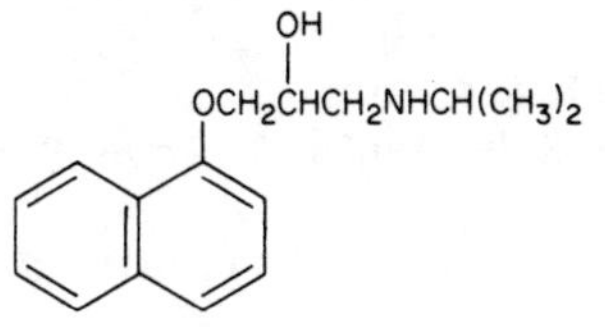

OH
OCH$_2$CHCH$_2$NHCH(CH$_3$)$_2$

Propanolol

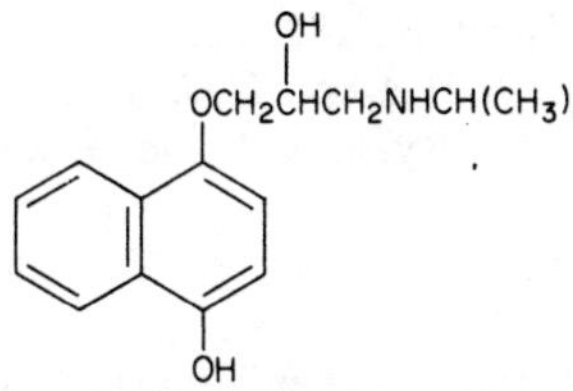

OH
OCH$_2$CHCH$_2$NHCH(CH$_3$)$_2$

OH

4-hydroxypropanolol

REFERENCES

Abou-El-Makarem, M. M., Millburn, P., Smith, R. L. and Williams, R. T. (1967) *Biochem. J.,* **105**, 1289.

Alexander, W. E., Ryan, A. J. and Wright, S. E. (1965) *Food Cosmet. Toxicol.,* **3**, 571.

Axelrod, J. (1954) *J. Pharmacol. exp. Ther.,* **110**, 315.

Beckett, A. H. and Rowland, M. (1965) *J. Pharm. Pharmacol.,* **17**, 628.

Bend, J. R., Holder, G. M. and Ryan, A. J. (1971) *Food Cosmet. Toxicol.*, **9**, 169.

Beyer, K. H., Russo, H. F., Tillson, E. K., Miller, A. K., Verwey, W. F. and Gass, S. R. (1951) *Amer. J. Physiol.*, **166**, 625.

Bond, P. A. (1967) *Nature (Lond.)*, **213**, 721.

Boyland, E. and Manson, D. (1966) *Biochem. J.*, **101**, 84.

Bridges, J. W., French, M. R., Smith, R. L. and Williams, R. T. (1970) *Biochem. J.*, **118**, 47.

Caldwell, J., Dring, L. G. and Williams, R. T. (1971a) *Biochem. J.*, **124**, 16P.

Caldwell, J., Dring, L. G. and Williams, R. T. (1971b) *Biochem. J.*, **123**, 27P.

Capel, I., French, M. R., Millburn, P., Smith, R. L. and Williams, R. T. (1972) *Xenobiotica*, **2**, 25.

Charconnet-Harding, F., Dalgliesh, C. E. and Neuberger, A. (1953) *Biochem. J.*, **53**, 513.

Dacre, J. C. and Williams, R. T. (1968) *J. Pharm. Pharmacol.*, **20**, 610.

Daniel, J. W. and Gage, J. C. (1965) *Food Cosmet. Toxicol.*, **3**, 405.

Davison, C. and Williams, R. T. (1968) *J. Pharm. Pharmacol.*, **20**, 12.

Dieke, S. H. and Richter, C. P. (1946) *Proc. Soc. exp. Biol. (N.Y.)*, **62**, 22.

Dring, L. G., Smith, R. L. and Williams, R. T. (1970) *Biochem. J.*, **116**, 425.

Earle, D. P. Jr. and Brodie, B. B. (1947) *J. Pharmacol. exp. Ther.*, **91**, 250.

Gross, M. and Greenberg, L. A. (1948) *The Salicylates* p. 49, Hillhouse Press, New Haven.

Guarino, A. M. and Schanker, L. S. (1968) *J. Pharmacol. exp. Ther.*, **164**, 387.

Hertting, G. and La Brosse, E. H. (1962) *J. biol. Chem.*, **237**, 2291.

Hertting, G. (1964) *Biochem. Pharmacol.*, **13**, 1119.

James, M. O., Smith, R. L., Williams, R. T. and Reidenberg, M. (1972) *Proc. roy. Soc. Lond. B.*, **182**, 25.

Javitt, N. B. (1966) *Amer. J. Physiol.*, **211**, 424.

Ladomery, L. G., Ryan, A. J. and Wright, S. E. (1967a) *J. Pharm. Pharmacol.*, **19**, 383.

Ladomery, L. G., Ryan, A. J. and Wright, S. E. (1967b) *J. Pharm. Pharmacol.*, **19**, 388.

Lethco, E. J., and Brouwer, E. A. (1966) *J. agric. food Chem.*, **14**, 532.

Millburn, P. M. (1970) In *Metabolic Conjugation and Metabolic Hydrolysis*, vol. 2. p. 1, edited by W. H. Fishman, Academic Press, New York and London.

Mitsuba, K. and Ichihara, K. (1927) *Hoppe-Seylers Z. physiol. Chem.*, **164**, 244.

Parke, D. V. (1960) *Biochem. J.*, **77**, 493.

Quick, A. J. (1932) *J. biol. Chem.*, **96**, 83.

Richter, C. P. and Clisby, K. H. (1942) *Arch. Path.*, **33**, 46.

Robinson, D. and Williams, R. T. (1958) *Biochem. J.*, **68**, 23P.

Scheline, R. R., Smith, R. L. and Williams, R. T. (1961) *J. med. pharm. Chem.*, **4**, 109.

Schmid, K. and Tripod, J. (1959) *Leprosy Rev.*, **30**, 85.

Smith, R. L. (1970) *Proc. Europ. Soc. Study Drug Toxicity*, **11**, 19.

Vree, T. B. and Rossum, J. M. van (1970) In *Amphetamines and Related Compounds*, p. 165, edited by E. Costa and S. Garattini, Raven Press, New York.

Williams, R. T. (1959) In *Detoxication Mechanisms*, 2nd ed. p. 359, Chapman and Hall, London.

Williams, R. T., Millburn, P. and Smith, R. L. (1965) *Ann. N.Y. Acad. Sci.*, **123**, 110.

CHAPTER ELEVEN

Sulphonamides

The biliary excretion of several sulphonamides was first investigated a few years after their discovery and development in the mid-1930's. This aspect of their behaviour became of interest because of their potential application in the treatment of infections of the hepatobiliary system. In general most sulphonamide drugs are cleared from the body by renal excretion though for some, depending upon the structure and animal species, significant biliary excretion occurs. Sulphonamides of relatively low molecular weight such as sulphanilamide and sulphathiazole are eliminated mainly by renal excretion whereas drugs of higher molecular weight, have, as might be expected, a significant biliary excretion. Thus in the rat, sulphonamides of molecular weight in excess of 300 or so and having a polar group (e.g. succinyl- and phthalyl-sulphathiazole) or which acquire one by metabolism (e.g. sulphapyridine and sulphadimethoxine) are extensively excreted in the bile (Table 33).

Most sulphonamides undergo metabolism in the body. The extent and nature of metabolism varies with the particular drug and species concerned. As a consequence, most sulphonamides appear in the bile to some extent unchanged together with their transformation products. The most important metabolic reactions of these drugs are those involving the N^4- and N^1-amino groups. Metabolism of the N^4-amino group is usually the more important and this group can undergo three reactions, namely, acetylation, N^4-glucuronide formation and N^4-sulphate synthesis.

$$\text{RNHSO}_2 - \langle \text{ring} \rangle - \text{NH}_2 \begin{cases} -\text{NHCOCH}_3 & N^4\text{-acetyl conjugate} \\ -\text{NHCH} \cdot [\text{CHOH}]_3 \text{CH} \cdot \text{COOH} & N^4\text{-glucuronide} \\ -\text{NHSO}_2\text{OH} & \text{sulphamate} \end{cases}$$

Table 33
Biliary excretion of sulphonamides in the rat

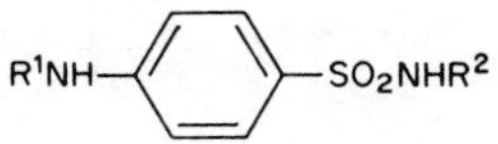

R¹NH—⟨benzene⟩—SO$_2$NHR²

Dose 50 mg/kg injected intraperitoneally as aqueous solution of the sodium salts

Compound	R¹	R²	Mol wt.	% dose in bile	Nature of compounds in bile
Sulphanilamide	H	H	172	4	Sulphanilamide and N^1- and N^4-monoacetyl and N^1, N^4-diacetyl derivatives
Sulphacetamide	H	COCH$_3$	214	0.5	Sulphacetamide
Sulphaguanidine	H	C(:NH)NH$_2$	214	trace	Sulphaguanidine and N^4-acetylsulphaguanidine
Sulphapyridine	H	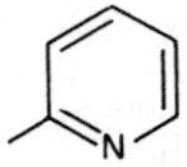 ⟨2-methylpyridinyl⟩	249	11	A glucuronide and traces of N^4-acetylsulphapyridine
Sulphadiazine	H	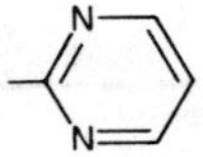 ⟨2-pyrimidinyl⟩	250	2	Sulphadiazine

139

Table 33 (continued)

Compound	R^1	R^2	Mol wt.	% dose in bile	Nature of compounds in bile
Sulphathiazole	H		255	2	Sulphathiazole
Sulphisoxazole	H		267	0.5	Sulphisoxazole
Sulphasomidine	H		278	7	Sulphasomidine and N^4-acetylsulphasomidine
Sulphamethoxy-pyridazine	H		280	8	Glucuronide conjugate
Sulphamethomidine	H		294	7	Sulphamethomidine, N^4-acetylsulphamethomidine, N^1- and N^4-glucuronide

Name			Structure	Name	Substituent
Sulphadimethoxine and N^1-glucuronide	310	9		Sulphadimethoxine	H
N^4-acetylsulphasomidine	320	5		N^4-acetylsulphasomidine	CH_3CO-
N^4-acetylsulphamethomidine	336	4		N^4-acetylsulphamethomidine	CH_3CO
N^4-acetylsulphadimethoxine	352	3		N^4-acetylsulpha-dimethoxine	CH_3CO-
Succinylsulphathiazole	355	43		Succinylsulphathiazole	CH_2COOH $-CH_2CO-$

141

Table 33 (continued)

Compound	R^1	R^2	Mol wt.	% dose in bile	Nature of compounds in bile
Phthalylsulphathiazole	COOH structure	thiazole structure	403	11	Phthalylsulphathiazole
Sulphadimethoxine N^1-glucuronide	H	OCH₃ pyrimidine structure and glucuronide structure	487	78	Sulphadimethoxine N^1-glucuronide
Sulphadimethoxine N^4-glucuronide	glucuronide structure	OCH₃ pyrimidine structure	487	44	Sulphadimethoxine N^4-glucuronide and sulphadimethoxine (2%)

Of these reactions N^4-acetylation is the most extensive but the extent to which it occurs varies with the sulphonamide, species and individual. N^4-glucuronides and N^4-sulphates are usually relatively minor products. The former appear to be produced by the spontaneous combination of the sulphonamide 4-amino group with free glucuronic acid. Reactions involving the N^1-group are less common but two have been described to occur namely acetylation and N^1-glucuronide formation. N^1-acetylation occurs in the case of sulphanilamide while the long acting sulpha drug sulphadimethoxine forms, in man and other primate species, a highly water-soluble N^1-glucuronide. Oxidative metabolism of the heterocyclic group of sulphonamides such as sulphapyridine and sulphasomizole and of the aromatic ring of sulphanilamide occurs, the products being eliminated as conjugates.

Sulphanilamide

Biliary excretion is of limited significance in the elimination of sulphanilamide and its metabolites. Thus, rats excrete about 4% of an injected dose of the drug in the bile in 24 h, 3% as the unchanged drug and 1% as N^4-acetylsulphanilamide (Millburn et al., 1967). Dogs also eliminate small amounts of sulphanilamide by this pathway (Carryer and Ivy, 1939). In man the drug occurs in the bile free and as its N-acetyl conjugate following its oral administration (Bettman and Spier, 1939; Hubbard and Anderson, 1940; Hubbard and Butsch, 1941; Spink et al., 1941). The level of sulphanilamide in gall-bladder bile is higher than that of the blood but the concentration in hepatic bile is less. In man and other species the drug is eliminated largely in the urine partly unchanged and partly as its N^1-acetyl conjugate, except in the dog which does not acetylate sulphonamides. In addition small amounts of the N^1,N^4-diacetyl derivative (Bridges and Williams, 1963) and conjugated 3-hydroxysulphanilamide may be excreted (Williams, 1946). N^1-acetylsulphanilamide is itself poorly excreted (0.5% of dose) in rat bile and is eliminated in the urine.

Sulphapyridine

The biliary excretion of this drug is somewhat greater than that seen with most sulphonamides. Thus, rats eliminate up to 20% of an injected dose of sulphapyridine in the bile partly as N^4-acetylsulphapyridine but largely as an unidentified glucuronide conjugate (Millburn et al., 1967). This glucuronide may be similar to that isolated from the urine of dogs given the drug and identified by Scudi and Childress (1956) as the glucuronic acid conjugate of the metabolite formed by hydroxylation of the 5-position of the pyridine ring. This polar conjugate has a molecular weight of 461 and might therefore be expected to be extensively excreted in the bile. The cat has also been reported to eliminate sulphapyridine in bile (Taylor and Agren, 1940). In man the drug occurs both free and as its N^4-acetyl conjugate in the hepatic bile of patients treated with the drug (Hubbard and Butsch, 1941; Spink *et al.*, 1941); most of the dose, however, can be recovered from the urine.

Sulphapyridine   5'-Hydroxysulphapyridine (R=H) and its
                        glucuronide (R = $C_6H_9O_6$)

Sulphathiazole

Biliary excretion is of little importance in the elimination of this drug and most of the dose can be recovered in the urine of man and experimental animals as the free drug and its N^4-acetyl conjugate together with a small amount of a hydroxylated derivative, possibly 3-hydroxysulphathiazole (Thorpe and Williams, 1940; Smith and Williams, 1948). Rats eliminate about 1% of an injected dose in the bile unchanged (Millburn *et al.*, 1967); the drug also appears in dog bile at a level about twice that of the blood (Shay *et al.*, 1944). N^4-acetylsulphathiazole is also poorly eliminated in the bile and is largely excreted by the kidneys.

Sulphasomidine

This drug is an isomer of sulphamethazine and is a short-acting antibacterial agent. Its biliary elimination is low; when injected intraperitoneally into rats only about 6% of the dose appears in the 24 h bile (2% free and 4% acetylated). N^4-acetylsulphasomidine is also poorly (5% of dose) excreted unchanged in rat bile (Bridges *et al.*, 1969) and the main excretory pathway is the urine. Thus, in man 80—90% of a dose appears in the urine mainly in the free state and about 10% is acetylated (Prior and Saslaw, 1951).

Sulphamethomidine

Sulphamethomidine is a medium to long-acting drug in man. Its biliary excretion is of a low order since rats excrete only about 7% of an injected dose in the bile in 24 h during which time about 40% appears in the urine. Bile contains the unchanged drug (1%), the N^4-acetyl derivative (3%) and small amounts of the N^1- and N^4-glucuronides. The urine contains mainly

N^4-acetylsulphamethomidine and the unchanged drug and small amounts of the N^4-sulphate and N^4-glucuronide conjugates. Curiously, the N^1-glucuronide which occurs to a small extent in bile appears to be absent from the urine (Bridges et al., 1969). The N^4-acetyl conjugate when injected into rats is poorly eliminated (4% of dose) in the bile.

Sulphadimethoxine

Sulphadimethoxine is an antibacterial agent with a prolonged action. Appreciable biliary excretion of this drug occurs both in man and the rat although the renal route is the main pathway for its elimination. Rats eliminate about 12% of an injected dose in the bile in 24 h and this is composed mainly of the N^1-glucuronide (11% of dose) together with small amounts of the unchanged drug and the N^4-glucuronide. The latter metabolite may be formed spontaneously by the interaction of sulphadimethoxine with glucuronic acid whereas the N^1-glucuronide appears to be formed enzymically. In the rat there is an interesting difference in the types of metabolites excreted in the bile and the urine, for the N^1-glucuronide is the main metabolite in the bile but a relatively minor one (1% of dose) in the urine. The main metabolite in the urine is the acetyl conjugate, namely N^4-acetylsulphadimethoxine (6% of dose), together with some unchanged drug (Bridges et al., 1968).

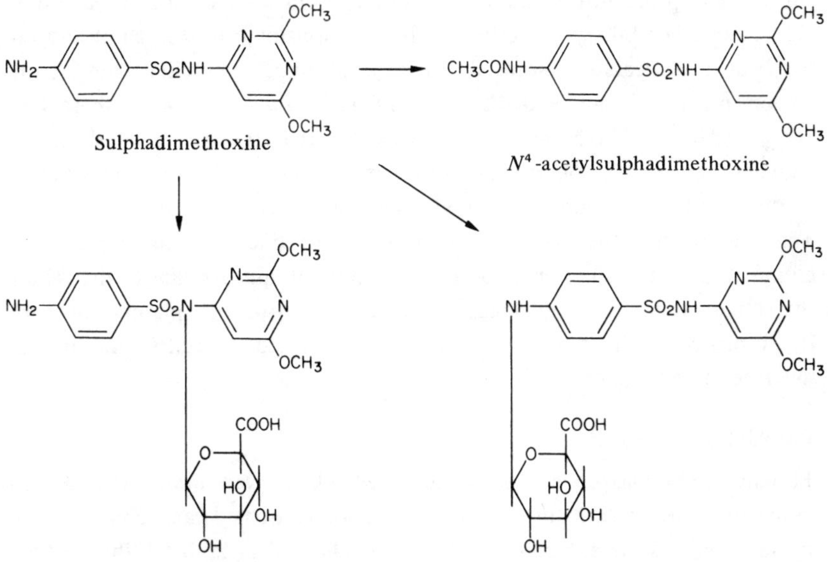

Sulphadimethoxine

N^4-acetylsulphadimethoxine

Sulphadimethoxine N^1-glucuronide

Sulphadimethoxine N^4-glucuronide

Considerable amounts of both free sulphadimethoxine and a glucuronide conjugate of the drug have been reported to occur in the bile of human patients with biliary fistulae treated with the drug (Kawerau, 1962).

Because of their polarity and relatively high molecular weight both the N^1- and N^4-glucuronides of sulphadimethoxine as might be expected are highly excreted (80% and 40% respectively) in rat bile when injected intraperitoneally. In contrast, the N^4-acetyl and N^4-sulphate conjugates are poorly excreted in the bile (2–3% of dose).

Species differences occur in the extent to which injected sulphadimethoxine N^1-glucuronide is excreted in bile since the rabbit and guinea pig eliminate about 10–20% of the dose in the bile in 3 h whereas both the rat and the dog excrete over 40% of the dose by this route (Abou-El-Makarem et al., 1967a).

Succinylsulphathiazole

Succinylsulphathiazole is used to treat infections of the gastrointestinal tract. It is poorly absorbed from the gut when given orally and its effectiveness probably depends upon some local breakdown to sulphathiazole. When injected it is extensively excreted unchanged in the bile of some species and poorly in others. Thus, the dog, hen, fruit bat and rat excrete 20–30% of an injected dose of succinylsulphathiazole in the bile in 3 h whereas only 1% or less appears in the bile of the guinea pig, rabbit, pig and rhesus monkey. The cat and sheep are intermediate and excrete about 7% (Abou-El-Makarem et al., 1967a). The biliary excretion of this sulphonamide in the rabbit and rat has been investigated in some detail in an attempt to elucidate the factors responsible for the marked difference in its biliary excretion in these two species (Abou-El-Makarem et al., 1967b). In the rat, ligation of the renal pedicles increases the biliary excretion from 34% in 3 h to over 80% whereas in the rabbit the amount eliminated in the bile rises only from 1.3% to 2.5%. This shows that the species difference is not due to more rapid renal elimination of the sulphonamide by the rabbit. It appears that in the rabbit the sulphonamide does not readily enter the liver from the plasma and there is, compared with the rat, a deficiency of the concentrative mechanism involved in its transfer to bile.

Phthalylsulphathiazole

Phthalylsulphathiazole is poorly absorbed when given orally and is used clinically for the treatment of gastrointestinal infections. In rats about 11% of an injected dose is excreted in the bile unchanged in 24 h (Millburn et al., 1967). It is also found in high concentrations in dog bile in which the levels can be 200 times that in the blood (Shay et al., 1944).

The following sulphonamides have also been reported to be excreted in rat bile: sulphaguanidine (0.5% of dose); sulphadiazine (2%), sulphisoxazole (0.5%); sulphasomizole (0.5%) (Millburn *et al.*, 1967) (see Table 33).

Chlorothiazide

Chlorothiazide has diuretic properties and is used for treating oedematous conditions. It behaves as a dibasic acid with pK_a values of 6.7 and 9.5 and at physiological pH it exists largely as an anion. The drug is eliminated mainly in the urine though some biliary excretion also occurs. Thus rats, with ligated renal pedicles to prevent urine formation, eliminate unchanged about 20% of an injected dose of chlorothiazide in the bile in 90 min. The bile to plasma ratio for the unbound drug is about 7:1 showing that its transfer occurs against a large concentration gradient.

If allowance is made for the extensive plasma protein binding of chlorothiazide (>90%) the concentration of the drug in the bile is about 80 times that of the unbound drug in the plasma (Hart and Schanker, 1966). Its biliary excretion is suppressed by probenecid and the drug itself interferes with the hepatic elimination of *p*-acetamidohippuric acid; probably both effects are due to competitive phenomena.

Dogs eliminate 90% of a dose in the urine unchanged within 6 h but nephrectomised animals excrete about 40% of a dose of the drug in the bile in 4 h. In these dogs the blood and bile levels of chlorothiazide are similar (Baer *et al.*, 1959).

Chlorothiazide
(mol. wt. 296)

Hydrochlorothiazide (mol. wt. 296)

This drug is an analogue of chlorothiazide and like the latter has diuretic properties. It is a slightly weaker acid and has pK_a values of 7.9 and 9.2. In dogs the main pathway of elimination is the urine but small amounts (3% of dose) can be recovered in the bile. Its biliary excretion is not enhanced by secretin or bromsulphthalein both of which increase bile flow (Pratt and Aikawa, 1962).

REFERENCES

Abou-El-Makarem, M. M., Millburn, P., Smith, R. L. and Williams, R. T. (1967a) *Biochem. J.*, **105**, 1289.

Abou-El-Makarem, M. M., Millburn, P. and Smith, R. L. (1967b) *Biochem. J.*, **105**, 1295.

Baer, J. E., Leidy, H. L., Brooks, A. V. and Beyer, K. H. (1959) *J. Pharmacol. exp. Ther.*, **125**, 295.

Bettman, R. and Spier, E. (1939) *Proc. Soc. exp. Biol. (N.Y.)*, **41**, 463.

Bridges, J. W. and Williams, R. T. (1963) *Biochem. J.*, **87**, 19P–20P.

Bridges, J. W., Kibby, M. R., Walker, S. R. and Williams, R. T. (1968) *Biochem. J.*, **109**, 851.

Bridges, J. W., Walker, S. R. and Williams, R. T. (1969) *Biochem. J.*, **111**, 173.

Carryer, H. M. and Ivy, A. C. (1939) *J. Pharmacol. exp. Ther.*, **66**, 302.

Hart, L. G. and Schanker, L. S. (1966) *Amer. J. Physiol.*, **211**, 643.

Hubbard, R. S. and Anderson, R. K. (1940) *Proc. Soc. exp. Biol. (N.Y.)*, **44**, 487.

Hubbard, R. S. and Butsch, W. L. (1941) *Proc. Soc. exp. Biol. (N.Y.)*, **46**, 484.

Kawerau, E. (1962) Quoted by J. W. Bridges (1963) Ph.D. Thesis, p. 31, University of London.

Millburn, P., Smith, R. L. and Williams, R. T. (1967) *Biochem. J.*, **105**, 1283.

Pratt, E. B. and Aikawa, J. K. (1962) *Amer. J. Physiol.*, **202**, 1083.

Prior, J. A. and Saslaw, S. (1951) *J. Lab. clin. Med.*, **38**, 420.

Scudi, J. V. and Childress, S. J. (1956) *J. biol. Chem.*, **218**, 587.

Shay, H., Komarov, S. A., Siplet, H. and Fels, S. S. (1944) *Gastroenterology*, **2**, 432.

Spink, W. W., Bergh, G. S. and Jermsta, J. (1941) *Surgery*, **9**, 853.

Smith, J. N. and Williams, R. T. (1948) *Biochem. J.*, **42**, 351.

Taylor, A. and Agren, G. (1940) *Acta. physiol. scand.*, **1**, 79.

Thorpe, W. V. and Williams, R. T. (1940) *Nature (Lond.)*, **146**, 686.

Williams, R. T. (1946) *Biochem. J.*, **40**, 219.

CHAPTER TWELVE

Aromatic Hydrocarbons

The metabolism and disposition of the aromatic hydrocarbons, especially the polycyclic hydrocarbons, is of particular interest in view of the carcinogenic properties of some of these compounds. Indeed their biological properties may arise as a consequence of the metabolic transformations they undergo and their particular distribution in the body. With the simple aromatic hydrocarbons such as benzene and toluene relatively little of these materials appears in the bile and elimination in the urine is the predominant pathway of excretion but with the larger hydrocarbons, extensive excretion in the bile occurs, and as a consequence a considerable proportion appears finally in the faeces.

Benzene (mol. wt. 78)

In the rat only 0.8% of an injected dose of $[^{14}C]$ benzene appears in the bile. It is eliminated largely in the expired air unchanged and in the urine as conjugates of its oxidation products, phenol, catechol, quinol and hydroxy-quinol together with phenylmercapturic acid and *trans-trans*-muconic acid (Parke and Williams, 1953). The bile contains four metabolites one of which is phenylglucuronide accounting for 16% of the biliary radioactivity. The other three metabolites have not been identified (Abou-El-Makarem *et al.*, 1967).

Toluene (mol. wt. 92)

Less than 2% of an injected dose of $[^{14}C]$ toluene is excreted in rat bile; the nature of the biliary material has not been determined. (Abou-El-Makarem *et al.*, 1967). It is excreted mainly in the urine as hippuric acid but some unchanged toluene is found in the expired air (El Masry *et al.*, 1956).

Biphenyl (mol. wt. 154)

Biphenyl is used as a fungistat for oranges by applying it to the inside of shipping containers or to wrappers. It is also used as a heat transfer agent. About 10% of a dose, injected intraperitoneally into rats, is excreted in the bile mainly as the glucuronides of 4-hydroxy- and 4,4'-dihydroxy-biphenyl (Levine *et al.*, 1970).

Biphenyl   4-hydroxybiphenyl   4-hydroxybiphenylglucuronide

4,4'-dihydroxybiphenyl   4,4'-dihydroxybiphenylglucuronide

The biliary excretion of biphenyl in rats is considerably enhanced by pretreatment with phenobarbitone and this is probably due to the inductive effect of the barbiturate on microsomal enzymes thereby enhancing the rate of formation of the hydroxylated biphenyls and their glucuronides. The hydroxybiphenyls are themselves extensively excreted in the bile when administered to rats. Thus, 4-hydroxybiphenyl appears in rat bile to the extent of 37% of the dose as its glucuronide (21% of dose) and as the monoglucuronide of 4,4'-dihydroxybiphenyl (16%) together with traces of the aglycones (Millburn *et al.*, 1967). The preformed glucuronides when injected intraperitoneally are also rapidly and extensively excreted unchanged in the bile of rats. About 60% of the dose of 4-hydroxybiphenylglucuronide is excreted in the 24 h bile and over 90% in the case of 4,4'-dihydroxy-biphenylglucuronide.

Naphthalene (mol. wt. 128)

The biliary excretion of this aromatic hydrocarbon in rats has been studied in detail by Boyland *et al.* (1961). Its fate in this respect is of considerable interest since several of the biliary metabolites are different from those appearing in the urine. Most of the biliary material consists of conjugates containing glucuronic acid and glutathione. The main glucuronides are those of 1-naphthol, the 1- and 2-glucuronides of *trans*-1,2-dihydro-1,2-dihydroxy-naphthalene and metabolites believed to be the 1- and 2-glucuronides of 1,2-dihydroxynaphthalene. Small amounts of free *trans*-1,2-dihydro-1,2-dihydroxynaphthalene also occur in the bile.

Several conjugates of naphthalene with amino acids also appear in the bile, the main one being the glutathione conjugate, *S*-(1,2-dihydro-2-hydroxy-1-naphthyl)glutathione. Two other biliary metabolites occur, one in which the glutathione conjugate has lost the glutamic acid residue and the other in

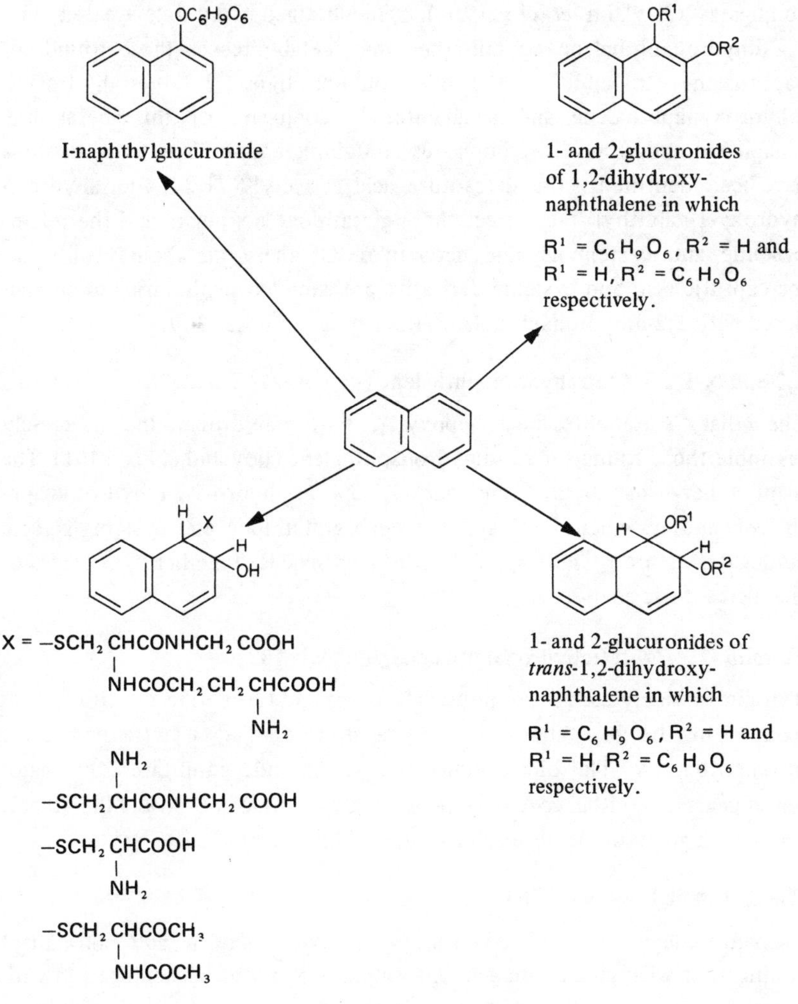

I-naphthylglucuronide

1- and 2-glucuronides
of 1,2-dihydroxy-
naphthalene in which

$R^1 = C_6H_9O_6$, $R^2 = H$ and
$R^1 = H$, $R^2 = C_6H_9O_6$
respectively.

X = —SCH$_2$CHCONHCH$_2$COOH
         |
         NHCOCH$_2$CH$_2$CHCOOH
                            |
                            NH$_2$

         NH$_2$
         |
—SCH$_2$CHCONHCH$_2$COOH

—SCH$_2$CHCOOH
         |
         NH$_2$

—SCH$_2$CHCOCH$_3$
         |
         NHCOCH$_3$

1- and 2-glucuronides of
trans-1,2-dihydroxy-
naphthalene in which

$R^1 = C_6H_9O_6$, $R^2 = H$ and
$R^1 = H$, $R^2 = C_6H_9O_6$
respectively.

which both the glutamic acid and the glycine residues have been lost. In addition, there occur in the bile small amounts of two other metabolites, which appear to be taurine derivatives of the glutathione conjugate. It is of interest that while the urine of rats dosed with naphthalene contains large amounts of 1-naphthylsulphate and the isomeric sulphates of 1,2-dihydroxynaphthalene, these metabolites do not occur in the bile. Similarly, the mercapturic acid, *N*-acetyl-*S*-(1,2-dihydro-2-hydroxy-1-naphthyl)-L-cysteine, is found in considerable amounts in urine but only in traces in the bile.

1,2-dihydronaphthalene (mol. wt. 130)

This hydrocarbon is excreted in rat bile as glucuronic acid and amino acid conjugates (Boyland *et al*., 1961). Bile obtained from rats treated with 1,2-dihydronaphthalene contain the same metabolites as those found for naphthalene. In addition the bile contains trans-1,2,3,4-tetrahydro-1,2-dihydroxynaphthalene and a glucuronide conjugate of this metabolite, 2-naphthol and some five conjugates containing amino acids. Four of these have been identified as the mercapturic acid, *N*-acetyl-*S*-(1,2,3,4-tetrahydro-2-hydroxy-1-naphthyl)-L-cysteine, the 1-glutathione conjugate and the related cysteine and cysteinylglycine derivatives. Of these metabolites only the mercapturic acid and cysteine derivative are excreted in the urine of animals dosed with 1,2-dihydronaphthalene (Boyland and Sims, 1960).

1,2-epoxy-1,2,3,4-tetrahydronaphthalene (mol. wt. 148).

The biliary metabolites of 1,2-epoxy-1,2,3,4-tetrahydronaphthalene closely resemble those found for 1,2-dihydronaphthalene (Boyland *et al.*, 1961). The main biliary metabolites are *trans*-1,2,3,4-tetrahydro-1,2-dihydroxynaphthalene and its glucuronide and the same glutathione and cysteinylglycine conjugates as are found for 1,2-dihydronaphthalene, together with traces of the mercapturic acid.

Tetralin (1,2,3,4-tetrahydronaphthalene; mol. wt. 132).

Tetralin is widely used as an industrial solvent and turpentine substitute. Rats excrete in the bile about 13% of a dose of $[1-^{14}C]$ tetralin injected intraperitoneally. The bile contains two glucuronide conjugates, the major one appears to be either *ac*-α- or *ac*-β-tetralylglucuronide or both and the other is probably a glucuronide of tetralin-1,2-diol (Millburn *et al.*, 1967).

Phenanthrene (mol. wt. 178)

Phenanthrene is metabolized mainly by hydroxylation and subsequent conjugation with glucuronic acid and sulphate and also by conjugation with glutathione (Boyland and Sims, 1962; Sims, 1962). The bile of rats dosed with phenanthrene contains S-(9,10-dihydro-9-hydroxy-10-phenanthryl)-glutathione and the corresponding cysteinylglycine, N-acetylcysteine and cysteine conjugates. Both the mercapturic acid and cysteine derivatives also occur in the urine but not the other two metabolites. The glutathione and cysteinylglycine conjugates are probably intermediates in the formation of the mercapturic acid.

$$R = — SCH_2CHCONHCH_2COOH$$

$$NHCOCH_2CH_2CH\ COOH$$

$$NH_2$$

Glutathione conjugate

$$NH_2$$

$$— SCH_2CHCONHCH_2COOH$$

Cysteinylglycine conjugate

$$—SCH_2CHCOOH$$

$$NH_2$$

Cysteine conjugate

$$—SCH_2CH\ COOH$$

$$NHCOCH_3$$

Mercapturic acid

Biliary metabolites of phenanthrene

Pyrene (mol. wt. 202)

Pyrene occurs in cigarette smoke but has not been shown to be carcinogenic. It is eliminated in both the urine and bile of rats as conjugates of hydroxylated derivatives. The bile of rats dosed orally with pyrene dissolved in arachis oil, contains the following metabolites: N-acetyl-S-(4,5-dihydro-4-hydroxy-5-pyrenyl)-L-cysteine, together with the corresponding cysteine, cysteinylglycine and glutathione conjugates as well as the glucuronic acid conjugates of 1-hydroxypyrene and trans-4,5-dihydro-4,5-dihydroxy-pyrene (Boyland and Sims, 1964).

The urine contains the sulphate and glucuronic acid conjugates of 1-hydroxypyrene, 1,6- and 1,8-dihydroxypyrene and trans-4,5-dihydro-4,5-dihydroxypyrene together with some N-acetyl-S-(4,5-dihydro-4-hydroxy-5-pyrenyl)-L-cysteine. The glutathione, cysteinylglycine and cysteine conjugates thus appear to be metabolites that are peculiar to bile. There also appears to be a difference in the nature of the conjugates of 1-hydroxypyrene

Biliary metabolites of pyrene

found in the urine and bile since the former contains mainly the sulphate conjugate of the phenol whereas the latter contains the glucuronide.

Harper (1957) has isolated from the faeces of rats and mice dosed with pyrene its 3-hydroxy derivative and its 3:8- and 3:10-quinones, these presumably being derived from the metabolites eliminated in the bile.

1:2-benzanthracene (mol. wt. 228)

1:2-benzanthracene has carcinogenic properties. Early work suggested that the hydrocarbon undergoes significant biliary excretion since a metabolite, 4'-hydroxy-1:2-benzanthracene, could be detected in the faeces of animals dosed with the compound (Berenblum and Schoental, 1943; Dickens, 1945). Boyland and Sims (1964) have shown that the hydrocarbon is eliminated in both the bile and urine of rats as conjugates of hydroxylated derivatives. Thus, the bile of rats dosed orally with 1:2-benzanthracene dissolved in arachis oil, contains N-acetyl-S-(5,6-dihydro-6-hydroxy-5-benzanthracenyl)-cysteine and the corresponding conjugates with cysteine, cysteinylglycine and glutathione. Besides these derivatives, the bile also contains conjugates which are probably the glucuronides of 3- and 4-hydroxybenzanthracene and 8,9-dihydro-8,9-dihydroxybenzanthracene. The faeces of rats dosed with the carcinogen contain free 3- and 4-hydroxybenzanthracene and 8,9-dihydro-8,9-dihydroxy-benzanthracene which probably arise by the splitting in the gut by bacterial enzymes, of the conjugates eliminated with the bile.

The urinary metabolites appear to be more numerous and have been identified as *N*-acetyl-*S*-(5,6-dihydro-6-hydroxy-5-benzanthracenyl)-L-cysteine and the sulphate and glucuronic acid conjugates of 3-, 4-, 8- and 9-hydroxy-benzanthracene and of 3,4-dihydro-3,4-dihydroxy-, 5,6-dihydro-5,6-dihydroxy-, 8,8-dihydro-8,9-dihydroxy- and 10,11-dihydro-10,11-dihydroxy-benzanthracene.

$$R = -SCH_2\overset{\overset{\displaystyle NHCOCH_3}{|}}{C}HCOOH; \; -SCH_2\overset{\overset{\displaystyle NH_2}{|}}{C}H\;COOH;$$

$$-SCH_2\overset{\overset{\displaystyle NH-Glu}{|}}{C}HCO-Gly; \; -SCH_2\overset{\overset{\displaystyle NH_2}{|}}{C}HCO-Gly$$

Biliary metabolites of 1:2-benzanthracene

3,4-benzopyrene (mol. wt. 252)

This hydrocarbon is an active carcinogen found in coal tar. It is also present in trace amounts in urban atmospheres due to pollution by smoke and it occurs to a small extent in tobacco smoke. It has been suggested that this compound may be at least partly responsible for human lung tumours associated with smoking. The metabolism of 3,4-benzopyrene and related compounds is very complex and this is compounded by the fact that the primary metabolic transformation products are eliminated in the bile and these then undergo further extensive metabolism by the gut flora.

When 3,4-benzopyrene is injected intravenously into mice there occurs in the bile a substance, designated BPX with a brilliant blue fluorescence (Weigert and Mottram, 1946). This fluorescent material appears to be composed of conjugates of 8- and 10-benzopyrenol (Berenblum and Schoental, 1955). In the small intestine this material travels along with the gut contents until it reaches the ileocaecal valve when the fluorescence changes to green-blue. This appears to be due to breakdown of the conjugates and their conversion to the free phenols, namely 8- and 10-benzopyrenol and both of these occur in the faeces. Conjugates of 5-benzopyrenol may also occur in rat bile as Pihar and Spaleny (1956) have isolated 5- as well as 8-benzopyrenol

3,4-benzopyrene

10-benzopyrenol

8-benzopyrenol

from the faeces of rats given benzopyrene. Chalmers (1956) found that the bile of both mice and fowls treated with 3,4-benzopyrene contain a major metabolite which appeared to be the glucuronide of a benzopyrenol possibly 10-benzopyrenol. Rats excrete about 70–80% of an injected dose of $[^{14}C]$-benzopyrene in the bile in 6 h in the form of 26 metabolites most of which are conjugates (Falk, 1963). Soon after the injection the main biliary metabolite appears to be the glucuronide of 6-benzopyrenol together with small amounts of 1,6- and 3,6-dihydroxybenzopyrene conjugates and traces of 6,12-dihydroxy- and 4,5-dihydro-4,5-dihydroxybenzopyrene conjugates. One to two hours after administration of the hydrocarbon the main biliary metabolites are the glucuronide of 3-hydroxybenzpyrenol, conjugates of 2,3-dihydro-2,3-dihydroxybenzopyrene and a substance, possibly a dihydro-monohydroxy derivative which on treatment with acid yields 3,4-benzo-pyrene. Studies with the 3- and 6-benzopyrenols and the 1,6- and 3,6-quinones show that these substances are also highly excreted in the bile of rats as conjugates.

The biliary excretion of 3,4-benzopyrene is greatly enhanced in rats if the animals are pretreated with the microsomal enzyme inducing agents pheno-barbitone, methylcholanthrene or benzopyrene itself (Levine, 1970). This has been attributed to an increase in the rate at which the carcinogen is metabolically transformed to polar conjugates which can be rapidly excreted in the bile.

1:2:5:6-dibenzanthracene (mol. wt. 278)

1:2:5:6-dibenzanthracene was the first pure chemical shown to have carcinogenic properties and as a consequence its metabolism and excretion have been extensively studied. Its main channel of elimination is the bile, probably as conjugates of hydroxylated derivatives and it is eventually voided with the faeces. It persists in the body for long periods and this could be due to its enterohepatic circulation. Heidelberger and Weiss (1951) found that radioactivity persisted in the subcutaneous tissues of mice injected with [^{14}C]-1:2:5:6-dibenzanthracene for more than 85 days.

When given to mice intravenously, intraperitoneally or orally, most of the radioactivity from a dose of the ^{14}C-labelled hydrocarbon is excreted via the bile in the faeces (80%) and less than 10% appears in the urine (Heidelberger and Jones, 1948; Heidelberger et al., 1948). The nature of the biliary material has not been determined. A number of hydroxylated derivatives have however been isolated from the urine and faeces of various species dosed with the compound and it is possible that the bile contains these same metabolites or their conjugates. Thus, 4':8'-dihydroxy-1:2:5:6-dibenzanthracene occurs as a metabolite of the carcinogen in rat and mouse urine (Cason and Fieser, 1940). The faeces of rabbits dosed with 1:2:5:6-dibenzanthracene contain a monohydroxy derivative which is either the 4'- or 4-hydroxy derivative (Cook and Schoental, 1952).

5-hydroxy-1:2-naphthalic acid

4':8'-dihydroxy-1:2:5:6-dibenzanthracene

Further studies by Heidelberger and his colleagues (Heidelberger and Wiest, 1951; Heidelberger et al., 1953) have shown that the hydrocarbon is also converted to quinones and that these are split at the central ring to give acidic metabolites. Thus, one such product, 5-hydroxy-1:2-naphthalic acid, is found in the faeces and liver of mice injected intravenously or treated on the skin with the hydrocarbon. This metabolite is not found in the liver at 2 or 6 h after injection but is present after 22h. It is probably formed from 4':8'-dihydroxy-1:2:5:6-dibenz-9:10-anthraquinone which has also been detected in the livers of animals. It could arise from enterobacterial metabolism of metabolites secreted in the bile.

Biliary excretion of other aromatic hydrocarbons

Cholanthrene, methylcholanthrene, 2:6- and 2':1-dimethyl-1:2-benzanthracene and fluoranthene are excreted in the bile of fowls as fluorescent metabolites (Chalmers and Peacock, 1941).

REFERENCES

Abou-El-Makarem, M. M., Millburn, P., Smith, R. L. and Williams, R. T. (1967) *Biochem. J.,* **105**, 1269.

Berenblum, I. and Schoental, R. (1955) *Science,* **122**,470.

Berenblum, I. and Schoental, R. (1943) *Cancer Res.,* **3**, 686.

Boyland, E., Ramsay, G. S. and Sims, P. (1961) *Biochem. J.,* **78**, 376.

Boyland, E. and Sims, P. (1960) *Biochem. J.,* **77**, 175.

Boyland, E. and Sims, P. (1962) *Biochem. J.,* **84**,564.

Boyland, E. and Sims, P. (1964) *Biochem. J.,* **90**, 391.

Cason, J. and Fieser, L. F. (1940) *J. Amer. chem. Soc.,* **62**, 2681.

Chalmers, J. G. (1956) *Brit. J. Cancer,* **10**, 787.

Chalmers, J. G. and Peacock, P. R. (1941) *Biochem. J.,* **35**, 1276.

Cook, J. W. and Schoental. R. (1952) *J. chem. Soc.,* P.9.

Dickens, F. (1945) *A. R. Brit. Emp. Cancer Campaign,* **22**, 53.

Masry, A. M. El, Smith, J. N. and Williams, R. T. (1956) *Biochem. J.,* **64**, 50.

Falk, H. L. (1963) *Acta. Un. int. Cancr.,* **19**, 528.

Harper, K. H. (1957) *Brit. J. Cancer,* **11**, 499.

Heidelberger, C. and Jones, H. B. (1948) *Cancer,* **1**, 252.

Heidelberger, C., Kirk, M. R. and Perkins, M. S. (1948) *Cancer,* **1**, 261.

Heidelberger, C. and Weiss, S. M. (1951) *Cancer, Res.,* **11**, 885.

Heidelberger, C. and Wiest, W. G. (1951) *Cancer, Res.,* **11**, 511.

Heidelberger, C., Hadler, H. I and Wolf, G. (1953) *J. Amer. chem. Soc.,* **75**, 1303.

Levine, W. G., Millburn, P., Smith, R. L. and Williams, R. T. (1970) *Biochem. Pharmacol.,* **19**, 235.

Levine, W. G. (1970) *J. Pharmacol. exp. Ther.,* **175**, 301.

Millburn, P., Smith, R. L. and Williams, R. T. (1967) *Biochem. J.,* **105**, 1275.

Parke, D. V. and Williams, R. T. (1953) *Biochem. J.,* **54**, 231.

Pihar, O. and Spaleny, J. (1956) *Chem. Listy,* **50**, 296.

Sims, P. (1962) *Biochem. J.,* **84**, 558.

Weigert, F. and Mottram, J. C. (1946) *Cancer Res.,* **6**, 97.

CHAPTER THIRTEEN

Phthaleins

This group of compounds includes such well-known substances as phenolph-thalein, phenolsulphonphthalein (phenol red) and phenoltetrabromophthalein (BSP). Phenolphthalein is used as a cathartic while the latter two phthaleins are important diagnostic agents. Other phthaleins such as bromocresol green and bromothymol blue are used as acid-base indicators.

Most phthaleins have an affinity for excretion in the bile and the extent to which this occurs depends upon their structure. Phenolphthalein itself is highly excreted in the bile of several species largely in the form of its polar glucuronide conjugate. By contrast phenolsulphonphthalein which has a molecular weight (354) comparable with phenolphthalein (318) is less effectively excreted in bile and appears in the urine largely unchanged. This may be a reflection of the difficulty which the body apparently has in converting it to a polar glucuronic acid conjugate with a larger molecular weight. However, the halogenation of phenolsulphonphthalein to give polar compounds of higher molecular weight such as bromocresol green and bromophenol blue results in a change of emphasis from kidney excretion to hepatic elimination. The extent of biliary excretion of compounds of this type is also influenced by the number of sulphonic acid groups in the molecule, since the mono- and di-sulphonates of phenoltetrabromphthalein for example, are more extensively excreted in rat bile than the tetra-sulphonate.

Phenolphthalein

Phenolphthalein R = H; mol. wt. 318

Phenolphthalein
glucuronide

mol. wt. 495   R =

The extensive elimination of phenolphthalein and related compounds in bile was first observed by Abel and Rowntree (1909). This proved to be an important empirical observation since it later led to the development of phthalein based compounds for use as X-ray contrast media for the gall-bladder and for assessment of liver function.

Phenolphthalein is extensively excreted (40–85% of dose) in the bile of the rat, dog and hen and less so in the guinea pig, rabbit and cat (Table 34). The rat, rabbit, guinea pig and hen excrete in the bile largely phenolphthalein glucuronide while cat and dog bile contains, besides some unchanged phenolphthalein and its glucuronide, a second unidentified metabolite which appears to be another glucuronide. Other reports indicate that phenolphthalein is excreted in cat bile as a glucuronide conjugate (Pekanmaki and Salmi, 1961a, Steigmann et al., 1938). Dogs have been reported to excrete in the bile within 72 h over 40% of a dose $[^{14}C]$ phenolphthalein injected intravenously; a further 35% appears in the urine and 11% in the faeces (Visek et al., 1956).

Table 34
Biliary excretion of phenolphthalein in various species
Dose 10 mg/kg

Species	Route of administration	% dose found in bile in 3 h.
Rat	intraperitoneal	85
Guinea pig	intraperitoneal	22
Rabbit	intravenous	25
Cat	intravenous	13
Dog	intravenous	57
Hen	intravenous	43

Data from Abou-El-Makarem (1967)

In man, phenolphthalein is eliminated in the bile as its glucuronide and its prolonged laxative effect has been attributed to enterohepatic circulation (Steigmann *et al.*, 1938; Pekanmaki and Salmi, 1961b). One patient with a biliary fistula excreted 26% of an oral dose of phenolphthalein in the bile, 21% conjugated and the remainder free. Its biliary excretion is much reduced in non-obstructive jaundice; in this situation the blood levels increase and more is eliminated in the urine (Fantus *et al.*, 1941). One curious observation is that in the absence of bile, phenolphthalein loses it cathartic action. Thus, it apparently has no laxative effect in clinical obstructive jaundice when no bile is secreted into the intestine. Similarly, the drug has no cathartic action in cats with experimental obstructive jaundice (Steigmann *et al.*, 1938). Whether phenolphthalein is excreted in the bile as a metabolite with cathartic properties or that bile is necessary for the absorption of the drug into the intestinal wall has not been investigated.

The main metabolite of phenolphthalein, namely the glucuronide, is extensively excreted in the bile of several species when given as such. Thus, the dog, rat and hen excrete 50–80% of an injected dose of the glucuronide in the bile unchanged, while moderate excretion (30–40%) occurs in the cat and sheep but relatively little (6–13%) in the rabbit, guinea pig and rhesus monkey (Abou-El-Makarem *et al.*, 1967). In rats, the rate of biliary excretion of phenolphthalein is enhanced by pretreatment with phenobarbitone and this has been attributed to an enhanced rate of glucuronide formation due to the stimulant effect of the barbiturate on the microsomal enzymes (Levine *et al.*, 1970). Conversely, the microsomal enzyme inhibitor SKF-525 retards the biliary excretion of phenolphthalein by suppressing its conversion to a glucuronide conjugate. These two facts indicate the importance of glucuronide formation for the biliary excretion of phenolpthalein.

Phenolsulphonphthalein (phenol red) (mol. wt. 354)

Phenol red is widely used in tests of kidney function since in several species including man it is excreted partially by glomerular filtration and by tubular secretion. It appears to be so rapidly excreted in the urine unchanged that little biliary elimination occurs though this increases markedly if the renal route is blocked. In anaesthetized dogs only about 3% of a dose (20 mg/kg) injected intravenously appears in the bile in 3 h and 75% in the urine. Nephrectomy however increases the biliary excretion to 30% in 3 h (Kim and Hong 1962). Rats with ligated renal pedicles eliminate over 80% of an intravenous dose in the bile in 2 h largely unchanged but partly (25% of dose) as a glucuronide (Hart and Schanker, 1966). Phenol red also appears to be secreted in the bile of chickens (Sperber, 1957) and of frogs (Höber and Titajew, 1929).

Bromophenol blue and bromocresol green

Bromocresol green
(mol. wt. 698)

Bromophenol blue
(mol. wt. 670)

Both bromocresol green and bromophenol blue are highly excreted in the bile and this may be associated with the introduction of several halogen groups into the phenolsulphonphthalein molecule. Rats excrete about 60% of an intravenous dose of bromocresol green in the bile in 3 h largely unchanged and about 4% as a metabolite. It is also excreted in the bile of chickens (Sperber, 1957). In dogs about 20–30% of the dose of both bromocresol green and bromophenol blue appears in the bile in 3 h with about 4% in the urine (Kim and Hong, 1962).

Sulphobromophthalein (phenoltetrabromphthalein; bromsulphalein)
(mol. wt. 838)

From the point of view of biliary excretion one of the most interesting phthalein derivatives is sulphobromophthalein (BSP), a diagnostic agent used in liver function tests. Sulphobromophthalein is rapidly excreted by the liver in the bile and the rate of disappearance of an injected dose of the dye from the plasma due to hepatic elimination forms the basis of a test for liver function. BSP is highly excreted in the bile of all species so far investigated mainly in the form of transformation products. The rat excretes 95–100% of an injected dose of BSP in the bile (Javitt, 1965) mainly in the form of two metabolites (Krebs, 1959). The latter when isolated and injected intravenously into rats are rapidly eliminated in the bile. The dog (Cantarow *et al.,* 1948; Brauer and Pessotti, 1950) and the guinea pig (Schenker *et al.,* 1965) also rapidly excrete the dye in the bile. In man 50–80% of injected doses (5 mg/kg) of BSP have been recovered within 2 h in the bile of subjects with biliary fistulae following choledochotomy (Monroe and Kittinger, 1961). However, patients with biliary and portal cirrhosis excreted only 23% of the dose in the bile. The bile contained at least 4 or 5 metabolites derived from BSP.

The nature of the biliary metabolites remains to be fully determined. There also occurs marked species variations in the nature, number and amounts of the various metabolites of BSP excreted in the bile (Krebs and Brauer, 1958). The main biliary metabolites of the dye are probably the various isomeric forms of the glutathione conjugate and its partial breakdown products such as BSP-cysteinylglycine and BSP-cysteine. Conjugation appears to occur through the sulphydryl group of glutathione by replacement of one of the bromine groups of BSP with formation of a thioether linkage (Combes and Stakelum, 1960; Javitt *et al.,* 1960).

Glutathione conjugates excreted in the bile may be hydrolysed in the gut since the small intestine contains the enzyme glutathionase which can split glutathione and its conjugates (Bray *et al.*, 1959). Progressive hydrolysis of the conjugate in the enteric tract would release first glutamic acid and then glycine leaving the *S*-cysteine conjugate which, if absorbed and then *N*-acetylated, would provide a source of the mercapturic acid.

The biliary excretion of BSP in rats is enhanced by pretreatment with phenobarbitone and this has been attributed to increased bile flow and bile transport capacity (Klaassen and Plaa, 1968).

Javitt (1965) has made a comparative study of the biliary excretion in the rat of two phthaleins closely related to BSP namely, phenoltetrabromphthalein monosulphonate and tetrasulphonate. While both BSP (the disulphonate) and the monosulphonate are highly excreted (95—100% of dose) in bile the reverse is true of the tetrasulphonate derivative (10% in bile). The monosulphonate disappeared rapidly from the plasma and appeared in the bile as a glutathione conjugate and as a double conjugate containing both glutathione and glucuronic acid. While the tetrasulphonate was poorly excreted in the bile a synthetic glutathione derivative was rapidly eliminated by the liver.

Tetraiodophenolphthalein

Tetraiodophenolphthalein sodium
(mol. wt. 920)

Tetraiodophenolphthalein is highly excreted in bile and is of interest since it was the first substance to be used as a radiopaque medium for X-ray visualization of the gall-bladder (Graham *et al.*, 1928). It has now, however, been largely replaced by better tolerated and less toxic substances.

FLUORESCEIN AND ITS DERIVATIVES

The fluoresceins are structurally related to the phthaleins and like the latter they tend to be extensively excreted in bile. Their metabolism and excretion is of considerable interest because of their use as colouring agents in food and cosmetics.

Webb *et al.* (1962) have investigated the biliary excretion in rats, of fluorescein and its halogenated derivatives and their findings are summarized in Table 35.

Table 35
Excretion patterns of fluorescein and some halogenated derivatives in the rat

| | | % dose in 2 h in | |
Compound	mol. wt.	Bile	Urine
Fluorescein	332	14	30
4,5-Dibromofluorescein	490	29	5
4,5-Diiodofluorescein	584	32	5
4,5-Dibromo-2,7-diiodofluorescein	742	52	3
2,4,5,7-Tetrabromo-12,13,14,15- tetrachlorofluorescein	836	55	1
2,4,5,7-Tetraiodofluorescein	786	66	0

Fluorescein on injection into rats appears in both the urine and bile whereas on increasing halogenation the proportion excreted in the bile rises with a concomitant fall in the urinary excretion. Fluorescein and its 4,5-dibromo-, 4,5-diiodo- and 2,7-dichloro- derivatives appear in the bile partly unchanged and in the form of glucuronide conjugates. By contrast, the tri- and tetra-halogenated fluoresceins and the tetrachlorotetrabromo compound are metabolically inert and appear in the bile unchanged. The hepatic excretion of the monohalogenated fluoresceins (the 4-iodo- and 4-bromo-derivatives) is more complex since besides forming glucuronide conjugates both substances undergo some dehalogenation to give fluorescein. Heavily halogenated fluoresceins are less toxic than the simpler fluoresceins and this might be related to their more rapid elimination in the bile (Hansen *et al*., 1958).

The various fluorescein dyes investigated appear to be resistant to metabolic degradation in the gut since they can be isolated unchanged from rat faeces several days after their oral administration.

Rose bengal (4,5,6,7-tetrachloro-2′,4′,5′,7′-tetraiodofluorescein)

Rose bengal (mol. wt. 974)

Rose bengal is used in the form of its sodium or potassium salt as a dye and biological stain and as the ^{131}I-labelled compound for liver function tests. Rabbits excrete about 60% of the radioactivity from an intravenous dose of $[^{131}I]$ Rose bengal in the bile within one hour (Nosslin and Morgan, 1965). Its biliary excretion in this species is suppressed, apparently by interference with its hepatic uptake, by favaspidic acid. This substance is present in male-fern extracts and may contribute to the transient clinical jaundice sometimes observed after the use of such extracts. Similarly, rats excrete 70–90% of an injected dose of $[^{131}I]$ Rose bengal in the bile in 3 h apparently without undergoing metabolic change. Carbon tetrachloride induced centrilobular necrosis reduces the hepatic elimination of the dye in rats (Meurman, 1960). Rose bengal is also rapidly excreted in the bile of dogs and humans (Delprat and Stowe, 1931). Its rate of disappearance from the plasma by biliary excretion is influenced by liver damage and this is the basis of its use in a diagnostic test for the latter.

REFERENCES

Abel, J. J. and Rowntree, L. G. (1909) *J. Pharmacol. exp. Ther.*, **1**, 231.
Abou-El-Makarem, M. M. (1967) Ph.D. Thesis, University of London.
Abou-El-Makarem, M. M., Millburn, P., Smith, R. L. and Williams, R. T. (1967) *Biochem. J.*, **105**, 1289.

Brauer, R. W. and Pessotti, R. L. (1950) *Amer. J. Physiol.,* **162,** 565.

Bray, H. G., Franklin, T. J. and James, S. P. (1959) *Biochem. J.,* **71,** 690.

Cantarow, A., Wirts, C. W., Snape, W. J. and Miller, L. L. (1948) *Amer. J. Physiol.,* **154,** 211.

Combes, B. and Stakelum, G. S. (1960) *J. clin. Invest.,* **39,** 1214.

Delprat, G. D. and Stowe, W. P. (1931) *J. Lab. clin. Med.,* **16,** 923.

Fantus, B., Steigmann, F. and Dyniewicz, J. M. (1941) *J. Pharmacol. exp. Ther.,* **72,** 252.

Graham, E. A., Cole, W. H., Copher, G. H. and Moore, S. (1928) *Diseases of the Gall-bladder and Bile ducts,* Lea and Febiger, Philadelphia.

Hansen, W. H., Fitzhugh, O. G. and Williams, M. W. (1958) *J. Pharmacol. exp. Ther.,* **122,** 29 A.

Hart, L. G. and Schanker, L. S. (1966) *Proc. Soc. exp. Biol. (N.Y.),* **123,** 433.

Höber, R. and Titajew, A. A. (1930) *Pflüger's Arch. ges. Physiol.,* **223,** 180.

Javitt, N. B. (1965) *Amer. J. Physiol.,* **208,** 555.

Javitt, N. B., Wheeler, H. O., Baker, K. J., Ramos, O. L. and Bradley, S. E. (1960) *J. clin. Invest.,* **39,** 1570.

Kim, J. H. and Hong, S. K. (1962) *Amer, J. Physiol.,* **202,** 174.

Klaassen, C. D. and Plaa, G. L. (1968) *J. Pharmacol. exp. Ther.,* **161,** 361.

Krebs, J. S. (1959) *Amer. J. Physiol.,* **197,** 292.

Krebs, J. S. and Brauer, R. W. (1958) *Amer. J. Physiol.,* **194,** 37.

Levine, W. G., Millburn, P., Smith, R. L. and Williams, R. T. (1970) *Biochem. Pharmacol.,* **19,** 235.

Meurman, L. (1960) *Acta. med. scand., Suppl.* 354.

Monroe, L. S. and Kittinger, M. S. (1961) *J. Lab. clin. Med.,* **58,** 468.

Nosslin, B. and Morgan, E. H. (1965) *J. Lab. clin. Med.,* **65,** 891.

Pekanmäki, K., and Salmi, H. A. (1961a) *Acta pharmacol. (Kbh),* **18,** 133.

Pekanmäki, K. and Salmi, H. A. (1961b) *Ann. Med. exp. Fenn.,* **39,** 302.

Schenker, S., Goldstein, J. and Combes, B. (1965) *Amer. J. Physiol.,* **208,** 563.

Smith, R. L. (1970) *Proc. Europ. Soc. Study Drug Toxicity,* **11,** 19.

Sperber, I. (1957) *Acta physiol. scand.,* **42**; Suppl. 145, 129.

Steigmann, F., Barnard, R. D. and Dyniewicz, J. M. (1938) *Amer. J. med. Sci.,* **196,** 673.

Visek, W. J., Liu, W. C. and Roth, L. J. (1956) *J. Pharmacol. exp. Ther.,* **117,** 347.

Webb, J. N., Fonda, M. and Brouwer, E. A. (1962) *J. Pharmacol. exp. Ther.,* **137,** 141.

CHAPTER FOURTEEN

Azo Compounds

Azo compounds have long been the most common synthetic colour agents used in foods, pharmaceuticals and cosmetics. In recent years there has occurred an increasing awareness of the possible health hazards associated with their use particularly as some azo compounds have carcinogenic properties. Because of the latter much interest has focussed upon the metabolism and elimination of azo compounds (see Walker, 1970) as in some cases the carcinogen is probably an active metabolite. The study of the fate of these compounds is also of considerable historical interest since it was from an exploration of the metabolism of the antibacterial azo dye, prontosil, that the present range of sulphonamide drugs became available.

The earliest studies were concerned mainly with the nature of the urinary metabolites but in recent years it has been realized that biliary excretion is an important aspect of their overall fate. Furthermore, their excretion in the bile brings the azo compounds into contact with the gut flora which can reduce them to potentially toxic arylamines. The latter may be voided with the faeces or absorbed and then excreted in the urine.

P-Dimethylaminoazobenzene (butter yellow; mol. wt. 225).

The metabolism and excretion of this compound has been extensively investigated in view of its carcinogenic properties. Studies by Ishidate and his co-workers (1962) have shown that in rats biliary excretion is an important aspect of its physiological disposition. The bile of rats injected with the dye contains six metabolites, all of them being conjugates. These are the glucuronide and sulphate conjugates of 4'-hydroxy-4-dimethylaminoazobenzene and its mono- and di-demethylated derivatives. The urine however contains metabolites formed predominantly by splitting of the azo linkage. It is probable that the latter are formed by enterobacterial metabolism of the compounds excreted in bile which are then absorbed and eliminated in the urine.

Biliary metabolites of p-*dimethylaminoazobenzene*

R¹	R²	R³
$O-C_6H_9O_6$ or OSO_2OH	CH_3	CH_3
$O-C_6H_9O_6$ or OSO_2OH	H	CH_3
$O-C_6H_9O_6$ or OSO_2OH	H	H

$-C_6H_9O_6$ = glucuronic acid; OSO_2OH = sulphate

Related fat-soluble azo dyes are also excreted in the bile of rabbits. Thus, Salant and Bengis (1916) found that the following dyes appeared in rabbit bile after intravenous or intraperitoneal injection: 1-benzeneazo-β-naphthyl-amine, 1-benzeneazo-β-naphthol, and 1-azobenzene-β-naphthol. The quantitative and qualitative aspects of their biliary excretion were not determined though it seems probable that they would largely be present as polar conjugates.

O-aminoazotoluene (4-amino-2′,3-dimethylazobenzene; mol. wt. 225)

This dye causes hepatomas in both rats and mice (Crabtree, 1949) and it is excreted in rat bile in the form of a large number of metabolites (Samejima *et al.*, 1967). These have been identified to be as follows: 4-amino-2′,3-di-methylazobenzene *N*-glucuronide (a major metabolite), 4-amino-2′-carboxyl-3-methylazobenzene *N*-glucuronide, the sulphate and glucuronic acid conjugates of 4-amino-2′,3-dimethyl-4′-hydroxyazobenzene and a double conjugate which appears to be 4-amino-2′,3-dimethyl-4′-hydroxy toluene *N*-glucuronide *O*-sulphate.

Yellow OB (1-[*o*-tolylazo]-2-naphthylamine; mol. wt. 261)

Yellow OB is a fat-soluble dye. In rats the dye appears in the bile as four polar metabolites all of which retain the azo linkage. These have been suggested by Radomski and Harrow (1966) to be as follow: 1-(*o*-tolylazo)-6-hydroxy-2-naphthylamine *N*-glucuronide, 1-(*o*-tolylazo)-2-sulphaminonaph-thalene *O*-glucuronide, 1-(*o*-tolylazo)-6-hydroxy-2-naphthylamine *N*-glu-curonide and 1-(*o*-tolylazo)-2-sulphaminonaphthalene.

1-phenylazo-2-naphthol (mol. wt. 248)

1-phenylazo-2-naphthol was formerly used as a margarine colour. It appears to be a mild carcinogen. Both the bile and urine of rabbits dosed orally with 1-phenylazo-2-naphthol contain the glucuronides of 4′,6-dihydroxy-1-phenyl-azo-2-naphthol and 4′- and 6-hydroxy-1-phenyl-azo-2-naphthol. The urine however, contains in addition to these metabolites, the *N*-glucuronides of 1-phenylhydrazo-2-naphthol and 4′-hydroxy-1-phenylhydrazo-2-naphthol and two metabolites, namely 1-amino-2-naphthyl hydrogen sulphate and 1-amino-2-naphthyl glucuronide derived from splitting of the azo linkage (Childs and Clayson, 1966).

The Prontosils

Prontosil
(mol. wt. 291)

Neoprontosil
(mol. wt. 589)

Prontosil, the forerunner of the modern sulpha drugs, is excreted to a small extent (10% of dose in 24 h) in the bile of rats following its intraperitoneal injection; less (5%) is excreted following its oral administration (Gingell *et al.*, 1969). The bile contains mainly a polar metabolite which appears to be an *N*-glucuronide of prontosil together with small amounts of free sulphanilamide and its *N*-acetyl conjugate (Gingell, 1970). The conjugated prontosil undergoes, at least in part, some enterobacterial metabolism in the gut to form sulphanilamide and 1,2,4-triaminobenzene which are both absorbed.

Injected neoprontosil is even more extensively eliminated in the bile of rats after injection (70% of dose in 24 h) apparently unchanged. Like prontosil the material excreted in the bile is metabolized by the gut flora to amines which are absorbed and eliminated in the urine.

WATER-SOLUBLE SULPHONATED AZO DYES

Several water-soluble sulphonated azo dyes are used as food colours. Such sulphonates, because of their highly polar character are not readily absorbed nor readily metabolized by the tissues, though in recent years work has shown that they can be broken down by the gut bacteria. Some dyes are sulphonated on both sides of the azo linkage so that if reductive fission occurs then the two sulphonated fragments may still be readily excreted. Ryan and Wright (1961) have investigated the biliary excretion in rats of several sulphonated azo dyes and they found that although some are eliminated predominantly in the bile there appears to be no obvious correlation between their chemical structure and hepatic clearance.

Biliary excretion of water-soluble sulphonated azo dyes in the rat

Compound	Colour index no.	% dose in bile in 6 h
Azobenzenes		
Methyl orange	13025	55
3'-Sulpho-4-dimethylaminoazobenzene	–	27
Fast yellow	13015	10
Phenylazonaphthalenes		
Naphthalene fast orange 2GS	15510	46
Red 10BS	17200	12
Geranine 2GS	18050	64
Ponceau RS	16150	15
Orange GCN	15980	23
Sunset yellow	15985	22
Scarlet GN	14815	0
Ponceau SX	14700	48
Azonaphthalenes		
Carmoisine	14720	38
Brilliant scarlet	16255	34
Amaranth	16185	53

Thus, the biliary excretion of Red 10BS is only about 12% of the dose whereas its *N*-acetyl derivative (Geranine 2GS) which is less polar and less water-soluble is excreted in bile to the extent of 60% of the dose.

Red 10BS, R = H
Geranine 2GS, R = COCH$_3$

Similarly, Scarlet GN does not appear to be excreted in the bile whereas its isomer Ponceau SX is eliminated unchanged to about 50% of the dose.

Scarlet GN, R = R^{111} = SO$_3$Na; R^1= R^{11} = H
Ponceau SX, R = R^{111} = H; R^1 = R^{11}SO$_3$Na

The reasons for these differences are not clear; they may be related to differences in metabolism or the polar/non-polar balance of the molecule as determined by the relative distribution of lipophilic and hydrophilic groups.

Radomski and Mellinger (1962) have studied in detail the fate in rats of three sulphonated dyes namely, Amaranth, Ponceau SX and Sunset yellow. When given by intrasplenic infusion the three dyes appear in the bile unchanged. The extent to which this occurs appears to depend upon the degree of sulphonation. Thus, Amaranth with three sulphonic acid groups appears only in the bile whereas Ponceau SX and Sunset Yellow which are both disulphonates are eliminated in the urine as well as the bile. When given orally only small amounts of unchanged dye are detectable in the faeces and large amounts of amines appear in the urine. Suppression of the gut flora by treatment with neomycin and tetracycline however, is accompanied by an increased faecal excretion of Amaranth clearly indicating the importance of enterobacterial metabolism for the degradation of the dye. This suggests that any dye excreted in the bile is probably degraded in the intestine and the amines formed absorbed and excreted in the urine.

Amaranth
(mol. wt. 604)

Methyl orange (mol. wt. 327).

Rats excrete about 70% of an injected dose of [³H] methyl orange in the bile in 6 h. Most of the biliary material consists of the monodesmethyl and didesmethyl derivatives of methyl orange, namely 4′-sulpho-4-methyl-aminoazobenzene and 4′-sulpho-4-aminoazobenzene (Barrett *et al.*, 1966) together with small amounts of the unchanged dye. *m*-methyl orange is also eliminated in the bile of rats largely as its desmethyl derivative, namely, 4-methylamino-3′-sulphoazobenzene, together with smaller amounts of 4-amino-3′-sulphoazobenzene and unchanged *m*-methyl orange. The two metabolites of methyl orange are excreted much more rapidly in rat bile than the parent compound (O'Reilly *et al.*, 1971).

Tartrazine (mol. wt. 468)

Tartrazine is widely used as a colouring agent as its water-soluble tri-sodium salt. Its biliary excretion is an important aspect of its overall fate in animals though the extent to which this occurs varies with species and in the case of the rat, with sex. The first studies on its biliary excretion (Ryan and Wright, 1961; Ryan and Wright, 1962) seemed to show that this is of a low order since only 1—2% of an injected dose could be recovered in the bile. This was later re-investigated since the relatively high molecular weight of the compound and its polarity suggested that extensive biliary excretion was to be expected. These studies (Gregson *et al.*, 1972) showed that female rats excrete about 40% of an injected dose (50 μmole/kg) of tartrazine in the bile in 3 h and about 45% in the urine unchanged. By contrast male rats eliminate only 17% of an injected dose in the bile but much more (70%) in the urine. At a lower dose (4.5 μmole/kg) male rats excrete less (9% of dose) in the bile and females (30%). There also occurs a marked species difference since while both rats and guinea pigs eliminate about 40% of an injected dose of tartrazine by the biliary route, the female rabbit excretes only 6% by this pathway. The sex difference in rats in the elimination pattern is, at least in part, hormone dependent, since following the pretreatment of female rats with testosterone their ability to excrete tartrazine in the bile becomes more like that of male rats. The sex difference is not due to a difference in renal function i.e. the males might have a greater ability to eliminate the dye in the urine since the same difference remains apparent in rats with ligated renal pedicles to prevent loss in the urine.

Other azo dyes, structurally related to tartrazine such as dichlorotartrazine, and Lissamine fast yellow 2G are also extensively eliminated in rat bile (Ryan and Wright, 1962).

Evans blue and trypan blue (mol. wt. 871)

Evans blue $R^1 = R^3 = SO_3Na$; $R^2 = R^4 = H$
Trypan blue $R^1 = R^3 = H$; $R^2 = R^4 = SO_3Na$

Evans blue is a bisazo dye used to estimate blood volume. Trypan blue is a structural isomer of Evans blue and has teratogenic properties. Despite their apparently suitably high molecular weight (871) and polar character neither are found in rat bile after their intravenous injection. Dogs also excrete only about 4% of an injected dose of Evans blue in the bile and the levels of the dye in the bile are less than those of the plasma and thoracic duct lymph.

A related dye *congo red* (mol. wt. 697) appears to undergo some elimination in the bile of the rabbit and cat (Richardson, 1939). The apparently anomalous biliary excretion of these compounds may be due to their existence in solution as high molecular weight aggregates. Congo red for example occurs in solution as aggregate particles having an apparent molecular weight of about 8000.

REFERENCES

Barrett, J. F., Pitt, P. A., Ryan, A. J. and Wright, S. E. (1966) *Biochem. Pharmacol*, **15**, 675.
Childs, J. J. and Clayson, D. B. (1966) *Biochem. Pharmacol.*, **15**, 1247.
Crabtree, H. G. (1949) *Brit. J. Cancer*, **3**, 387.

Gingell, R. (1970) Ph.D. Thesis, University of London.

Gingell, R., Bridges, J. W. and Williams, R. T. (1969) *Biochem. J.*, **114**, 5P.

Gregson, R. H. S., Hirom, P. C., Millburn, P., Smith, R. L., Turbert, H. B. and Williams, R. T. (1972) *J. Pharm. Pharmacol.*, **24**, 20.

Ishidate, M., Tamura, Z., Nakajima, T. and Samejima, K. (1962) *Chem. pharm. Bull.*, **10**, 75.

O'Reilly, W. J., Pitt, P. A., and Ryan, A. J. (1971) *Brit. J. Pharmacol.*, **43**, 167.

Radomski, J. L. and Mellinger, T. J. (1962) *J. Pharmacol. exp. Ther.*, **136**, 259.

Radomski, J. L. and Harrow, L. S. (1966) *Indian J. Med. Surg.*, **35**, 882.

Richardson, A. P. (1939) *Amer. J. med. Sci.*, **198**, 82.

Ryan, A. J. and Wright, S. E. (1961) *J. Pharm. Pharmacol.*, **13**, 492.

Ryan, A. J. and Wright, S. E. (1962) *Nature (Lond)*, **195**, 1009.

Salant, W. and Bengis, R. (1916) *J. biol. Chem.*, **27**, 403.

Samejima, K., Tamura, Z. and Ishidate, M. (1967) *Chem. pharm. Bull.*, **15**, 964.

Walker, R. (1970) *Food Cosmet. Toxicol.*, **8**, 659.

CHAPTER FIFTEEN

Cholecystographic Media

Radio-opaque or contrast media cause organs to appear as bright white shadows on an X-ray negative film in contrast to the dark surrounding soft tissues. For this effect the radio-opaques depend upon their ability to absorb X-rays and this is a function of the elemental composition of the material. The higher the atomic number of the heaviest element of the molecule the greater is the absorption. The first radio-opaques were inorganic compounds such as lead acetate, bismuth subnitrate and later barium sulphate.

The first organic radio-opaques were developed by Graham and Cole in 1924 for X-ray investigation of the gall-bladder. Several years earlier Abel and Rowntree (1909) had shown that tetrachlorophenolphthalein was eliminated almost entirely in the bile. Arguing from this empirical observation Graham suggested that it should be possible to opacify the gall-bladder by replacing the chlorine atoms in tetrachlorophenolphthalein with other atoms of greater radiopacity. Using the iodinated analogue, namely tetraiodophenolphthalein, Graham and Cole described the first successful X-ray visualization of the gall-bladder. This represented a major breakthrough in radiology which

Tetrachlorophenolphthalein (X = Cl)
Tetraiodophenolphthalein (X = I)

altered the entire course of its techniques. Now organic radio-opaques are available for opacifying most areas of the human body besides the gall-bladder and bile duct system.

Cholecystographic media are highly excreted in the bile and being opaque to X-rays can be used for the visualization of the gall-bladder and perhaps the hepatic, cystic and common bile ducts. They are usually given orally (e.g. iopanoic acid, pheniodol and sodium ipodate) or intravenously (iodipamide). Tetraiodophenolphthalein was formerly given by injection but it is no longer used because of its toxicity. Chemically, they are compounds of relatively high molecular weight (500–1000 approx) and contain about 50–70% by weight of iodine. The general features of a satisfactory cholecystographic agent have been suggested to be: (1) a high iodine content to provide radiopacity (2) a lipophilic group of optimal size to direct excretion in the bile rather than into the urine, (3) a proper balance between lipophilic and hydrophilic groups to ensure absorption from the intestinal tract and (4) the compound should be rapidly eliminated following completion of the diagnostic procedure (McChesney and Hoppe, 1954).

Biochemical studies on the cholecystographic agents are surprisingly few and little is known about their metabolic transformations and other factors involved in their hepatic elimination.

Tetraiodophenolphthalein (iodophthalein; mol. wt. 822)

Tetraiodophenolphthalein was the first cholecystographic agent to be used. Its use was later abandoned both because of its toxicity and because new agents which could be given orally were developed.

Pheniodol (iodoalphionic acid. mol. wt. 494)

Pheniodol was introduced in 1940 as an oral cholecystographic agent. (Dohrn and Diedrich, 1940). The compound is well excreted in the bile both of humans and laboratory species. Thus, cats with biliary fistulae excrete in the bile in 6 h about 36% of a dose of $[^{131}I]$ pheniodol given by intraduodenal injection. Rats excrete about 50% of an intravenous dose in the faeces in 3 days – this almost certainly arising from elimination in the bile (Free et al., 1951). Whether or not the compound in the bile is in a free or conjugated form is not known.

In humans, studies show that 60–80% of a dose appears in the urine 3 days (Junkman, 1941) suggesting that much of the material excreted in the bile is absorbed from the intestine and re-eliminated by the kidneys.

Iopanoic acid (mol. wt. 571)

Iopanoic acid is a very effective oral cholecystographic agent which is extensively excreted in the bile as an ester glucuronide (McChesney and Hoppe, 1954).

In cats, 18 h after its intravenous injection about 75% of the dose is found associated with the liver, bile and intestinal contents with less than 10% in the urine. It would appear therefore, that the bile is the main route for its excretion in the cat. Dogs also excrete large amounts of iopanoic acid in the bile as the ester glucuronide. The glucuronide has a marked affinity for excretion in the bile for when given intravenously to a cat, it is rapidly concentrated in the liver and gall-bladder (McChesney and Hoppe, 1956). Human subjects also extensively excrete the drug in the bile and it can give good quality gall-bladder shadows on X-ray visualization. Of an oral dose of 3g, 62% is recovered in the faeces in 5 days and about 36% in the urine in the same time.

Iophenoxic acid (mol. wt. 572)

Iophenoxic acid is an analogue of iopanoic acid in which the amino group of the former has been replaced by a phenolic hydroxyl group. Iophenoxic acid (Teridax) was used as radio-opaque medium for oral cholecystography from about 1955 to 1957 after which it was withdrawn from clinical use because of its extremely long persistence in the plasma. Indeed, crystalline iophenoxic acid has been isolated from the plasma of patients who had received the drug many years previously and Astwood (1957) has calculated its half-life in man to be about 2½ years and even this may be an underestimate (Carakushansky, *et al.*, 1969). It is readily transmitted across the placenta to the foetus and it has been speculated that there is a possibility of maternal transmission from mother to daughter and then to a third generation. The failure of the organism to excrete iophenoxic acid along the normal excretion pathways thus has several important implications.

One important factor in its delayed excretion is the extensive enterohepatic circulation that occurs coupled with an inability of the kidney to secrete iophenoxic acid when present in the plasma at low levels (Mudge *et al.*, 1971). Dogs injected intravenously with $[^{125}I]$ iophenoxic acid excrete about 35% of the radioactivity in the urine and 60% in the stools in 10 days. During this time the plasma level of radioactivity declined from 284 $\mu g/ml$ to 115 $\mu g/ml$ for one dog and from 490 to 80 $\mu g/ml$ for a second dog over a period of 10 days. Of the material that is excreted in the bile 90–99% is reabsorbed from the intestine into an enterohepatic circulation.

acyl monoglucuronide   ethereal monoglucuronide   diglucuronide

Only traces of iophenoxic acid are excreted in dog bile and most of the compound is in the form of three glucuronides, namely, the acyl and ethereal glucuronides and the diglucuronide conjugate (Wade *et al.*, 1971). Interestingly, these metabolites although less lipid soluble than the parent iophenoxic acid do retain a high degree of lipophilic character.

Iodipamide (mol. wt. 1140)

Iodipamide is an X-ray contrast agent of low toxicity which can be given intravenously. It can give satisfactory X-ray visualization of the hepatic, cystic and common bile ducts as well as the gall-bladder (Link *et al.*, 1955; Sutton and Tillet, 1954). About 90% of a dose of iodipamide is excreted in the bile, the remainder being excreted by the kidneys (Frommhold, 1953; Hornykiewytsch and Stender, 1953).

OTHER CHOLECYSTOGRAPHIC AGENTS

More recently introduced oral cholecystographic agents are ioglycamid, an analogue of iodipamide, tyropanoate, buniodyl and sodium iopodate. The latter two agents are rapidly absorbed when given orally and are rapidly excreted in the bile so that the biliary duct system is usually well visualized. Both tyropanoate and buniodyl are eliminated in cat bile conjugated with glucuronic acid (McChesney, 1964)

Ioglycamid (mol. wt. 620)

Buniodyl sodium (mol. wt. 661)

Tyropanoate (mol. wt. 641)

Ipodate (mol. wt. 598)

REFERENCES

Abel, J. J. and Rowntree, L. G. (1909) *J. Pharmacol. exp. Ther.*, **1**, 231.

Astwood, E. B. (1957) *Trans. Ass. Amer. Phycns.*, **70**, 183.

Carakushansky, G., Cárdenas, L. E. and Gardner, L. I. (1969) *Pediatrics*, **44**, 1020.

Dohrn, M., and Diedrich, P. (1940) *Dtsch. med. Wschr.*, **66**, 1133.

Free, A. A., Page, J. E. and Woollett, E. A. (1951) *Biochem. J.*, **48**, 490.

Frommhold, W. (1953) *Fortschr. Röntgenstr.*, **79**. 283.

Graham, E. A. and Cole, W. H. (1924) *J. Amer. med. Ass.*, **82**, 613.

Hornykiewytsch, T. and Stender, H. S. (1953) *Fortschr. Röntgenstr.*, **79**, 292.

Junkmann, K. (1941) *Klin. Wschr.*, **20**, 125.

Link, A. J., Parida, R. K., Heydemann, J. and Kark, R. M. (1955) *J. Amer. med. Ass.* **158**, 1491.

McChesney, E. W. and Hoppe, J. O. (1954) *Arch. int. pharmacodyn.*, **99**, 127.

McChesney, E. W. and Hoppe, J. O. (1956) *Arch. int. pharmacodyn.*, **105**, 306.

McChesney, E. W. (1964) *Biochem. Pharmacol.,* **13**, 1366.
Mudge, G. H., Strewler, G. J. Jr., Desbiens, N., Berndt, W. O. and Wade, D. N.
    (1971) *J. Pharmacol. exp. Ther.,* **178**, 159.
Sutton, D. and Tillett, J. V. (1954) *Brit. J. Radiol.,* **27**, 575.
Wade, D. N., Desbiens, N., Strewler, G. J. Jr., Berndt, W. O. and Mudge, G. H.
    (1971) *J. Pharmacol. exp. Ther.,* **178**, 173.

CHAPTER SIXTEEN

Chlorinated Hydrocarbon Pesticides

Pesticides continue to play an important role in the protection of agricultural and horticultural crops, livestock and stored food and for suppressing various insect-borne infections. Without their use farm productivity and the quality of food would drop and the control of diseases such as malaria would prove more difficult. An important group of synthetic pesticides are based upon the halogenated hydrocarbon structure and it includes compounds such as DDT, dieldrin and endosulphan. As a consequence of the concern over their persistence in the body and the possible long-term implications, their use is now strictly controlled in many countries.

Because of the persistence of many of these compounds in the animal body the question of their excretion becomes of paramount importance since this is a major means of protection against accumulation and poisoning. The metabolism and urinary excretion of these compounds have been extensively investigated (see Hayes, 1965). Their biliary excretion has however received comparatively little attention despite its importance; for a number of pesticides it is the main mode of elimination.

DDT (2,2-bis(*p*-chlorophenyl)-1,1,1-trichloroethane; mol. wt. 355)

The metabolic fate of DDT is complex and has not been fully resolved. Its excretion in bile is an important aspect of its overall fate since in the rat about 65% of an intravenous dose of radioactive DDT appears in the bile with a further 2% in the urine and 0.3% in the faeces (Jensen *et al.*, 1957). The bile contains only small amounts of DDT and the product of its dehydrochlorination, namely, DDE; most of the biliary material consists of DDA in a free and complexed form. Acid hydrolysis converts the latter to DDA. The proportions of the various metabolites excreted in the bile may change from day to day since the concentration of water-soluble metabolites increases with time particularly on the third and fourth day. Faecal excretion is the main ultimate pathway of elimination of DDT in the rat and this is a consequence of the extensive biliary excretion of the pesticide. The faeces of rats contain free DDA (Judah, 1949) though Jensen *et al.* (1957) found that the faecal DDA also occurs as acidic complexes or conjugates. Pinto *et al.* (1965) have isolated from the faeces of rats, given DDT orally, a conjugate of DDA containing aspartic acid and serine and other amino acid conjugates also appear to be present. The urinary excretion of DDT and its metabolites is normally low but this is markedly increased in rats in which the bile duct has been ligated to prevent loss in the bile (Burns *et al.* 1957).

The extensive biliary excretion of DDT and its metabolites and their potential involvement in enterobacterial metabolism and in an enterohepatic circulation may have an important bearing on their persistence in the body.

Metabolites of DDT

Perthane (1,1-dichloro-2,2-bis(*p*-ethylphenyl)ethane; mol. wt. 307)

Perthane is an analogue of DDT with insecticidal properties. It can cause adrenal cortical atrophy in the dog but not in the rat. Rats excrete most (70–90%) of an injected or oral dose of [^{14}C] perthane in the faeces with only small amounts in the urine (Bleiberg and Larson, 1957). The faecal material is derived from biliary elimination since following the intravenous injection of the pesticide in rats, up to about half the dose is recovered in the bile in 8 h. The nature of the material excreted in the bile has not been determined. When the latter bile is given orally to rats, about 70% of the ^{14}C appeared in the faeces and 13% in the urine over a 3 day period indicating that some enterohepatic circulation occurs.

Methoxychlor (1,1,1-trichloro-2,2-bis(p-methoxyphenyl)ethane mol. wt. 346)

Methoxychlor is an analogue of DDT having slightly lower insecticidal activity but it is less toxic to mammals. In the rat its main pathway of elimination is the faeces, this arising from extensive biliary excretion. Following the intravenous injection of [^{14}C] methoxychlor, 40% of the dose is recovered in the 6 h bile (Weikel, 1956); only 0.1% appears in the urine in this time, and at 48 h the urinary excretion accounts for only 5%. The bile contains an unidentified water-soluble metabolite of methoxychlor.

Dieldrin (1,2,3,4,10,10-hexachloro-6,7,-epoxy-1,4,4a,5,6,7,8,8a,-octahydro-exo-1,4-$endo$-5,8-dimethanonaphthalene; mol. wt. 381)

Dieldrin has been widely used in insecticidal dips, sprays and dusting powders in agriculture and horticulture. It is readily absorbed from the gastro-intestinal tract, the respiratory system and the skin. It tends to persist in the human and animal body for long periods, particularly in the body fat. Dieldrin is extensively excreted in the bile over a period of days and then ultimately eliminated in the faeces (Heath and Vandekar, 1964; Mörsdorf *et al.*, 1963). Rats excrete about 5% daily of an injected dose of [^{36}Cl] dieldrin in the bile but this is more than doubled if the rats are starved for a few days (Heath and Vandekar, 1964). The material excreted in the bile undergoes an enterohepatic circulation. The bile contains only traces of dieldrin and most of the radioactivity is associated with a single metabolite, possibly a glucuronide of a compound designated by Heath and Vandekar (1964) as 'metabolite I'. The latter is neutral but more polar than dieldrin. The faeces of rats treated with [^{36}Cl] dieldrin contain mainly 'metabolite I', some free dieldrin and small amounts of other metabolites. Mörsdorf *et al.* (1963) also found that dieldrin appears in both bile and liver as a hydrophilic metabolite.

Aldrin (1,2,3,4,10,10-hexachloro-1,4,4*a*,5,8,8*a*-hexahydro-*exo*-1,4-*endo*-5,8-dimethanonaphthalene; mol. wt. 365)

Aldrin has been used as a seed dressing and for the control of pests such as wireworms, cabbage root fly and vine-weevils. It is converted in plants, soils and animal tissues by epoxidation to dieldrin. Aldrin is excreted in the bile of the rat in the form of a hydrophilic metabolite identical with that formed from dieldrin (Mörsdorf *et al* (1963). The main path of excretion of dieldrin is eventually via the faeces (Hunter *et al.*, 1960; Ludwig *et al.*, 1964).

Endosulfan (6,7,8,9,10,10-hexachloro-1,5,5*a*,6,9,9*a*-hexahydro-6,9-methano-2,3,4-benzo-[*e*] dioxathiepin-3-oxide; mol. wt. 407)

Technical endosulfan (Thiodan) consists of two principal isomers, endosulfan A and endosulfan B; isomer A predominating in the ratio of about 4:1. Both isomers are excreted in the bile and eventually in the faeces of rats mainly in the form of metabolites. The bile of rats treated with endosulfan A contains large amounts of the endoketone together with small amounts of an unknown metabolite. Endosulphan B, however, gives rise to the presence in bile of large amounts of an unknown metabolite and traces of endolactone. The faeces of rats given the separate isomers orally or by injection contain the unchanged compound, endosulphate, α-hydroxy-endoether and endolactone (Schupan *et al.*, 1968).

REFERENCES

Bleiberg, M. J. and Larson, P. S. (1957) *J. Pharm. exp. Ther.*, **121**, 421.
Burns, E. C., Dahm, P. A. and Lindquist, D. A. (1957) *J. Pharmacol. exp. Ther.*, **121**, 55.
Hayes, W. J. Jr., (1965) *Ann. Rev. Pharmacol.*, **5**, 27.
Heath, D. F. and Vandekar, M. (1964) *Brit. J. industr. Med.*, **21**, 269.

Hunter, C. G., Rosen, A., Williams, R. T., Reynolds, J. G. and Worden, A. M. (1960) *Meded. LandbHoogesch. OpzoekStn, Gent,* 25, 1296.

Jensen, J. A., Cueto, C., Dale, W. E., Rothe, C. F., Pearce, G. W. and Mattson, A. M. (1957) *J. agric. food Chem.,* 5, 919.

Judah, J. D. (1949) *Brit. J. Pharmacol.,* 4, 120.

Ludwig, G., Weis, J. and Korte, F. (1964) *Life Sci.,* 3, 123.

Mörsdorf, K., Ludwig, G., Vogel, J. and Korte, F. (1963) *Med. exp. (Basel),* 8, 90.

Pinto, J. D., Camien, M. N. and Dunn, M. S. (1965) *J. biol. Chem.,* 240, 2148.

Schuphan, I., Ballschmiter, K. and Tölg, G. (1968) *Z. Naturforsch.,* 23B, 701.

Weikel, J. H. Jr. (1956) *J. Pharmacol. exp. Ther.,* 116, 60.

CHAPTER SEVENTEEN

Quaternary Ammonium Compounds

Quaternary ammonium compounds have the general structure $R^1 R^2 R^3 R^4 N^+$ where the R groups may be alkyl, aryl, cycloalkyl or heterocyclic. They are very strong bases and form salts which are completely ionized at physiological pH. A number of quaternary ammonium or onium compounds are used as drugs and others as antiseptics and detergents. Examples of drugs containing the quaternary ammonium group are neostigmine (anticholinesterase), hexamethonium (antihypertensive), decamethonium (muscle relaxant) and cetiprin (atropine-like) and the onium derivative, cetalkonium, which finds application as an antibacterial detergent.

They are poorly absorbed from the gastrointestinal tract so that when given orally they are mainly eliminated in the faeces. When injected they are excreted in the urine and bile and the relative importance of the two pathways appears to depend upon the molecular weight and structure of the compound. Mono-onium compounds of relatively low molecular weight are in general poorly excreted in the bile. Quaternary ammonium compounds of higher molecular weight e.g. benzomethamine, cetiprin, aprobit and poldine, which have molecular weights greater than 300, are extensively excreted in rat bile. The biliary excretion of these cations appears to be a relatively non-specific process since these chemicals have very diverse chemical structures. However, they do have one characteristic in common, namely, the presence in their structures of a single quaternary ammonium group separated at a distance from a large non-polar group.

The problem of the biliary excretion of cations has not been systematically studied as has been done for anions, so that it is not possible to correlate physico-chemical parameters with the extent of biliary excretion. The quaternary ammonium group seems to be important for extensive biliary excretion to occur. Thus, the tertiary amine analogues of benzomethamine and its derivatives, which themselves are significantly eliminated in bile, are by comparison, poorly excreted by this route (Levine and Clark, 1955). There are indications that the molecular weight factor for significant biliary excretion of cations may be different from that for anions. Thus, Hughes *et al*. (1972) have investigated the extent of biliary excretion in the rat of the three simple quaternary ammonium derivatives shown in Table 36; all three appear in the bile largely unchanged. The biliary excretion of trimethyl-phenylammonium (mol. wt. 136) is very low (1% of dose) and most of an injected dose is eliminated in the urine. The biliary excretion of the tribenzylmethylammonium (mol. wt. 302) is high (39% in 3 h) as might be expected on the basis of its relatively high molecular weight. Of considerable interest however is the observation that the extent of biliary elimination of dibenzyldimethylammonium (mol. wt. 226) is also of a high order (24% of dose in 3 h). It has been suggested that the threshold molecular weight for appreciable (i.e. >10% of dose) biliary excretion of mono-quaternary ammonium compounds in the rat is about 225 ± 25.

Table 36
Biliary excretion of cations in the rat

	Mol. wt.	% dose in bile
$\langle\!\!\!\!\!\!\!\rangle$—$\overset{+}{N}(CH_3)_3$ Trimethylphenylammonium	136	1
$C_6H_5CH_2$\\$\overset{+}{N}$/$CH_3$ $C_6H_5CH_2$/ \\$CH_3$ Dibenzyldimethylammonium	226	24
$C_6H_5CH_2$\\$\overset{+}{N}$/$CH_3$ $C_6H_5CH_2$/ \\$CH_2C_6H_5$ Tribenzylmethylammonium	302	39

Structural factors may also influence the extent of biliary excretion of quaternary ammonium compounds. The presence of the two onium groups in a molecule appears to reduce the extent of biliary excretion as in the case of hexamethonium and its analogues. *d*-tubocurarine, a bis-onium compound of high molecular weight (625), is poorly excreted in the bile of dogs though this increases if kidney function is impaired.

It has been suggested that the liver may possess an active secretory process for the transport of certain quaternary ammonium ions from blood to bile. Furthermore, it has been proposed that this process is different from that responsible for the active secretion of organic anions into bile (Schanker and Solomon, 1963). This view has been based largely on the observation that anions which are excreted in the bile, do not compete with cations for excretion, whereas a pair of different anions or a pair of cations can compete with each other for hepatic elimination. The findings that cations differ from anions in terms of their threshold molecular weights for biliary excretion and also in the species variations in biliary elimination, may be seen to support the view that the processes involved in the hepatic transport of anions and cations are not the same.

If the liver has a separate mechanism for the excretion of cations the interesting question arises as to the possible natural substrates for such a mechanism. Possible substrates are choline and the phospholipids. The main phospholipid present in human and animal bile is lecithin which accounts for 96% or more of the total phospholipid (Spitzer et al., 1964; Phillips, 1960). Human bile also contains small amounts of choline (Merlevede et al., 1959).

Neostigmine

| Neostigmine (mol. wt. 223) | Trimethyl-(3-hydroxy-phenyl)ammonium (mol. wt. 152) | Pyridostigmine (mol. wt. 181) |

Neostigmine is an anticholinesterase agent used clinically for the treatment of myasthenia gravis and to reverse the action of tubocurarine-like drugs. In rats the biliary pathway is quantitatively of little significance since only about 2% of an injected dose of $[^{14}C]$neostigmine appears in the bile as compared to 82% found in the urine (Calvey, 1966). Removal of the renal pathway by ligation of the renal pedicles however increases the biliary excretion to 8% of the dose. The bile contains a hydrolysis product of neostigmine, namely, trimethyl-(3-hydroxyphenyl)ammonium, formed by hydrolysis of the carbamate ester link, a second unidentified metabolite and traces of the unchanged drug. The bile levels of both neostigmine and its hydrolysis product are about three times those of the plasma.

The hydrolysis product of neostigmine, trimethyl-(3-hydroxyphenyl)-ammonium, is also poorly excreted in bile; Wistar rats eliminate about 3% of a dose of the compound in the bile in 4 h The bile contains mainly the glucuronic acid conjugates of the parent compound and of its demethylated derivative, namely 3-dimethylaminophenol. By contrast, biliary excretion appears to be much higher in the homozygous jaundiced Gunn rat. When injected into this strain of rat, 26% of a dose of neostigmine is eliminated in the bile, entirely in the form of the O-glucuronide (mol. wt. 328) which presumably exists at physiological pH as a zwitterion (Calvey *et al.*, 1970).

The biliary excretion of the related anticholinesterase agent *pyridostigmine* is also of a low order. Rats eliminate only 0.3% of an injected dose of the drug in the bile in 6 h; 90% of the dose appears in the urine, the unchanged drug accounting for 60% and its metabolite, 3-hydroxy-*N*-methylpyridinium, for 30% (Birtley *et al.*, 1966).

Hexamethonium and related compounds

$$(CH_3)_3\overset{+}{N}-(CH_2)_6-\overset{+}{N}(CH_3)_3$$
Hexamethonium (mol. wt. 202)

$$(CH_3)_3\overset{+}{N}-(CH_2)_{10}-\overset{+}{N}(CH_3)_3$$
Decamethonium (mol. wt. 258)

$$(CH_3)_2-\overset{+}{N}-(CH_2)_6-\overset{+}{N}(CH_3)_2$$
$$\qquad\quad |\qquad\qquad\qquad |$$
$$\qquad CH_2C_6H_5\quad CH_2C_6H_5$$

Hexamethylene-1:6-bis(benzyldimethylammonium) (mol. wt. 354)

Bisonium compounds such as *hexamethonium* and its derivatives are poorly absorbed when given orally and when injected they are eliminated mainly via the kidneys with only small amounts in the bile. Thus, Levine (1960) found that the biliary excretion of hexamethonium and six of its derivatives given intravenously to rats is only about 4% of the dose in 3 h. The series included the relatively high molecular weight bisonium compound hexamethylene-1:6-bis(benzyldimethylammonium) (mol. wt. 354). It is possible that bisonium compounds are relatively poorly excreted in bile compared to mono-onium derivatives. This is also seen with *d*-tubocurarine, a bisonium derivative of high molecular weight (625) which is also relatively poorly excreted in bile.

Decamethonium

Decamethonium, a skeletal muscle relaxant, is poorly excreted in rat bile (Schanker, 1962) even if loss in the urine is prevented by ligation of the renal pedicles (Christensen, 1965). Bilaterally nephrectomised rabbits eliminate only about 2% of an injected dose of $[^{14}C]$ decamethonium in the bile in 4 h; the drug is taken up by the tissues, particularly the striated muscle. Some dealkylation occurs since about 0.5% of the radioactivity appears in the expired air as $[^{14}C]CO_2$. The low affinity of decamethonium for biliary excretion is reflected by its low concentration in bile which is less than that of plasma.

Procaine amide ethobromide (mol. wt. 264)

Procaine amide ethobromide is significantly excreted in bile and has been extensively used for studies on the mechanism of biliary excretion of bases. Rats with ligated renal pedicles excrete about 9% of an injected dose of procaine amide ethobromide in the bile in 30 min (Muranishi and Schanker, 1970). The bile contains the unchanged drug together with two conjugates in which the aromatic amino group is conjugated (Schanker, 1962). The concentration of procaine amide ethobromide and its conjugates in the bile can be 80 times or more that of the plasma. The biliary excretion of the compound can be reduced by the administration of other quaternary ammonium compounds (darstine, benzomethamine and oxyphenonium which are also eliminated in the bile. Its biliary elimination is not, however, affected by organic anions such as bromsulphthalein and glycocholate (Schanker and Solomon, 1963) nor by other non-nitrogenous onium compounds such as methyltriphenylphosphonium and tetraphenylarsonium (Muranishi and Schanker, 1970).

Cetiprin (ethyl[3,3-diphenyl-1-methylpropyl] dimethylammonium; mol. wt. 282)

Cetiprin is a synthetic anticholinergic agent. The drug is extensively excreted in both urine and bile when injected into rats. Thus, 4 h after an intravenous injection of $[^{14}C]$ cetiprin about 16% of the dose occurs in the bile and 11%

in the urine. Both excreta contain mainly unchanged cetiprin together with two metabolites which may be conjugates. After intramuscular injection 40% of a dose of [^{14}C] cetiprin appears in the urine and a similar amount in the faeces, the faecal material arising from the excretion of the drug in the bile (Hansson and Schmiterlöw, 1961b).

Tiemonium (4-[3-hydroxy-3-phenyl-3-(2'-thienyl)propyl]-4-methylmorpholinium; mol. wt. 319)

Tiemonium is a synthetic drug with anticholinergic and antispasmodic properties. It is highly excreted in the bile in rats since 75% of an intravenous dose is eliminated by this route. After oral administration to rats 16% of the dose appears in the bile in 6 h and 9% in the urine (Beau *et al.*, 1968).

Aprobit (*N*-hydroxyethylpromethazine; mol. wt. 330)

Aprobit has antihistaminic properties but is without the sedative properties of promethazine. About 20% of an intravenous dose of [^{35}S] aprobit is excreted in rat bile in 4 h. Intact animals eliminate 60% of the ^{35}S in the urine in 72 h and 20% in the faeces, the latter arising from material excreted in the bile. The bile and urine contain mainly unchanged aprobit together with small amounts of aprobit sulphoxide and two other more polar metabolites which have not been identified (Hansson and Schmiterlöw, 1961a).

Poldine (2-hydroxymethyl-1,1-dimethylpyrrolidinium benzilate; mol. wt. 342)

Poldine is used in the form of its methylsulphate salt as an anticholinergic drug to reduce gastric acid secretion. When injected it is eliminated in the urine and faeces; faecal excretion arises from extensive excretion of the drug in the bile. Thus, after intravenous injection in rats 38% of the dose is eliminated in the urine and 64% in the faeces. Biliary cannulated rats excrete as much as 36% of a dose of $[^{14}C]$ poldine in the bile in 24 h and only 11% in the urine. The drug is extensively metabolized since the bile and urine contain seven or eight metabolites of poldine. It is poorly absorbed when given orally to rats; about 50–70% of an oral dose appears in the faeces and 3% in the urine in 3 days while biliary cannulated animals excrete only about 7% of a dose in the bile (Langley *et al.*, 1966).

Oxyphenonium (cyclohexylhydroxyphenylacet-2-oxyethyl)diethylmethyl-ammonium; mol. wt. 349)

Oxyphenonium is also a synthetic anticholinergic drug. When injected into rats about 11% of the dose is excreted in the bile in 3 h. Two analogues of oxyphenonium, namely, BA 3762 and BA 3854 are also excreted in the bile of rats to the extent of 7% and 18% respectively of the dose in 3 h (Levine and Clark, 1957). Oxyphenonium is poorly absorbed when given orally since only 0.3% of an oral dose is excreted in rat urine compared to 32% after intravenous injection.

Benzomethamine (hydroxydiphenylacetyl-*N*-methylaminoethyl)diethyl-methylammonium; mol. wt. 356)

Benzomethamine has anticholinergic properties and inhibits human gastric acid secretion. This compound is rapidly excreted in the bile of dogs and rats since soon after its intravenous injection large amounts of the drug appear in the small intestine. Biliary cannulated rabbits and rats eliminate about 31% of an intravenous dose in the bile in 3 h. The biliary excretion is however, much lower after oral administration since the drug is poorly absorbed from the intestinal tract (Levine and Clark, 1955).

Benzomethamine also appears to be significantly excreted in human bile since a single patient with a bile duct fistula excreted about 14% of a dose of the drug injected intramuscularly in the bile in 4 h.

The quaternary ammonium group appears to be important for biliary excretion since the tertiary amine analogue of benzomethamine is poorly excreted in the bile. Similarly, the biliary elimination in rats of three quaternary ammonium derivatives closely related to benzomethamine is about 6–11% of the dose in 2 h but the corresponding tertiary amines show no or little excretion in the bile.

Diquat and paraquat

Diquat and paraquat are dipyridinium compounds which have been developed as herbicides.

Diquat (mol. wt. 184)   Paraquat (mol. wt. 186)

Both compounds are poorly absorbed when administered orally and are therefore largely eliminated with the faeces (Daniel and Gage, 1966). When [14C] paraquat dimethosulphate is injected subcutaneously into rats about 85% of the radioactivity appears in the urine and about 15% in the faeces, the latter presumably arising from excretion in the bile. After oral doses of [14C] diquat, but not paraquat, small amounts (1–5% of dose) of radioactivity appear in rat bile.

d-tubocurarine (mol. wt. 625)

d-tubocurarine is one of the active principles of curare and is used in surgery as a skeletal muscle relaxant. It is a bisonium compound and despite its relatively high molecular weight the main channel for its elimination in the dog is the urine. When injected intravenously, dogs excrete 75% of the dose in the urine mainly unchanged in 24 h. Biliary cannulated dogs excrete 11% of the dose in the bile but this increases to nearly 40% in the absence of kidney function due to ligation of the renal pedicles. The bile contains in addition to unchanged d-tubocurarine a metabolite accounting for 1—10% of the total drug present and this appears to be formed by dealkylation of the parent compound. The ratio of d-tubocurarine in the bile to that of the plasma is 40:1 indicating that a concentrative transfer occurs (Cohen *et al.*, 1967).

Calabash curarine-I, another curare alkaloid, is excreted in the bile of cats (Waser *et al.*, 1954).

PHENANTHRIDIUM COMPOUNDS

Phenanthridium compounds have trypanocidal properties and two of these, ethidium and prothidium, are used as curative and prophylactic agents against cattle trypanosomiasis. Other phenanthridium compounds have antibacterial and antitumour activity. For these compounds, excretion in the bile appears to be the main channel for their elimination from the body.

Ethidium (homidium; 3,8-diamino-5-ethyl-6-phenyl phenanthridium; mol. wt. 314)

Ethidium has marked trypanocidal properties and is used for its curative and prophylactic properties against trypanosome infections. A single dose of ethidium bromide acts as a prophylactic for about one month. As for other phenanthridium compounds, ethidium is extensively excreted in bile. Rats with ligated renal pedicles eliminate more than 50% of an intravenously injected dose of the bromide salt of ethidium in the bile within 16—18 h. Unchanged ethidium accounts for about 10% of the dose and the remainder of the material in the bile appears to consist of two acetyl derivatives of ethidium (MacGregor and Clarkson, 1971).

Carbidium (2-amino-6-*p*-carbethoxyaminophenyl-5-methylphenanthridium; mol. wt. 372)

When injected intravenously into rats with ligated renal pedicles about 60–65% of the dose is recovered in the bile in 10–16 h mainly as the *N*-acetyl conjugate (47%) and as unchanged carbidium (15%) (MacGregor and Clarkson, 1971). Rabbits also excrete the injected drug (20% in 3 h) with little if any in the urine (Goodwin *et al*., 1950). Carbidium fluoresces a bright orange colour in ultra-violet light and this property can be used to follow visually the fate of the drug after injection. Within two minutes of the intravenous injection of the drug in rats, the bile and liver show the characteristic orange fluorescence which persists for several hours. The upper part of the small intestine also shows fluorescence and segments of fluorescent material pass down to the caecum.

Prothidium (pyrithidium; 3-amino-8-(2-amino-6-methyl-pyrimidin-4-ylamino)-6-*p*-aminophenylphenanthridine; mol. wt. 437)

Prothidium is a bisonium compound used as a prophylactic agent for protecting cattle against trypanosome infections. A single dose can provide protection for 6 months. It is excreted in the bile of cattle and this may be important for its prolonged action. Rats and rabbits excrete the drug in the bile and little if any, appears in the urine. Thus, rats slowly excrete about

30% of a dose of the drug in the bile over a period of 9 days apparently unchanged. The metabolic inertness of the drug appears to be confirmed by the finding that when the isolated rat liver is perfused with blood containing prothidium only the unchanged drug is found in the bile, plasma and liver (Taylor, 1960).

Guanethidine (mol. wt. 198)

Guanethidine, although not a quaternary ammonium compound is strongly basic due to the guanidine group and it is convenient to consider its disposition here. It is used in the form of its sulphate salt for treating hypertension. The main channel of excretion in rats is the urine and only 0.2% of an injected dose appears in the bile in 2 h. The concentration of the drug in bile however is 25 times that of the plasma indicating that a concentrative transfer process occurs. After intravenous injection most of the dose appears in the urine and about 8% in the faeces in 8 h. The origin of the latter is not clear in view of the low biliary excretion of guanethidine. Some of the drug is localized in a number of tissues, particularly the heart, lungs, intestine, skeletal muscle, spleen and kidney (Schanker and Morrison, 1965).

REFERENCES

Beau, G., Constantin, M., Talvard, J. and Duchene-Marullaz, P. (1968) *Thérapie*, **23**, 399.

Birtley, R. D. N., Roberts, J. B., Thomas, B. H. and Wilson, A. (1966) *Brit. J. Pharmacol.*, **26**, 393.

Calvey, T. N. (1966) *Brit. J. Pharmacol.*, **28**, 348.

Calvey, T. N., Somani, S. M. and Wright, A. (1970) *Biochem. J.*, **119**, 659.

Christensen, C. B. (1965) *Acta pharmacol.* (Kbh), **23**, 275.

Cohen, E. N., Brewer, H. W. and Smith, D. (1967) *Anesthesiology*, **28**, 309.

Daniel, J. W. and Gage, J. C. (1966) *Brit. J. industr. Med.*, **23**, 133.

Goodwin, L. G., Goss, M. D. and Lock, J. A. (1950) *Brit. J. Pharmacol.*, **5**, 287.

Hansson, E. and Schmiterlöw, C. G. (1961a) *Arch. int. Pharmacodyn.*, **131**, 309.

Hansson, E. and Schmiterlöw, C. G. (1961b) *Acta pharmacol.* (Kbh), **18**, 183.

Hughes, R. D., Millburn, P., Smith, R. L. and Williams, R. T. (1972) *Biochem. J.* **128**, 144p.

Langley, P. F., Lewis, J. D., Mansford, K. R. L. and Smith, D. (1966) *Biochem. Pharmacol.,* **15**, 1821.

Levine, R. M. and Clark, B. B. (1957) *J. Pharmacol. exp. Ther.,* **121**, 63.

Levine, R. M. and Clark, B. B. (1955) *J. Pharmacol. exp. Ther.,* **114**, 63.

Levine, R. R. (1960) *J. Pharmacol. exp. Ther.,* **129**, 296.

MacGregor, J. T. and Clarkson, T. W. (1971) *Biochem. Pharmacol.,* **20**, 2833.

Merlevede, E., Pottiez, F. and Vandamme, E. (1959) *Arch int. Pharmacodyn.,* **122**, 474.

Muranishi, S. and Schanker, L. S. (1970) *Europ. J. Pharmacol.,* **9**, 116.

Phillips, G. B. (1960) *Biochim. biophys. Acta* (Amst.), **41**, 361.

Schanker, L. S. and Morrison, A. S. (1965) *Int. J. Neuropharmacol.,* **4**, 27.

Schanker, L. S. (1962) *Biochem. Pharmacol.,* **11**, 253.

Schanker, L. S. and Solomon, H. M. (1963) *Amer. J. Physiol.,* **204**, 329.

Spitzer, H. L., Kyriakides, E. S. and Balint, J. A. (1964) *Nature (Lond.),* **204**, 288.

Taylor, A. E. R. (1960) *Brit. J. Pharmacol.,* **15**, 235.

Waser, P., Schmid, R. and Schmid, K. (1954) *Arch. int. Pharmacol.,* **96**, 586.

CHAPTER EIGHTEEN

Steroids

The discovery of the biliary excretion of the steroids has been important for the fuller understanding of their metabolic fate and disposition in the body. Early studies concentrated very largely on the qualitative and quantitative aspects of their urinary excretion and such analyses could, in the absence of an understanding of the importance of the biliary excretion and enterohepatic circulation of steroids, give only an incomplete picture of the behaviour of these substances. The first report of the biliary excretion of a steroid hormone was that of Cantarow *et al.* (1943) who found that oestrogens are eliminated in dog bile and furthermore that these hormones undergo enterohepatic circulation.

That steroid hormones should undergo biliary excretion is not surprising firstly, because of their relatively high molecular weight (270–360 approx.) and secondly because they give rise metabolically, to polar conjugates of molecular weight in the region of 400–500. However, marked variations do occur in the extent of biliary excretion of steroids, probably due to differences in structure and metabolite formation. Marked species variations also occur in the extent of biliary excretion of certain steroids. Thus, hydrocortisone is extensively excreted (90% of dose) in rat bile but poorly so by humans (4%). In contrast oestradiol is well excreted in bile by both humans and the rat, as well as by the guinea pig and bull. There also occur marked species differences in the enterohepatic circulation and overall pattern of excretion of the steroids. Thus, in the rat, enterohepatic circulation results eventually in faecal excretion being the dominant channel of elimination as in the case of testosterone. In other species such as man and the guinea pig, extensive biliary excretion may occur at first, and then the material in the bile is absorbed from the intestine and ultimately eliminated in the urine. In this situation, biliary excretion and enterohepatic circulation have a delaying effect upon the elimination of the steroid.

In man, the steroids may be divided into three groups according to the extent of their hepatic elimination (Sandberg and Slaunwhite, 1956a). Group 1 includes oestrone and progesterone (30–50% of dose in bile), group 2, testosterone and corticosterone (12–25%) and group 3, cortisone and cortisol (1–5%). Steroids of the group 1 type tend to undergo enterohepatic circulation and are eventually eliminated mainly in the urine. In this situation, biliary excretion has a clearly defined delaying effect upon their ultimate clearance from the body. Thus, in the case of cortisol, testosterone or corticosterone, whose excretion in bile is relatively restricted in man, over one-third of the dose is excreted in the urine in the first 4 h and over 60–70% in 24 h and excretion is essentially complete within 48 h. On the other hand, with oestrone and oestradiol, both of which are extensively excreted in bile, only 12% of a dose is eliminated in the urine in the first 4 h and about 33% after 12 h and urinary excretion continues for 4–5 days after administration of the steroid. This effect is attributed to the extensive biliary excretion and enterohepatic circulation which these two steroids undergo.

The metabolism of certain steroids is complicated by their undergoing enterobacterial metabolism in the gut as a consequence of their elimination with the bile. The nature of the faecal metabolites of most steroids remains to be elucidated but it is known that in some cases (e.g. testosterone) they are different from the primary metabolites excreted in the bile.

Oestrone and oestradiol

These two compounds may be considered together as they are metabolically interchangeable. Oestrone is extensively excreted in the bile. Thus, the extent of excretion of the hormone in 4–6 h for the rat, guinea pig and rabbit was found to be 58, 59 and 17% of the injected dose respectively. In the guinea pig much of the material excreted in the bile is reabsorbed, as intact animals excrete over 60% of an injected dose in the urine and only 8% in the faeces (Sandberg et al., 1967). Extensive biliary excretion also occurs in the bull; in one experiment Pearson and Martin (1966) found over 50% of an injected

Oestrone (mol. wt. 270)   Oestradiol (mol. wt. 272)

dose of [^{14}C]oestradiol in the 3 h bile of a bull with a biliary fistula and only 4% in the urine.

Human subjects with T-tube bile drainage, eliminate 50–75% of an injected dose of [^{14}C]oestradiol in the bile. Most of the material excreted in the bile is reabsorbed since patients without a bile fistula excrete about 80% of an injected dose in the urine within 96–120 h and only 7% occurs in the stools (Sandberg and Slaunwhite, 1957; 1965). Little free oestrogen occurs in the bile and most of the compound is present as conjugated metabolites. Thus, the main biliary metabolites of oestradiol in the bull are glucuronide conjugates of oestrone and oestradiol (Pearson and Martin, 1966). In humans injected oestradiol also appears in the bile mainly in a conjugated form. Using a gas-chromatographic procedure the following metabolites of oestradiol were found in human bile: oestriol, 16-keto-17β-oestradiol, oestrone, 16α-hydroxy-oestrone, 17β-oestradiol, 16-epi-oestriol and 2-methoxyoestrone (Adlercreutz and Luukkainen, 1967).

The sulphate conjugates of both oestrone and oestradiol are also excreted in human bile when given as such. Thus, Twombly and Levitz (1960) found that patients taking oestrone-16-sulphate orally, excrete about equal amounts in the bile and urine, partly in the form of glucuronide conjugates. Oestradiol-3-sulphate given orally or by intramuscular injection appears in bile as oestradiol glucuronide, oestriol glucuronide and the sulphate and glucuronide conjugates of oestrone (Adlercreutz, 1962).

Oestriol (mol. wt. 288)

Oestriol also undergoes extensive biliary excretion in both laboratory species and man. The rat, guinea pig and rabbit excrete in the bile 36%, 72% and 45% respectively of an injected dose in 4–6 h. Women with T-tube drainage excrete 23% of a dose of [^{14}C]oestriol in the bile (Sandberg and Slaunwhite, 1965). Similarly, a man with a biliary fistula was found by Støa and Levitz (1968) to eliminate about 20% of an injected dose of labelled oestriol by the biliary route. In the guinea pig, rabbit and humans most of the material excreted in the bile is reabsorbed from the intestine and eventually eliminated in the urine. Thus, although human subjects excrete over 20% of a dose of oestriol in the bile, ultimately most of the oestrogen can be recovered in the urine and only 2% or so is found in the faeces.

Oestriol occurs in human bile mainly in the form of a double conjugate, namely, oestriol 3-sulphate 16-glucuronide together with a small amount of oestriol 16-glucuronide (Støa and Levitz, 1968). The urine however, contains mainly oestriol 16-glucuronide together with some 3-glucuronide. It appears that the double conjugate of oestriol is very effectively excreted in the bile (Emerman *et al.*, 1967). In the intestine both the sulphate and glucuronide groups are removed by hydrolysis and the oestriol so released, is partly conjugated in the intestinal wall in the 3-position, and the glucuronide formed is excreted in the urine. Some of the steroid is conjugated in the 16-position which is excreted in the urine or re-excreted in the bile following conjugation with sulphate to give the double conjugate. The glucuronide conjugate of oestriol, namely, oestriol-16-glucuronide is not excreted in human bile when injected as such and most of the dose is found in the urine (Sandberg and Slaunwhite, 1965). By contrast, oestriol 3-sulphate when infused into human subjects with T-tube drainage is appreciably excreted in the bile as oestriol 3-sulphate-16-glucuronide, oestriol 16-glucuronide and oestriol 3-sulphate (Emerman *et al.*, 1967). When the double conjugate was injected intraduodenally into two women with bile drainage 23% of the dose appeared in the bile and 53% in the urine. The bile contained mainly oestriol 3-sulphate-16-glucuronide and some oestriol 6-glucuronide but no 3-glucuronide. By contrast the urine contained the 3- and 6-glucuronide but the double conjugate was absent (Levitz and Katz, 1968).

Testosterone (mol. wt. 288)

Biliary excretion of this steroid is marked in the rat, mouse and cat but less so in man. In one study in which [^{14}C] testosterone was injected intravenously into human subjects with T-tube drainage, only about 12–14% of the radioactivity appeared in the bile. One patient who had suffered from ascending cholangitis however, excreted much more (56% of dose) in the bile. All the material eliminated in the bile was in a conjugated form. Patients without a biliary fistula excreted only 6% of the dose in the faeces indicating that at least part of the material eliminated in the bile undergoes reabsorption from the gut (Sandberg and Slaunwhite, 1956b).

In the rat, injected [^{14}C] testosterone undergoes extensive biliary excretion and enterohepatic circulation and eventually one-third of the dose appears in the urine and two-thirds in the faeces. Biliary cannulated rats eliminate about 80% of the dose in the bile. The faecal metabolites are different from those found in the bile indicating that the latter undergo alteration in the gut (Ashmore *et al.*, 1953). According to Staub *et al.* (1961) testosterone is excreted in rat bile as the glucuronide conjugates of aetiocholanolone and androsterone and their respective 11-hydroxy derivatives. Extensive biliary excretion of [^{14}C] testosterone also occurs in the mouse as a consequence of which much of an injected dose is eventually eliminated in the faeces (Barry *et al.*, 1952). The cat also extensively excretes testosterone in the bile and probably ultimately in the faeces. Archer *et al.* (1965) found that male cats eliminated about 70–80% of the radioactivity from an intravenous dose of [^{14}C] testosterone in the bile and only about 3–6% in the urine. Most of the material excreted in the bile appeared to be in a conjugated form.

Rabbits given the ^{14}C-labelled steroid as a single intravenous dose excrete about 40% of the dose in the bile and 24% in the urine. Most of the excreted material is in a conjugated form (Taylor and Scratcherd, 1967). Testosterone is also excreted in dog bile (Paschkis *et al.*, 1944).

Testosterone cyclopentylpropionate (mol. wt. 413)

Testosterone cyclopentylpropionate is a synthetic long acting derivative of testosterone. When injected intramuscularly in rabbits it is excreted in bile and undergoes enterohepatic circulation. Bile contains some unchanged compound, testosterone and dehydroepiandrosterone (Okada, 1957).

Dehydroepiandrosterone (mol. wt. 288)

Dehydroepiandrosterone is an androgenic hormone which is extensively excreted in the bile of the guinea pig largely as sulphate and glucuronide conjugates. The sulphate conjugate is excreted largely unchanged in the bile following its injection (Knapstein *et al.*, 1967).

Progesterone (mol. wt. 314)

Progesterone is extensively excreted in the bile of all the species so far studied. Rats excrete about 73% of a dose of $[^{14}C]$ progesterone in the bile and about 22% in the urine (Grady *et al.*, 1952). Intact rats eliminate 22% of the dose in the urine and 66% in the faeces suggesting that only a limited enterohepatic circulation occurs. In the cat 67% of an intravenous dose appears in the bile, mainly as conjugated metabolites with less than 1% in the urine (Taylor and Scratcherd, 1961). Rabbits excrete less (23–40% of dose) in the bile in 6 h and more (11–24%) in the urine, once again in a conjugated form (Taylor and Scratcherd, 1965). Human subjects, with a bile fistula, excrete about 30% of an injected dose of $[^{14}C]$ progesterone in the bile and much of this is absorbed into an enterohepatic circulation since only about 13% appears in the faeces of non-fistula subjects (Sandberg and Slaunwhite, 1958). Most of the biliary material is in a conjugated form which is different from the metabolites found in the urine. Some of the biliary metabolites have been shown to be conjugates of pregnanediol, allopregnanedione, pregnanolone and progesterone (Chang *et al.*, 1960). It has been suggested that hydroxylated metabolites of progesterone are eliminated chiefly in the urine while the corresponding ketonic derivatives are found mainly in the bile.

17-α-hydroxyprogesterone (mol. wt. 330)

17-α-hydroxyprogesterone is an important intermediate in the biosynthesis of steroid hormones. It is a precursor of cortisol and androstenedione, the latter

COCH₃
CH₃
-----OH
CH₃
O

being a precursor of testosterone and the oestrogens. It is excreted to a moderate extent in human bile. Thus Slaunwhite and Sandberg (1961) found that 15–20% of the radioactivity from an intravenous dose of [^{14}C] 17-α-hydroxyprogesterone was excreted in the bile of three women with bile fistulas; about 60% was found in the urine. Both bile and urine contained mainly pregnane-3α,17α,20α-triol and pregnane-3α,17α-diol-20-one together with small amounts of other metabolites largely in a conjugated form.

Corticosterone (mol. wt. 346)

Corticosterone is extensively eliminated in both human and cat bile mainly in the form of conjugates. In one study with two subjects with biliary fistulae, 21% and 31% respectively of an injected dose of the steroid was excreted in the bile. The urinary excretion of the ^{14}C-labelled steroid by the bile fistula subjects was lower than that of controls indicating that some enterohepatic circulation occurs (Migeon et al., 1956).

CH₂OH
CO
CH₃
HO
CH₃
O

The biliary metabolites of corticosterone in human bile have not been identified but they are probably similar to those occurring in urine which have been identified as the glucuronides of pregnane-3α, 11β, 21-triol-20-one and its allopregnane isomer and pregnane-3α, 20α-diol-11-one together with other unknown metabolites (Engel et al., 1955).

In the cat biliary excretion is even more extensive since the biliary cannulated animal eliminates 90% of an intravenous dose of the ^{14}C-labelled steroid in the bile mainly as conjugates and only 1% in the urine (Scratcherd and Taylor, 1961).

In the isolated perfused rat liver, infused [^{14}C] corticosterone is eliminated in the bile in the form of water-soluble metabolites about one-third of which consists of glucuronide and sulphate conjugates (Berliner et al., 1962).

Deoxycorticosterone (mol. wt. 330)

Deoxycorticosterone, an intermediate adrenocortical steroid in the biosynthesis of corticosterone from progesterone, is also extensively excreted in human bile. One patient with T-tube drainage excreted 43% of an intravenous dose of $[^{14}C]$ deoxycorticosterone in the bile in 72 h and 32% in the urine (Harris *et al.*, 1967).

Cortisone (mol. wt. 360) and hydrocortisone (362)

Both cortisone and hydrocortisone are poorly excreted in human bile but they are extensively eliminated in the bile of rodent species. Only 4% of the radioactivity from an intravenous dose of $[^{14}C]$ cortisone was excreted in the bile of human subjects with a biliary fistula; 90% of the ^{14}C was excreted in the urine within 72 h (Peterson *et al.*, 1957). Similarly, only 4% of a dose of $[^{14}C]$ hydrocortisone infused intravenously was excreted in the bile of a single human subject with T-tube drainage (Peterson *et al.*, 1955).

After intravenous injection in rats, more than 90% of a dose of $[^{14}C]$ hydrocortisone was found in the bile, mainly as polar metabolites, particularly glucuronides (Hyde and Williams, 1957). Much of this is reabsorbed into an enterohepatic circulation so that intact rats eventually excrete about 30% in the urine and about 50–70% is eliminated with the faeces (Wyngaarden *et al.*, 1955; Bocklage *et al.*, 1955). Most of the material excreted in the faeces was not conjugated showing that extensive deconjugation occurs in the gut. In the guinea pig although biliary excretion of the steroid is extensive (65% of dose) most of this is reabsorbed and eliminated in the urine. The chemical nature of the material excreted in the bile has not been identified.

Norethynodrel (mol. wt. 298)

Norethynodrel is an orally active progestational agent used with mestranol as an oral contraceptive. Studies in rabbits have shown that the drug undergoes extensive biliary excretion and enterohepatic circulation which delay its eventual elimination. Thus, rabbits with biliary fistulae excrete 20—40% of an oral dose of [³H] norethynodrel in the bile in 7 days and about 21% in the urine and 17% in the faeces. Intact animals however excrete over 52% of the dose in the urine and 16% in the faeces showing that much of the material eliminated in the bile is absorbed from the intestine and excreted in the urine. Most of the biliary material consists of the glucuronide of 17α-ethynyl-3β, 17β-dihydroxy-5(10)-oestrene and less than 1% of the radioactivity in the bile is unconjugated.

The faeces contain unchanged norethynodrel together with three other compounds namely, 17α-ethynyl-17β-hydroxy-19-norandrost-4-ene-3-one, 17α-ethynyl-10β, 17β-dihydroxy-19-norandrost-4-ene-3-one together with an unidentified ketone. The same metabolites are formed when norethynodrel is incubated with gastric juice or blood (Arai *et al.*, 1962).

Ethynyloestradiol (mol. wt. 296)

Ethynyloestradiol is a synthetic compound with potent oestrogenic properties. Male rats with biliary fistulae excrete nearly 60% of an oral dose of [³H] ethynyloestradiol in the bile in 5 h in the form of conjugates with glucuronic acid and sulphate. No unchanged drug is excreted.

Some of the conjugates found in bile retain uterotrophic activity when given orally but this is less than that of the parent drug (Steinetz *et al.*, 1967).

Quinestrol (ethynyloestradiol-3-cyclopentyl ether; mol. wt. 365)

Quinestrol is also a potent oral oestrogen which unlike its parent compound is stored in and slowly released from the body fat. Male rats eliminate nearly 40% of an oral dose of [^{3}H]quinestrol in the bile in 5 h and this undergoes enterohepatic circulation. No unaltered quinestrol appears in the bile and the drug is present as conjugated metabolites some of which have oestrogenic properties. The drug undergoes some splitting of the ether linkage since derivatives of cyclopentanol are excreted in the urine (Meli *et al.*, 1968).

Stilboestrol (mol. wt. 268)

Stilboestrol is a potent synthetic oestrogen. It is used clinically for its oestrogenic properties, and as its diphosphate derivative, for the treatment of prostatic carcinoma. It is also used in animal husbandry as a growth stimulant. Stilboestrol seems to have a low level of carcinogenic activity for it has been found to induce malignant tumours in experimental animals when given chronically in large doses (see Twombly and Schoenewaldt, 1951) and some men have developed breast cancer while undergoing stilboestrol treatment for prostatic carcinoma (Huggins, 1949).

Stilboestrol undergoes extensive biliary excretion and enterohepatic circulation in the rat (Fischer *et al.*, 1966; Clark *et al.*, 1969). When injected intraperitoneally into rats up to 100% of the dose is excreted in the bile mainly in the form of stilboestrol glucuronide. This undergoes deconjugation in the gut by bacterial β-glucuronidase and the aglycone released is taken up into an enterohepatic circulation. Because of the enterohepatic cycling, excretion by intact animals is very slow. Thus, intact rats eliminate about 11% of an injected dose in the urine in 7 days and about 70% in the faeces (see Smith 1971).

REFERENCES

Adlercreutz, H. (1962) *Acta endocr.* (Kbh), Suppl. 72, 220.

Adlercreutz, H. and Luukkainen, T. (1967) *Acta endocr.* (Kbh), Suppl., 124, 101.

Arai, K., Golab, T., Layne, D. S. and Pincus, G. (1962) *Endocrinology*, 71, 639.

Archer, S. E. H., Scratcherd, T. and Taylor, W. (1965) *Biochem. J.*, 94, 778.

Ashmore, J., Elliott, W. H., Doisy, E. A. Jr. and Doisy, E. A. (1953) *J. biol. Chem.*, 200, 661.

Barry, M. C., Eidinoff, M. L., Dobriner, K. and Gallagher, T. F. (1952) *Endocrinology*, 50, 587.

Berliner, D. L., Leong, G. F., Cazes, D. M. and Berliner, M. L. (1962) *Amer. J. Physiol.*, 202, 420.

Bocklage, B. C., Doisy, E. A. Jr., Elliott, W. H. and Doisy, E. A. (1955) *J. biol. Chem.*, 212, 935.

Cantarow, A., Rakoff, A. E., Paschkis, K. E., Hansen, L. P. and Walkling, A. A. (1943) *Proc. soc. exp. Biol. (N.Y.)*, 52, 256.

Chang, E., Slaunwhite, W. R. Jr. and Sandberg, A. A. (1960) *J. clin. Endocrinol. Metab.*, 20, 1586.

Clark, A. G., Fischer, L. J., Millburn, P., Smith, R. L. and Williams, R. T. (1969) *Biochem. J.*, 112, 17P.

Emerman, S., Twombly, G. H. and Levitz, M. (1967) *J. clin. Endocrin.*, 27, 539.

Engel, L. L., Carter, P. and Fielding, L. L. (1955) *J. biol. Chem.*, 213, 99.

Fischer, L. J., Millburn, P., Smith, R. L. and Williams, R. T. (1966) *Biochem. J.*, 100, 69P.

Grady, H. J., Elliott, W. H., Doisy, E. A. Jr., Bocklage, B. C. and Doisy, E. A. (1952) *J. biol. Chem.*, 195, 755.

Harris, J. J., Hoegel, C. and Crane, M. G. (1967) *J. clin. Endocr.*, 27, 106.

Huggins, C. (1949) *J. Amer. med. Ass.*, 141, 750.

Hyde, P. M. and Williams, R. H. (1957) *J. biol. Chem.*, 227, 1063.

Knapstein, P., Rindt, W. and Oertel, G. W. (1967) *Sympn. dtsch. ges. Endokr.*, 12, 296.

Levitz, M. and Katz, J. (1968) *J. clin. Endocr.*, 28, 862.

Meli, A., Steinetz, B. G., Giannina, T., Cargill, D. I. and Manning, J. P. (1968) *Proc. Soc. exp. Biol. (N.Y.)*, 127, 1042.

Migeon, C. J., Sandberg, A. A., Paul, A. C. and Samuels, L. T. (1956) *J. clin. Endocr.*, 16, 1291.

Okada, H. (1957) *Endocrinol. Japan*, 4, 147.

Paschkis, K. E., Cantarow, A., Rakoff, A. E., Hansen, L. and Walkling, A. A. (1944) *Proc. Soc. exp. Biol. (N.Y.)*, 55, 127.

Pearson, J. R. and Martin, R. P. (1966) *Endocrinology*, 78, 914.

Peterson, R. E., Wyngaarden, J. B., Guerra, S. L., Brodie, B. B. and Bunim, J. J. (1955) *J. clin. Invest.*, 34, 1779.

Peterson, R. E., Pierce, C. E., Wyngaarden, J. B., Bunim J. J. and Brodie, B. B. (1957) *J. clin. Invest.*, 36, 1301.

Sandberg, A. A. and Slaunwhite, W. R. Jr. (1956a) *J. clin. Endoc.*, **16**, 923.

Sandberg, A. A. and Slaunwhite, W. R. Jr. (1956b) *J. clin. Endoc.*, **35**, 1331.

Sandberg, A. A. and Slaunwhite, W. R. Jr. (1957) *J. clin. Invest.*, **36**, 1266.

Sandberg, A. A. and Slaunwhite, W. R. Jr. (1958) *J. clin. Endoc.*, **18**, 253.

Sandberg, A. A., Kirdani, R. T., Back, N., Weyman, P. and Slaunwhite, W. R. Jr. (1967) *Amer. J. Physiol.*, **213**, 1138.

Sandberg, A. A. and Slaunwhite, W. R. Jr. (1965) *J. clin. Invest.*, **44**, 694.

Scratcherd, T. and Taylor, W. (1961) *J. Physiol. (Lond.)*, **159**, 83P.

Slaunwhite, W. R. Jr. and Sandberg, A. A. (1961) *J. clin. Endoc.*, **21**, 753.

Smith, R. L. (1971 In *Mechanisms of Toxicity*, p. 229, edited by W. N. Aldridge, Macmillan, London.

Staub, W., Dönges, K. and Teller, W. (1961) *Hoppe-Seylers Z. physiol. Chem.*, **324**, 32.

Steinetz, B. G., Meli, A., Giannina, T. and Beach, V. L. (1967) *Proc. Soc. exp. Biol. (N.Y.)*, **124**, 1283.

Støa, K. F. and Levitz, M. (1968) *Acta endocr.* (Kbh), **57**, 657.

Taylor, W. and Scratcherd, T. (1961) *Biochem. J.*, **81**, 398.

Taylor, W. and Scratcherd, T. (1965) *Biochem. J.*, **97**, 89.

Taylor, W. and Scratcherd, T. (1967) *Biochem. J.*, **104**, 250.

Twombly, G. H. and Schoenewaldt, E. F. (1951) *Cancer (Philad.)*, **4**, 296.

Twombly, G. H. and Levitz, M. (1960) *Amer. J. Obstet. Gynec.*, **80**, 889.

Wyngaarden, J. B., Peterson, R. E. and Wolff, A. R. (1955) *J. biol. Chem.*, **212**, 963.

CHAPTER NINETEEN

Cardioactive Glycosides

The term cardioactive glycoside is applied to a group of naturally occurring substances having basically similar actions and chemical structure. They are steroid glycosides and they have a specific and powerful action on cardiac muscle. They are found in many plants particularly those belonging to the families Scrophulariaceae, Apocynaceae and Hiliaceae. In addition they occur in the venom of certain toads. They are widely used in clinical medicine because of their cardiotonic activity. The preparations commonly employed are obtained from digitalis but occasionally glycosides obtained from strophanthus are used. Preparations of squill are used as rodenticides and certain cardioactive glycosides are active components of arrow poisons.

Structurally, the cardioactive glycosides constitute a series of closely related compounds. They consist of a steroid ring with a characteristic unsaturated lactone ring at C17. In addition, methyl, hydroxyl, and aldehyde groups are attached in specific positions which vary with the particular aglycone. All carry OH groups at position 14 and most also at C3; sugar residues are usually attached through a glycoside link at position 3. The aglycones have pharmacological activity; they produce the same type of cardiac effect as the glycosides, though their activity may be more transient and less potent in this respect. The unsaturated lactone ring attached to C17 has the $\alpha\beta$ structure and is essential for activity; saturation is accompanied by a loss of activity. Two types of lactone ring are encountered; the digitalis-strophanthus group of aglycones have a five-membered lactone ring, whereas in the aglycones of the squill-toad venom group it is a six-membered lactone ring and doubly unsaturated.

Digitalis Glycosides

Metabolism and excretion have an important bearing on the pharmacological and toxic properties of the cardioactive glycosides. Several glycosides such as those of the digitalis group appear to be extensively metabolized in the body but, probably due to their chemical complexity, this problem has not yet been thoroughly investigated. It is clear however that biliary excretion is important in the elimination of some cardioactive glycosides and their metabolites from the body. Furthermore, as a consequence of biliary excretion some glycosides undergo enterohepatic circulation and may be converted by the gut flora to more toxic metabolites. These factors may have a bearing on the persistence, cumulative properties and toxicity of certain glycosides.

The extent of biliary excretion appears to vary according to the structure of the glycoside and species. The number and position of the hydroxyl groups present in the molecule as well as the type of sugar present appear to have an influence on the extent of biliary excretion probably by influencing the polarity of the molecule. Thus oubain, with five free hydroxyl groups in its aglycone is one of the more water-soluble glycosides and is highly excreted in rat bile unchanged. By contrast, the relatively non-polar glycosides digitoxin with one free hydroxyl group in the aglycone is poorly excreted in rat bile.

The digitalis glycosides are obtained from two species of *Digitalis*, namely, *D. purpurea* and *D. lanata*. There are two series of glycosides derived from two aglycones, namely, digitoxigenin and digoxigenin. The latter differs from digitoxigenin in having an additional hydroxyl group at C12. The metabolism and disposition of the digitalis glycosides are of considerable interest in view of their widespread use in clinical medicine.

Digitoxin is extensively excreted in bile; the extent of this depending upon species. Dogs excrete in 8 h about 40% of the radioactivity from an intravenous dose (0.02–0.05 mg/kg) of [^{3}H] digitoxin (Katzung and Meyers, 1965). Most of the biliary material is more polar than the original drug indicating that it is extensively metabolized. Some enterohepatic circulation of the glycoside and its metabolites occurs in the dog since its half-life in fistula animals is about 6 h compared to 14 h in sham-operated animals. The rat eliminates about 10% of a dose of digitoxin in the bile in 5 h. In addition to the unchanged glycoside (6% of dose) the bile also contains digoxin (4% of dose) formed by hydroxylation at C12 of the steroid nucleus (Cox and Wright, 1959). St. George *et al.* (1952) using a bioassay procedure also found that rats excrete about 10% of an intravenous dose of digitoxin (about 300 μg/rat) in the bile in 24 h; none was detected in the following

Digitoxigenin, R^1 and R^2 = H
Digoxigenin, R^1 = H; R^2 = OH
Digitoxin, R^1 = (digitoxose)$_3$; R^2 = H
Digoxin, R^1 = (digitoxose)$_3$; R^2 = OH
Lanatoside A, R^1 = (digitoxose)$_3$-glucose; R^2 = H
                         |
                   acetyl
Lantoside C, R^1 = (digitoxose)$_3$-glucose; R^2 = OH
                        |
                 acetyl

Digitalis glycosides

24 h bile. In man significant biliary excretion of the glycoside occurs. In humans with biliary fistulae, Okita *et al*. (1955) found that [^{14}C] digitoxin is extensively excreted in the bile as shown by the high concentration of the glycoside and transformation products present in gall-bladder bile and the intestine. They suggested that it undergoes enterohepatic circulation since about 70% can be recovered in the urine (Okita *et al*., 1953). However, urinary excretion is slow since unchanged digitoxin is detectable in urine up to fifty days after a single dose. Digoxin is also extensively excreted in bile. Thus, rats excrete about 40% of an injected dose of digoxin in the bile as the unchanged glycoside (Cox and Wright, 1959) and as a metabolite which has been identified as digoxigenin di-digitoxoside (Wright 1962). Dogs eliminate about 15% of an injected dose of [^{3}H] digoxin in bile in 5 days and about 50% in the urine. Intact dogs excrete nearly 20% of the dose in the faeces and this arises from biliary excretion of the drug. The biliary materials consist of unchanged digoxin (1% of dose) and a metabolite (14% of dose) (Harrison *et al*., 1966).

Cox and Wright (1959) have studied in detail the biliary excretion in the rat of various digitalis glycosides and their aglycones. It was suggested that the relative polarities of these substances may be important for determining the extent of their biliary elimination. Thus, the two polar glycosides Lanatoside A and C appear unchanged in the bile to the extent of about 70% of the dose (1 mg/kg intravenous). The desglucose glycosides, namely, digitoxin and digoxin are less well excreted: about 40% of the dose of digoxin is eliminated, 11% unchanged and nearly 30% as a metabolite thought to be digoxigenin di-digitoxoside. The excretion of digitoxin is less: 10% of the dose appears in the bile; 6% unchanged and 4% as digoxin. The biliary excretion of the two relatively non-polar aglycones is of a low order: 14% of administered digoxigenin is excreted unchanged and as two metabolites and only 15% of a dose of digitoxigenin appears in the bile partly unchanged and as an unidentified metabolite.

Biliary excretion of digitalis glycosides in the rat

Glycoside or aglycone	Mol. wt.	Sugars present	% dose excreted in bile	Substances in bile
Lanatoside A	969	(digitoxose)$_3$-glucose	75	unchanged
Lanatoside C	985	(digitoxose)$_3$-glucose	70	unchanged
Digoxin	781	(digitoxose)$_3$	40	unchanged + metabolite
Digitoxin	765	(digitoxose)$_3$	10	unchanged + digoxin
Digitoxigenin	375	–	15	digitoxigenin + unknown metabolite
Digoxigenin	391	–	14	unchanged & 2 metabolites

Lanatosides A and C each have 4 sugar residues and are more polar than their corresponding desglucose-glycosides digitoxin and digoxin and they are highly excreted in bile. The greater biliary clearance of digoxin compared to digitoxin may be due to its higher polarity associated with the extra polar hydroxyl group at C12. More recent work suggests that digoxin and digitoxin may appear in bile as polar conjugates. Thus, Kolenda *et al.* (1971) using the isolated perfused guinea pig liver found both glycosides to be extensively excreted in the bile. Digoxin appeared in the bile unchanged and as conjugates with glucuronic acid and/or sulphate. Digitoxin however appeared in conjugated form together with conjugates of digitoxigenin-bis- and digitoxigenin-mono-digitoxosides which arise from sugar cleavage.

Strophanthus Glycosides

Seeds of Strophanthus species contain various cardiotoxic glycosides which have been used traditionally in East and West Africa for the preparation of arrow poisons. One of the glycosides, ouabain, is occasionally used clinically in preference to digitalis glycosides. This substance, also known as G-strophan-thin, is the rhamnoside of the aglycone ouabagenin.

Ouabagenin (mol. wt. 439)

Excretion in the bile appears to be the major route of elimination of ouabain. Farah (1946) found that 80–85% of an infused dose of the glycoside is excreted in the bile of rats within 2–4 h. More recently, Cox *et al*. (1959) showed that small injected doses (1 mg/kg) of ouabain are excreted unchanged in the rat largely in the bile (90% of dose) with a small amount (4%) in the urine. However at ten times this dose two metabolites as well as the unchanged glycoside appear in the bile. In rats with ligated renal pedicles to prevent urine excretion 85% of an intravenous dose of ouabain is eliminated unchanged in the bile in 90 min (Kupferberg and Schanker, 1968). Ouabain has also been reported to be excreted in the bile of sheep (Dutta *et al*., 1963) and of man (Marks *et al*., 1964). Any enterohepatic circulation of ouabain is probably limited since oral doses of the glycoside are poorly absorbed (Hatcher and Eggleston, 1919). Several experiments indicate the importance of the hepatobiliary system of the rat for controlling the excretion and toxicity of ouabain. Thus, although the compound is not metabolized to any marked extent, partial or total hepatectomy is accompanied by a marked increase in the toxicity of injected ouabain, presumably because of the removal of its main channel of elimination. Regeneration of the liver is accompanied by a decrease in the toxicity of the glycoside (Farah, 1946).

The rat is one of the most resistant species to the toxic action of the cardioactive glycosides. This has been attributed not only to the greater resistance of the heart to the glycosides but also to the ability of this species to rapidly eliminate these compounds in the bile. In rats, Kupferberg and Schanker (1968) have shown ouabain to be concentrated by the liver and to be actively excreted in bile; the nature of this process is different from that which transfers organic anions and cations into the bile.

K-strophanthoside

This is a triose glycoside found in *Strophanthus kombé* and it consists of the aglycone strophanthidin linked to a molecule of the hexose sugar cymarose and to two molecules of glucose. Removal of one terminal β-glucose unit gives K-strophanthin-β and removal of the next β-glucose residue affords cymarin, a very toxic compound. After oral or subcutaneous administration to rats, K-strophanthoside is excreted partly unchanged in the bile and as the glycoside cymarin in the urine and faeces. The removal of the two β-linked glucose units is carried out by gut enzymes since tissue homogenates are unable to hydrolyse K-strophanthoside. The sequence of events in the metabolism of the glycoside in the rat appear to be as follows: secretion of the parent compound in the bile; hydrolysis in the gut to cymarin which is partly absorbed, circulated and then eliminated in the urine and bile and some of the cymarin eliminated in the latter appears in the faeces (Engler *et al.*, 1958; Holtz, 1958).

The hydrolysis product cymarin is probably at least partly responsible for the pharmacological effects of the parent glycoside. A number of less common strophanthin glycosides have been reported to be excreted in rat bile (Angarskaya *et al.*, 1967) Thus, *convallotoxin* (found in the blossoms of lily of the valley) and the desglucose derivative of *cheirotoxin* (from seeds of wall flowers) when injected intravenously (1 mg/kg) into rats are excreted in the bile unchanged. The cardiac glycoside *adonitoxin,* however, appears in bile unchanged and as an oxidation product.

Thevetin

Thevetin is one of the poisonous glycoside principles of the be-still nut or Malayan nut, the fruit of the tropical yellow oleandor tree. It produces typical digitalis actions but has no special advantage for clinical use. Structurally, it consists of the aglycone digitoxigenin linked to thevetose, and through this to two glucose units. Removal of the glucose groups gives the biologically active glycoside neriifolin. Following its subcutaneous injection in rats thevetin is eliminated in the bile unchanged; however neriifolin is found in the urine and faeces and it is probably formed as in the case of cymarin by enterobacterial hydrolysis of the glycoside excreted in the bile (Engler *et al.*, 1958). Neriifolin probably contributes to the *in vivo* activity of thevetin.

Scillaren A (mol. wt. 693)

Scillaren A is a cardioactive glycoside found in squill (*Urginea maritima*) The latter is occasionally used medicinally and as a component of rat poison. The glycoside consists of the aglycone scillaridin A which has a six-membered lactone ring attached to C17 linked at C3 to glucose and rhamnose. When injected into rats scillaren A is almost quantitatively excreted in the bile of rats unchanged (Simon and Wright, 1960).

OTHER GLYCOSIDES

Other glycosides besides those having cardiotoxic properties are extensively excreted via the bile and it is appropriate to consider these in this section.

Phloridzin (mol. wt. 436)

Phloridzin is a naturally occurring glycoside much used in early studies on carbohydrate metabolism. When injected intravenously into dogs as much as

60% of the dose appears in the bile within 6 h (Jenner and Smyth, 1959). The bile contains in addition to unchanged phloridzin three metabolites one of which may be a glucuronide conjugate. The glycoside has a powerful choleretic effect in the dog which lasts for several hours.

Aesculin (mol. wt. 340)

Aesculin is a naturally occurring glycoside of 6:7-dihydroxy-coumarin and is found in the leaves and bark of horse chestnut and the roots of wild jasmine. Using a fluorescence microscopy technique Grafflin and Bagley (1952) found aesculin is excreted in the bile of the frog, the adult salamander and the mouse.

Troxerutin (3',4',7-tri-(β-O-hydroxyethyl)rutoside; mol. wt. 743)

This flavanoid, also known as Factor P or Vitamin P_4 is a component of the drug Paroven which is used for the treatment of venous disorders. When injected intravenously into rats about 50—60% of the dose is excreted in the bile in 24 h and about 6—30% in the urine. The bile contains mainly the unchanged glycoside together with three metabolites. A related flavanoid, namely, 3',4',5,7-tetra-(β-O-hydroxyethyl)rutoside is also extensively (12—30% of dose) eliminated in rat bile. The high biliary excretion of these flavanoids explains why when they are given intraperitoneally to rats much of the dose is found in the faeces in the form of the aglycones. These arise from microfloral degradation of the glycosides eliminated in the bile (Barrow and Griffiths, 1971). Biliary elimination with subsequent excretion in the faeces is also of major importance in the clearance of the flavanoids *naringin* and (+)-*catechin*.

REFERENCES

Angarskaya, M. A., Sokolova, V. E., Lyubartseva, L. A. and Lutokhin, S. I. (1967) *Pharmacol. Toxicol.*, **30**, 207.

Barrow, A. and Griffiths, L. A. (1971) *Biochem. J.*, **125**, 24P.

Cox, E., Roxburgh, G. and Wright, S. E. (1959) *J. Pharm. Pharmacol.*, **11**, 535.

Cox, E. and Wright, S. E. (1959) *J. Pharmacol. exp. Ther.*, **126**,117.

Dutta, S., Marks, B. H. and Smith, C. R. (1963) *J. Pharmacol. exp. Ther.*, **142**, 223.

Engler, R., Holtz, P. and Raudonat, H. W. (1958) *Naunyn-Schmiedeberg's Arch. exp. Path. Pharmak.*, **233**, 393.

Farah, A. (1946) *J. Pharmacol. exp. Ther.*, **86**, 248.

Grafflin, A. L. and Bagley, E. H. (1952) *Bull. John Hopk. Hosp.*, **90**, 395.

Harrison, C. E. Jr., Brandenburg, R. O., Ongley, P. A., Orvis, A. L. and Owen, C. A. Jr. (1966) *J. Lab. clin. Med.*, **67**, 764.

Hatcher, R. A. and Eggleston, C. (1919) *J. Pharmacol. exp. Ther.*, **12**, 405.

Holtz, P. (1958) *Klin. Wschr.*, **36**, 238.

Jenner, F. A. and Smyth, D. H. (1959) *J. Physiol.*, **146**, 563.

Katzung, B. G. and Meyers, F. H. (1965) *J. Pharmacol. exp. Ther.*, **149**, 257.

Kolenda, K-D., Lüllman, H. and Peters, T. (1971) *Brit. J. Pharmacol.*, **41**, 661.

Kupferberg, H. J. and Schanker, L. S. (1968) *Amer. J. Physiol.*, **214**, 1048.

Marks, B. H., Dutta, S., Gauthier, J. and Elliott, D. (1964) *J. Pharmacol. exp. Ther.*, **145**, 351.

Okita, G. T., Kelsey, F. E., Talso, P. J., Smith, L. B. and Geiling, E. M. K. (1953) *Circulation*, **7**, 161.

Okita, G. T., Talso, P. J., Curry, J. P. Jr., Smith, F. D. Jr., and Geiling, E. M. K. (1955) *J. Pharmacol. exp. Ther.*, **115**, 371.

Simon, M. and Wright, S. E. (1960) *J. Pharm. Pharmacol.* **12**, 767.

St. George, S., Bine, R., Jr. and Friedman, M. (1952) *Circulation*, **6**, 661.

Wright, S. E. (1962) *J. Pharm. Pharmacol.*, **14**, 613.

CHAPTER TWENTY

Antibiotics

The elimination of antibiotics in the bile is of considerable interest in view of their possible use for the treatment of hepatobiliary infections. The biliary tract is liable to infection by micro-organisms and various parasites such as flukes. Bacterial infections of the biliary system are not uncommon and the main organisms responsible include: *E. coli, S. faecalis, Proteus mirabilis, Klebsiella, Clostridia, Salmonella typhosa* and allied strains. Similarly, parasite infections such as amoebiasis, helminthiasis, leishmaniasis and trypanosomiasis can involve the hepatobiliary system. These diseases are endemic in countries of the Middle and Far East, Africa, India and South America and are the sources of enormous medical, social and economic problems. Also the parasitic infestation of domestic animals such as the liver fluke in sheep is a major source of economic loss. For the treatment of such bacterial and parasitic diseases it is desirable to use drugs which are concentrated in the hepatobiliary system and eliminated in the bile in effective concentrations.

The biliary excretion of a large number of antibiotics has been investigated but these studies have usually been limited to the estimation of the concentration of active antibiotic excreted in the bile and little or no attention has been paid to the elimination of metabolic products. This is not surprising however, in view of the chemical complexity of many antibiotics which make metabolic studies difficult. In general the main factor influencing the pattern of excretion of antibiotics is the molecular weight. Antibiotics of low molecular weight such as cycloserine (mol. wt. 102), chloramphenicol (mol. wt. 323) and benzylpenicillin (mol. wt. 334), are poorly excreted in bile and are eliminated mainly by renal excretion. Antibiotics of higher molecular weight e.g. cloxacillin (436) rifamide (811) and erythromycin (734) are extensively excreted in the bile. They are concentratively transferred from the plasma to the bile and their concentration in the latter may be very high. They may also undergo enterohepatic circulation and this factor may contribute to the maintenance of blood levels.

There occur, as might be expected, marked species variations in the biliary excretion of the antibiotics and this should be taken into account when attempting to extrapolate excretion data found in laboratory species to man. Thus, chloramphenicol is extensively excreted in rat bile in the form of its glucuronide but in man the same conjugate is eliminated mainly by renal excretion.

THE PENICILLINS

Excretion of penicillins occurs in the bile of man and animals. The extent to which this occurs varies with species and the particular penicillin. In man it appears that renal excretion is the main pathway of elimination for the penicillins. In the rat, for which species most information is available, all the penicillin derivatives are significantly (10—40% of dose) eliminated in the bile following their intravenous injection. The extent of the biliary excretion of the penicillins has been correlated with the relative polarities of the side-chain of the penicillin molecule (Ryrfeldt, 1971).

Benzylpenicillin (penicillin G)

The biliary excretion of benzylpenicillin was first demonstrated by the Oxford group originally responsible for its development as a chemotherapeutic agent (Abraham et al., 1941). They found using a bioassay technique, that penicillin administered to both rabbits and cats, is eliminated in the bile as well as the urine. Later, Rammelkamp and Helm (1943) showed that penicillin injected intravenously into human subjects appears in bile at levels higher than those of blood and which were effective against Gram-positive organisms. The excretion of penicillin in human bile is however reduced by liver damage, obstructive jaundice and conditions that affect the patency of the cystic duct (Zaslow et al., 1947a, b). Benzylpenicillin is also excreted in high concentrations in the bile of the rat (Harrison and Stewart 1961, Ryrfeldt, 1971) and the dog (Struble and Bellows, 1944; Glassman et al., 1964).

Methicillin

Methicillin is one of the less potent penicillins. Rats excrete 2—3% of a dose of the antibiotic in the bile probably in the form of an active metabolite since the biliary material shows different chromatographic and anti-microbiological properties from the original compound (Harrison *et al.*, 1960). Dogs eliminate over 20% of a dose in the bile in 24 h. (Glassman *et al.*, 1964).

Ampicillin.

This is a semisynthetic penicillin with a broad range of activity against both Gram-positive and Gram-negative bacteria. It is stable to acid and is absorbed from the gut and therefore can be given orally. Ampicillin is excreted in relatively high concentrations in the bile of several species. Rats excrete about 5% of an oral dose and 11–18% of an injected dose, apparently unchanged, in the bile and part of this undergoes enterohepatic circulation (Stewart and Harrison, 1961). Acred *et al.* (1962) found that after oral doses in rats about 2% appears in the bile and 4% in the urine in 25 h. The levels in the bile are 200–400 times those of the blood. It is also excreted in the bile of dogs and the bile levels are 300 times those of the blood (Brown and Acred, 1961). Ampicillin is secreted in high concentrations in human bile and for this reason it is used against infections of the hepatobiliary system. In patients with normal biliary tracts the levels of ampicillin in the bile may be up to 48 times those of the serum. (Ayliffe and Davies, 1965). Excretion of the antibiotic however is much reduced in obstructive jaundice and in cases of obstructed bile duct (Mortimer *et al.*, 1969). Patients with diseased biliary tracts (cholecystitis and cholelithiasis) and having patent cystic ducts excrete bactericidal levels of the antibiotic in the bile. Ampicillin treatment has been found to be of some value in the treatment of Salmonella carriers (Bullock. 1963).

Nafcillin

This is a semisynthetic penicillin which is highly resistant to penicillinase. In dogs the main channel of elimination is the bile; over 90% appears in the bile in 4 h following intravenous injection of the antibiotic. Extensive reabsorption and re-excretion in the bile occurs and bactericidal levels are maintained for several hours (Glassman *et al.*, 1964). Renal excretion accounts for less than 10% of the dose; this route however, is important in the dog for the elimination of both methicillin and penicillin G.

Cloxacillin

Cloxacillin is an orally active semisynthetic penicillin which is stable to staphylococcal penicillinase. Rats excrete in the bile in 6 h about 23% of a dose of cloxacillin injected intramuscularly. At least part of the dose occurs in the bile in the form of an active metabolite probably formed in the liver. In the intestine the antibiotic appears to be transformed into a second active

Names and chemical structures of the various penicillins

$$R-CONH-CH-CH \overset{S}{\underset{CO-N-CH-COOH}{\overset{\displaystyle |}{|}}} C \overset{CH_3}{\underset{CH_3}{}}$$

Side chain R	Chemical name	Other names
—CH₂— (phenyl)	Benzylpenicillin (334)	Penicillin G
phenyl-CH— with NH₂	α-aminobenzylpenicillin (349)	Ampicillin
phenyl-OCH₂—	Phenoxymethylpenicillin (350)	Penicillin V
dimethoxyphenyl (OCH₃, OCH₃)	Dimethoxyphenylpenicillin (380)	Methicillin
naphthyl-OC₂H₅	6-(2-ethoxy-1-naphthamido)-penicillin (414)	Nafcillin
phenyl-isoxazolyl (CH₃)	5-methyl-3-phenyl-4-isoxazolyl-penicillin (419)	Oxacillin
(o-chlorophenyl)-isoxazolyl (CH₃)	[5-methyl-3-(o-chlorophenyl)-4-isoxazolyl] penicillin (436)	Cloxacillin

Molecular weights are shown in parentheses

metabolite which is more active than cloxacillin against Sarcina lutea (Acred and Brown, 1963).

Erythromycin

Erythromycin is an orally effective antibiotic and is a metabolic product of the organism *Streptomyces erythreus(Waksman)*, originally isolated from a soil sample collected in the Philippine Archipelago. It is a member of an important group of antibiotic substances called the macrolides. These are compounds of relatively high molecular weight consisting of a large macrocyclic lactone ring to which sugars are attached. Erythromycin is used as an antibacterial drug or more commonly in the form of its esters or salts which have more desirable pharmaceutical and pharmacological properties.

Erythromycin R = H (mol. wt. 734)
Erythromycin propionate R = CH_3CH_2CO- (mol. wt. 790)

The metabolism and excretion of erythromycin have not been fully elucidated though it is clear that the bile is an important channel for its elimination. Thus, extensive biliary excretion of the antibiotic occurs in the rat and dog (Lee *et al.*, 1954a, 1956a) and in man (Pulaski and Fusillo, 1955). When injected intravenously into rats about 40% of the radioactivity of a dose of [^{14}C-methyl]erythromycin is found in the intestinal tract and faeces in 20h, about 30% in the urine and a further 30% as CO_2 in the expired air. The latter arises from demethylation of the antibiotic. Most of the intestinal and faecal material arise from biliary excretion since cannulated animals eliminate about 15% of the dose in the bile in 2h (Lee *et al.*, 1956a). The bile contains besides unchanged erythromycin, des-*N*-methyl-erythromycin formed by demethylation, which is microbiologically active, and two other inactive and unidentified metabolites. The faeces contain in addition to erythromycin and its des-*N*-methyl metabolite two further metabolites which probably arise from enterobacterial metabolism of the material excreted into the gut with the bile (Lee *et al.*, 1956b). The propionate ester of erythromycin is less effectively excreted in the rat bile than the parent antibiotic; about 9% of a dose of the free base given intraduodenally is recovered in the bile in 2h while this is only 0.6% in the case of the propionate (Lee *et al.*, 1959).

Dogs excrete about 34% of an injected dose of erythromycin in the bile in 6h and about 16% in the urine. The bile is thus the main channel of elimination for the compound in this species (Lee *et al.*, 1954a). The bile contains the unchanged antibiotic and its metabolite des-*N*-methyl-erythromycin. The antibiotic but not the metabolite appears to undergo enterohepatic circulation (Lee *et al.*, 1954b; Welles, *et al.*, 1955).

The appearance of erythromycin in the bile of human subjects has been observed by several investigators (Pulaski and Fusillo, 1955; Twiss *et al.*, 1956; Uberti, 1956). The extent to which this occurs however, depends upon a number of factors including the patency of the bile duct, and the presence of jaundice or other liver disease (Zaslow, 1953).Takimura and Lopez-Belio (1955) found that non-jaundiced patients who had undergone cholecystectomy excrete in the bile in 12h about 13% of a dose of erythromycin lactobionate given intravenously. Jaundiced patients however excrete less in the bile suggesting that the ability to secrete the antibiotic is depressed.

Piller and Bernstein (1955) recovered about 30% of an intravenous dose of the antibiotic in the bile in 6 h and only 6–7% in the urine. The blood levels of the antibiotic drop to less than a therapeutic concentration within 4 h of the injection and this was attributed to its rapid excretion in the bile. Twiss *et al.*, (1956) found erythromycin in both the hepatic and gall bladder bile of patients taking the drug orally and by taking adequate doses, levels could be maintained in the bile to inhibit a number of pathogenic organisms.

Erythromycin propionate produces higher and more consistent serum levels in man than the free base and this has been attributed by Griffith (1959) to be at least partly due to the fact that less of the drug administered as the ester is lost by excretion in the bile.

Oleandomycin (mol. wt. 688)

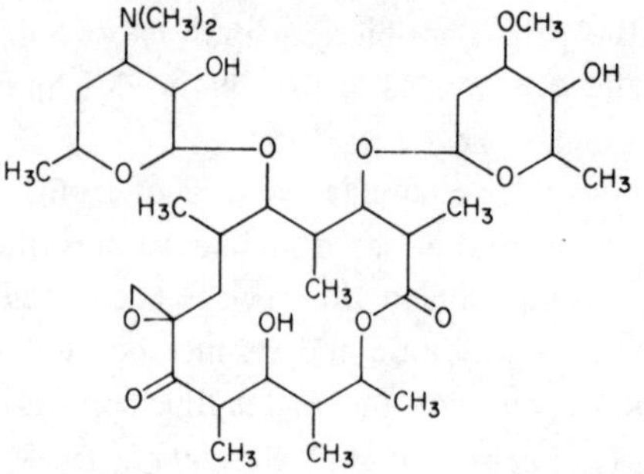

Oleandomycin is a macrolide antibiotic chemically related to erythromycin. The drug is excreted in high concentrations in the bile of rats and monkeys (Kazenko *et al.*, 1957). The rat excretes about 10% of an oral dose of oleandomycin in the bile in 4 h. In man, the drug when given orally or intravenously, appears in the bile in concentrations much higher than those in serum, but not if liver function is impaired (Preston *et al.*, 1962).

Spiramycin (Rovamycin)

Spiramycin is a macrolide antibiotic produced by the organism *Streptomyces ambofaciens* found in the soil of northern France. It can be separated into three components referred to as spiramycin I, II and III respectively.

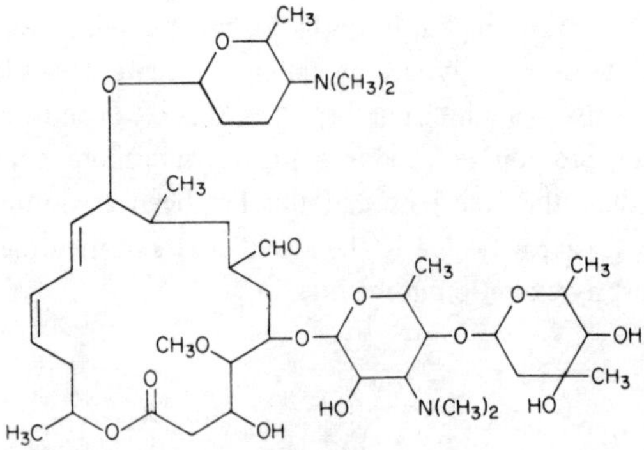

Spiramycin I
(mol. wt. 843)

The rat excretes the drug in the bile in high concentrations following its intramuscular injection (Lambert *et al.*, 1963a). It is eliminated in human bile at levels 20–40 times those of the serum and has been used for the treatment of cholangitis (Mulhardt, 1960).

THE TETRACYCLINES

The tetracyclines constitute a closely related group of tetracyclic antibacterial compounds having broad spectrum activity. Chlortetracycline, oxytetracycline and demethylchlortetracycline are obtained from cultures of *Streptomyces* while others such as tetracycline and rolitetracycline are produced semi-synthetically. Their metabolism and disposition has not been fully investigated but sufficient data is available to show that hepatobiliary elimination is an important aspect of their overall fate.

Structures of the various tetracyclines

		Mol. wt.	R^1	R^2	R^3	R^4
6-demethyl-6-deoxytetracycline	Norcycline	414	H	H	H	H
6-methyleneoxytetracycline	Methacycline	442	H	⌐CH₂⌐		OH
α-6-deoxyoxytetracycline	Doxycycline	444	H	CH₃	H	OH
Tetracycline	Achromycin	444	H	CH₃	OH	H
Oxytetracycline	Terramycin	460	H	CH₃	OH	OH
6-demethylchlortetracycline	Declomycin	465	Cl	H	OH	H

Chlortetracycline

This compound, also known as aureomycin, is a metabolic product of the organism *Streptomyces aureofaciens,* and it was the first tetracycline to be used in clinical medicine. It appears in human bile in concentrations several times those of blood (Pulaski and Fusillo, 1955; Levrat *et al.,* 1958) but the extent of its elimination by this route is unknown. In 4 days about 16% of an injected dose is found in the urine (Kunin *et al.,* 1959).

Oxytetracycline

This antibiotic is obtained from cultures of *Streptomyces rimosus.* Dogs excrete a small amount (2%) of an injected dose in the bile and about 55% in the urine as determined by bioassay (Schach von Wittenau and Yeary, 1963). The antibiotic appears in both the hepatic and gall-bladder bile of patients following its oral administration providing that liver function is not impaired and no jaundice is present (Zaslow and Rosenthal, 1954). Bile levels may be 4–5 times those of blood (Levrat et al., 1957) but the amount of antibiotic eliminated by this route is probably small since about 70% of an injected dose is recovered in the urine (Kunin et al., 1959).

Tetracycline

This antibiotic is produced semisynthetically from chlortetracycline. It appears to be extensively eliminated in the bile of rats since about 40% of an injected dose is recovered in the faeces in about 48 h; about 50% appears in the urine (Kelly and Buyske, 1960). Both urine and faeces appear to contain the unchanged drug. It is possible that the antibiotic is initially excreted in the bile as a polar conjugate and this is deconjugated in the intestine to give the free drug which is poorly absorbed and therefore passes out with the faeces. Tetracycline appears in the bile of patients following its oral (Andriola, 1954; Zaslow et al., 1955) or intravenous administration (Pulaski and Fusillo, 1955). Biliary levels of the antibiotic are higher after oral doses of tetracycline phosphate complex than with the hydrochloride salt (Pulaski and Isokane, 1957).

Demethylchlortetracycline

This antibiotic is produced by a mutant strain of Streptomyces aureofaciens from which chlortetracycline was first obtained. Dogs excrete unchanged about 75% of an injected dose of $[^{14}C]$ demethylchlortetracycline in the urine and about 15% in the faeces in 7 days (Kelly et al., 1961). The latter and the high concentration of drug found in the intestinal contents arise from extensive biliary excretion. The rat also excretes high concentrations of the antibiotic in the bile (Lambert et al., 1963b; Brette et al., 1966). In patients with T-tube bile drainage following cholecystectomy, biliary levels of the antibiotic may be up to thirty times greater than those of the blood (Kunin and Finland, 1959). The extent of biliary excretion of the antibiotic in man is not known; about 40% of an intravenous dose, however, is recovered in the urine (Kunin et al., 1959).

Pyrrolidonemethyltetracycline (Rolitetracycline; mol. wt. 528)

This is a semi-synthetic derivative of tetracycline which is more stable and soluble than the latter. Although about 60% of an injected dose of pyrrolidonemethyltetracycline can be recovered in the urine of human subjects (Cronk et al., 1961) high concentrations of the antibiotic appear in the bile (Lambrecht, 1958; Acocella et al., 1968).

Streptomycin (mol. wt. 582)

Streptomycin is an antibiotic substance produced by a strain of *Streptomycin griseus*. Structurally, it consists of the highly polar bisguanidine base streptidine linked to the sugars streptose and *N*-methylglucosamine. It forms salts which are very water-soluble. Probably because of its polarity and therefore low lipid solubility it is poorly absorbed when given orally.

Biliary elimination appears to be of little importance in the excretion of this antibiotic since for both man and the dog most of an injected dose can be recovered in the urine within 24h (Marshall, 1948). Low levels of streptomycin have been found in the bile of patients receiving the drug and undergoing cholecystectomy (Zaslow *et al.*, 1947b; Hegemann *et al.*, 1955).

Gentamycin

Gentamycin is a very water-soluble substance produced by the organism *Micromonospora purpurea* and has broad spectrum antibacterial properties. It has a molecular weight of 543 but its structure is unknown. It appears to be eliminated both by man and dogs mainly by renal excretion but it has been found in the bile of both the guinea pig and the dog (Black *et al.*, 1964).

Vancomycin

Vancomycin is a basic antibiotic substance of unknown structure having a molecular weight of about 3300. In both men and dogs it is apparently largely eliminated by renal excretion as determined by bio-assay (Geraci *et al.*, 1957; Kirby and Divelbiss, 1957); low concentrations however, occur in dog bile (Lee *et al.*, 1957).

Rifamycins

The rifamycins are a group of antibiotic substances isolated from broths of *Streptomyces mediteranei*. Four of these have been characterized and defined as rifamycin B, O, S and SV respectively. In addition a number of semi-synthetic rifamycin derivatives such as rifamide and rifampicin have been prepared for use as drugs. They are complex cyclic structures having molecular weights of about 700 or more. Of all the antibiotics the rifamycins

Rifamycin SV (mol. wt. 698)

appear to undergo the most extensive biliary excretion and this pathway is the main channel for their elimination from the body (Schiatti *et al.*, 1967). The rat excretes about 60% of an intravenous dose of rifamycin SV in the bile in 45 min (Maffii *et al.*, 1963). In this species the drug undergoes extensive enterohepatic circulation. In patients, injected rifamycin SV is largely eliminated in the bile and is passed out with the faeces; only small amounts appear in the urine. It has a short half-life in man (1 h) because of its rapid elimination in the bile (Fürész and Scotti, 1961). Rifamide, which is the semi-synthetic diethylamide derivative of rifamycin B is extensively excreted (about 60% of the dose) in the bile of patients with T-tube biliary drainage (Acocella *et al.*, 1966). The concentrations of the antibiotic in the bile are 100,000 times the minimal inhibitory concentration for Gram-positive and about 100 times that for Gram-negative organisms. The rat also largely eliminates the injected antibiotic in the bile, apparently unchanged (Maffii and Schiatti, 1966).

Another semi-synthetic derivative, namely rifampicin is also extensively eliminated in the bile of patients who had undergone cholecystectomy (Fürész *et al.*, 1967) and this explains its appearance in the faeces in large amounts following the intravenous injection of the drug. It undergoes marked enterohepatic circulation in the rat and this produces blood levels of the antibiotic much higher than those found in biliary cannulated animals in which recycling is prevented by drawing off the bile (Curci and Loscalzo, 1966).

Fusidic acid

Fusidic acid is an antibiotic substance formed by the organism *Fusidium coccineum*. Chemically, it is a tetracyclic triterpene and is structurally related to two other antibiotic substances, namely, cephalosporin P_1 and helvolic acid. It is effective in the treatment of staphylococcal infections. Rats and

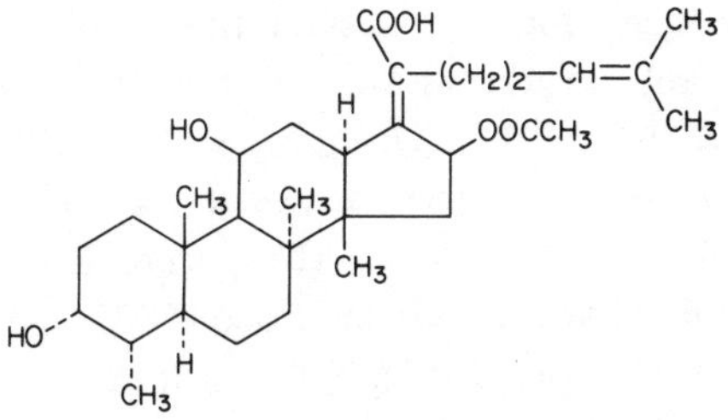

(mol. wt. 517)

rabbits eliminate the orally administered drug very largely in the bile mainly in an inactive form. Fusidic acid is also extensively excreted in the bile of patients following cholecystectomy. The bile contains some unchanged drug together with a glucuronide conjugate and at least six other unidentified metabolites four of which have antibiotic activity (Godtfredsen and Vangedal, 1966).

Chloramphenicol

Chloramphenicol is an antibiotic substance originally isolated from *Streptomyces venezuelas* and is now obtainable by synthesis. Marked species differences occur in the pattern of excretion of this compound. Thus, its biliary excretion is relatively low in man and the rhesus monkey but is high in the dog and rat. In man, the renal route is the main pathway for its elimination; about 90% of an oral dose of the drug is excreted in the urine in 24 h largely as the inactive 3-glucuronide together with small amounts of the unchanged drug and its amino-diol hydrolysis product (Glazko *et al.*, 1949; 1950).

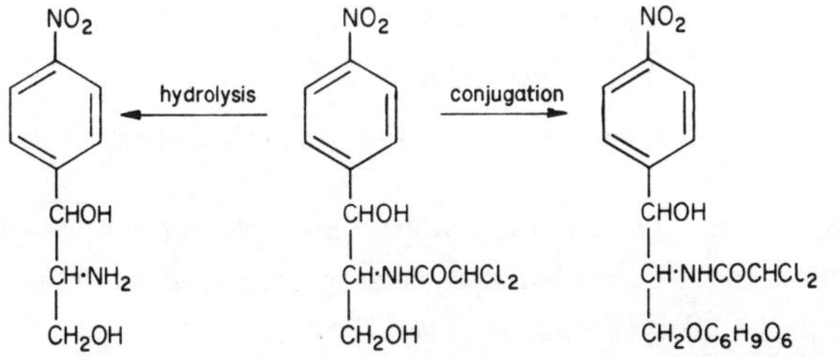

Chloramphenicol

Chloramphenicol glucuronide

One subject with an external biliary fistula given a 1g oral dose of chloramphenicol excreted 3% of the dose in the bile in 24 h largely in an inactive form and 82% in the urine. Despite the low excretion in bile, the concentrations of the antibiotic are several times those occurring in blood, as determined by microbiological assay, and the drug has therefore been suggested for use in liver disease (Danopoulos *et al.*, 1954). In the rhesus monkey biliary excretion is somewhat greater; about 15% of a dose is eliminated in the bile mainly as the inactive glucuronide conjugate (Glazko, 1967). The rat and dog however, eliminate about 80% and 50% respectively in the bile (Glazko *et al.*; 1949; 1952). In the rat the antibiotic appears in the bile as the 3-glucuronide and in the gut this is hydrolysed to release free chloramphenicol, part of which is absorbed into an enterohepatic circulation while the remainder undergoes enterobacterial reduction to arylamines. These are partly absorbed, acetylated and eliminated in the urine as *N*-acetyl conjugates while the unabsorbed material is voided with the faeces.

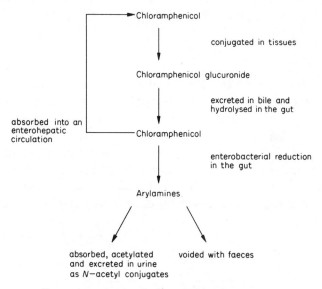

Enterohepatic circulation of chloramphenicol

The goitrogenic effect of chloramphenicol in the rat has been attributed to the formation of toxic arylamines by enterobacterial reduction of the drug eliminated in the bile (Thompson *et al.*, 1954).

Griseofulvin (mol. wt. 353)

Griseofulvin is an orally effective antifungal agent widely used in the treatment of fungal infections in both domestic animals and man. In the rat but not the rabbit, griseofulvin metabolism is characterized by extensive biliary excretion and enterohepatic circulation. The rat excretes nearly 80%

Griseofulvin (mol. wt. 353)

of an intravenous dose of griseofulvin in the bile in 24 h and 12% in the urine. Rat bile contains mainly free and conjugated 4-demethylgriseofulvin with small amounts of the 6-demethyl isomer and traces of unchanged griseofulvin. Rabbit bile however contains as the major metabolite 6-demethylgriseofulvin with only very small amounts of the 4-demethyl derivative (Symchowicz *et al.*, 1967).

REFERENCES

Abraham, E. P., Gardner, A. D., Chain. E., Heatley, N. G., Fletcher, C. M. Jennings, M. A. and Florey, H. W. (1941) *Lancet*, 2, 177.

Acocella, G., Lamarina, F., Tenconi, L. T. and Nicolis, F. B. (1966) *Gut*, 7, 380.

Acocella, G., Mattiussi, R., Nicolis, F. B., Pallanza, R. and Tenconi, L. T. (1968) *Gut*, 9, 536.

Acred, P., Brown, D.M., Turner, D. H. and Wilson, M. J. (1962) *Brit. J. Pharmacol.*, 18, 356.

Acred, P. and Brown, D. M. (1963) *Brit. J. Pharmacol.*, 21, 339.

Andriola, J. C. (1954) *Harlem Hosp. Bull.*, 7, 69.

Ayliffe, G. A. J. and Davies, A. (1965) *Brit. J. Pharmacol.*, 24, 189.

Black, J., Calesnick, B., Williams, D. and Weinstein, M. J. (1964) *Antimicrobial Agents and Chemotherapy* 1963, 138.

Brown, D. M. and Acred, P. (1961) *Brit. med. J.*, 2, 197.

Brette, R., Truchot, R. and Barthe, J. (1966) *Rev. int. Hépat.*, 16, 361.

Bullock. W. E. (1963) *Amer. J. med. Sci.*, 246, 42.

Cronk, G. A., Buckwalter, F. H., Wheatley, W. B. and Albright, H. (1961) *Amer. J. med. Sci.*, 241, 1.

Curci, G. and Loscalzo, B. (1966) Extracts from the Acts of the XVIII Italian Phthisiology Congress, Milan, Nov. 4-6. Riv. 1st Vacc. Consorzi antituberc, Supplementary Edition., 22.

Danopoulos, E., Angelopoulos, B., Ziordrou, C. and Amira, P. (1954) *Brit. J. Pharmacol.*, 9, 260.

Fürész, S. and Scotti, R. (1961) *Farmaco. Ed. sci.*, 16, 262.

Fürész, S., Scotti, R., Pallanza, R. and Mapelli, E. (1967) *Arzneimittel-Forsch.*, 17, 534.

Geraci, J. E., Heilman, F. R., Nichols, D. R., Wellman, W. E. and Ross, G. T. (1957) *Antibiot. Ann.*, 1956-1957, p.90.

Glassman, J. M., Warren, G. H., Rosenman, S. B. and Agersborg, H. P. K. (1964) *Toxicol. appl. Pharmacol,* **6**, 220.

Glazko, A. J., Wolf, L. M., Dill, W. A. and Bratton, A. C. Jr. (1949) *J. Pharmacol. exp. Ther.*, **96**, 445.

Glazko, A. J., Dill, W. A. and Rebstock, M. C. (1950) *J. Biol. Chem.*, **183**, 679.

Glazko, A. J., Dill, W. A. and Wolf, L. M. (1952) *J. Pharmacol. exp. Ther.*, **104**, 452.

Glazko, A. J. (1967) *Antimicrobial Agents and Chemotherapy 1966*, p. 655.

Griffith, R. S. (1959) *Antibiot. Ann.*, 1958-1959, p. 364.

Godtfredsen, W. O. and Vangedal, S. (1966) *Acta chem. scand.*, **20**, 1599.

Harrison, P. M., White, J. A. and Stewart, G. T. (1960) *Brit. J. Pharmacol.*, **15**, 571.

Harrison, P. M. and Stewart, G. T. (1961) *Brit. J. Pharmacol.*, **17**, 420.

Hegemann, F., Gleitz, K. and Wachtelborn, G. (1955) *Z. klin. Med.*, **153**, 162.

Kazenko, A., Sorenson, O. J. Jr., Wolf, L. M., Dill, W. A., Galbraith, M. and Glazko, A. J. (1957) *Antibiot. and Chemother.*, **7**, 410.

Kelly, R. G. and Buyske, D. A. (1960) *J. Pharmacol. exp. Ther.*, **130**, 144.

Kelly, R. G., Kanegis, L. A. and Buyske, D. A. (1961) *J. Pharmacol. exp. Ther.*, **134**, 321.

Kirby, W. M. M. and Divelbiss, C. L. (1957) *Antibiot. Ann.*, 1956-1957, p.107.

Kunin, C. M., Dornbush, A. C. and Finland, M. (1959) *J. clin. Invest.*, **38**, 1950.

Kunin, C. M. and Finland, M. (1959) *New Engl. J. Med.*, **261**, 1069.

Lambert, R., Brette, R., Salmon, F. and Maillard, M. A. (1963a) *C. R. Soc. Biol. (Paris)*, **157**, 1607.

Lambert, R., Brette, R., Salmon, F. and Maillard, M. A. (1963b) *C. R. Soc. Biol. (Paris)*, **157**, 1992.

Lambrecht, R. (1958) *Med. Klin.*, **53**, 1511.

Lee, C.-C., Anderson, R. C. and Chen, K. K. (1954a) *Antibiot. Ann.*, 1953-1954 p. 485.

Lee, C.-C., Anderson, R. C., Bird, H. L. Jr. and Chen, K. K. (1954b) *Antibiot. Ann.*, 1953-54, p. 493.

Lee, C.-C., Anderson, R. C. and Chen, K. K. (1954) *Antibiot. and Chemother.*, **4**, 926.

Lee, C.-C., Anderson, R. C. and Chen, K. K. (1956a) *J. Pharmacol. exp. Ther.*, **117**, 265.

Lee, C.-C., Anderson, R. C. and Chen, K. K. (1956b) *J. Pharmacol. exp. Ther.*, **117**, 274.

Lee, C. -C., Anderson, R. C., Henderson, F. G., Worth, H. M. and Harris, P. N. (1959) *Antibiot. Ann.*, 1958-1959 p. 354.

Lee, C.-C., Anderson, R. C. and Chen, K. K. (1957) *Antibiot. Ann.*, 1956-1957 p. 82.

Levrat, M., Brette, R., Thivolet, J. and Carraz, M. (1957) *Rev. int. Hépat.*, 7, 287.

Maffii, G., Schiatti, P. and Bianchi, G. (1963) *Chemotherapia*, 7, 158.

Maffii, G., and Schiatti, P. (1966) *Toxicol. appl. Pharmacol.*, 8, 138.

Marshall, E. K. Jr. (1948) *J. Pharmacol. exp. Ther.*, 92, 43.

Mortimer, P. R., Mackie, D. B. and Haynes, S. (1969) *Brit. Med. J.*, 3, 88.

Mulhardt, G. (1960) *Nouv. méd.*, 9, 251.

Piller, M. and Bernstein, A. (1955) *Schweiz. med. Wschr.*, 85, 104.

Preston, F. W., Silverman, M., Henegar, G. C. and Kurral, J. C. (1962) *Amer. J. digest. Dis., N. S.*, 7, 557.

Pulaski, E. J. and Fusillo, M. H. (1955) *Surg. Gynec. Obstet.*, 100, 571.

Pulaski, E. J. and Isokane, R. K. (1957) *Antibiot. Med.*, 4, 408.

Rammelkamp, C. H. and Helm, J. D. Jr. (1943) *Proc. Soc. exp. Biol. (N.Y.)*, 54, 31.

Ryrfeldt, Å. (1971) *J. Pharm. Pharmacol.*, 23, 463.

Schach von Wittenau, M. and Yeary, R. (1963) *J. Pharmacol. exp. Ther.*, 140, 258.

Schiatti, P., Maggi, N., Sensi, P. and Maffii, G. (1967) *Chemotherapia*, 12, 155.

Stewart, G. T. and Harrison, P. M. (1961) *Brit. J. Pharmacol.*, 17, 414.

Struble, G. C. and Bellows, J. G. (1944) *J. Amer. med. Ass.*, 125, 685.

Symchowicz, S., Staub, M. S. and Wong, K. K. (1967) *Biochem. Pharmacol.*, 16, 2405.

Takimura, Y. and Lopez-Belio, M. (1955) *Antibiot. Med.*, 1, 561.

Thompson, R. Q., Sturtevant, M., Bird, O. D. and Glazko, A. J. (1954) *Endocrinology*, 55, 665.

Twiss, J. R., Berger, W. V., Gillette, L., Aronson, A. R. and Siegel. L. (1956) *Surg. Gynec. Obstet.*, 102, 355.

Uberti, E. (1956) *G. ital. Chemioter.*, 3, 36.

Welles, J. S., Anderson, R. C. and Chen, K. K. (1955) *Antibiot. Ann.*, 1954-1955 p. 291.

Zaslow, J., Counseller, V. S., and Heilman, F. R. (1947a) *Surg. Gynec. Obstet.*, 84, 16.

Zaslow, J., Counseller, V. S., and Heilman, F. R. (1947b) *Surg. Gynec. Obstet.*, 84, 140.

Zaslow, J. (1953) *J. Amer. med. Ass.*, 152, 1683.

Zaslow, J. and Rosenthal, A. (1954) *Ann. Surg.*, 139, 478.

Zaslow, J., Cohn, E. M. and Ball, W. (1955) *Antibiot. Ann.*, 1954-1955 p. 663.

CHAPTER TWENTY-ONE
Iodothyronines

Studies on the fate of thyroxine and related compounds are of considerable interest in view of their physiological importance and their use in therapeutics. They are used for the correction of thyroid deficiency states and until recently for the treatment of hypercholesterolaemia. That the liver and biliary excretion play an important role in regulating the physiological effects of the thyroid hormones was suggested from the early work of Kellaway *et al.*, (1945) and Grad and Leblond (1950) who found that thyroxine produces a greater metabolic stimulation in hepatectomised animals or in animals with ligated bile ducts than in normal animals. It is however, only in more recent years that the complex metabolic changes undergone by the iodothyronines prior to excretion, have been evaluated. The iodothyronines can undergo a number of metabolic reactions and as a consequence they usually appear in the bile mainly as transformation products. The main metabolic reactions are: conjugation of the phenolic hydroxyl group with glucuronic acid or sulphate, deiodination, deamination and further oxidation of the side chain. Minor reactions are decarboxylation and rupture of the ether linkage. In the main the iodothyronines are excreted in bile as their glucuronide conjugates and to a lesser extent as their sulphates together with conjugates of their deiodination products and of the thyroacetic acid derivatives formed by oxidative deamination.

The extent of biliary excretion and enterohepatic circulation of thyroxine and its analogues varies considerably according to the species of animal used and the particular compound studied. Biliary elimination of the hormone appears to be generally high in rodents but is less in man. In rats about one-third of an injected dose of $[^{131}I]$ thyroxine is concentrated in the liver

236

within 1 min of injection and 50–70% of the radioactivity is excreted in the bile over a period of 24 h (Taurog *et al.*, 1952). The material excreted in the bile is subjected to intense enterohepatic circulation in this species. The rapidity of this recycling phenomenon is emphasized by the disparity found by Albert and Keating (1952) between the rate at which iodine radioactivity from [^{135}I] thyroxine is secreted into the bowel — more than 100% of the dose per hour, and the rate at which it leaves the gut in the faeces — about 3% per hour. Numerous studies have shown that the material excreted in the bile following thyroxine administration consists mainly of metabolites of the hormone. Flock and Bollman (1962) have characterized most of the metabolites of L-thyroxine excreted in the bile of rats and dogs and have shown these to be the *O*-glucuronide of thyroxine as the major metabolite together with small amounts of the glucuronide conjugates of 3, 3′,5- and 3,3′,5′-triiodothyronine and tetraiodothyroacetic acid. Also appearing in small amounts are the sulphate conjugates of thyroxine, 3,3′5-triiodothyronine and 3,3′-diiodothyronine. Although thyroxine has long been known to form a glucuronide in the body, the conjugate has never been isolated in

Some biliary metabolites of thyroxine

Thyroxine (R = H); glucuronide conjugate (R = $C_6H_9O_6$); sulphate conjugate (R = SO_2OH)

3,3′,5-triiodothyronine (R = H); glucuronide conjugate (R = $C_6H_9O_6$)
sulphate conjugate (R = SO_2OH)

Tetraiodothyroacetic acid

amounts sufficient for full chemical characterization. It is believed to be an ether glucuronide formed by conjugation through the phenolic hydroxyl group and this view is based upon the fact that the conjugate does not react with diazotised sulphanilic acid and that ninhydrin treatment of $[^{14}C]$-thyroxine glucuronide labelled in the carboxyl group of the hormone releases the quantitative amount of $^{14}CO_2$.

The enterohepatic circulation of thyroxine appears to depend, at least to some extent, on the hydrolysis of the glucuronide conjugate in the gut, since the absorption of L-thyroxine infused intraduodenally in rats is considerably more efficient than occurs for the glucuronide conjugate (Briggs *et al.*, 1953). That hydrolysis of the glucuronide occurs in the gut is clear for although this conjugate is present in quantity in the bile it is absent from the faeces; the major compound in the faeces is free thyroxine (Taurog *et al.*, 1952). The glucuronide is rapidly hydrolysed when incubated *in vitro* with the contents of the lower small or large intestine of rats. In some species the enterohepatic circulation of the thyroid hormones appears to be an important factor regulating the level of circulating hormones. Furthermore, it might be regarded as an economy mechanism functioning to recover iodine from compounds which might otherwise be rapidly lost by elimination with the faeces. There appears to exist species variations as regards the extent of enterohepatic circulation of the thyroid hormones. In man the extent of biliary excretion of thyroxine is less than in the rat (Johnson and Beierwaltes, 1953) as is also the enterohepatic circulation (Myant, 1956). The rat, dog and sheep appear to be intermediate as regards the extent of the enterohepatic circulation of the thyroid hormones (Taurog, 1955; Flock *et al.*, 1957; Clayton *et al.*, 1950).

The biliary excretion of thyroxine is markedly enhanced in rats by pretreatment with the microsomal enzyme inducing agent benzopyrene. Thus, treatment of rats with a single injection of the inducing agent 48 h before cannulation produces a 3–4 fold increase in biliary excretion of thyroxine due to enhanced formation of thyroxine glucuronide (Goldstein and Taurog, 1968).

Triiodothyronine (mol. wt. 651)

Triiodothyronine is extensively excreted in the bile of rats and dogs mainly as its glucuronide conjugate together with smaller amounts of other metabolites

(Flock *et al.*, 1957; Roche *et al.*,1953). The latter have been shown to be the sulphate conjugate of 3,5,3'-triiodothyronine (Fauvert *et al.*, 1958) and products arising from oxidative deamination of the side chain, namely 3,5,3'-triiodothyro-pyruvic, -lactic and -acetic acids (Roche *et al.*, 1961).

3,5,3'5'-tetraiodothyroacetic acid (Tetrac; mol. wt. 748)

3,5,3',5'-tetraiodothyroacetic acid is a metabolite of both administered and endogenous thyroxine. It has a hypocholesterolaemic effect. When injected it is only slowly excreted. Thus, dogs excrete about 4% of an injected dose of [^{131}I] Tetrac in the urine and about 6% in the bile in 24 h (Flock *et al.*, 1962). Rats eliminate about 9% of the radioactivity from an injected dose in the urine in 72 h and 45% in the faeces, the latter arising from excretion in the bile (Wilkinson, 1959). In the dog, nearly three-quarters of the material excreted in the bile is in the form of glucuronide conjugates; the main one is the glucuronic acid conjugate of the parent compound together with smaller amounts of the glucuronides of 3,3',5'-triiodothyroacetic acid, 3,5,3'-triiodothyroacetic acid and 3,3'-diiodothyroacetic acid.

3,5,3'-triiodothyroacetic acid (Triac; mol. wt. 622)

3,5,3'-triiodothyroacetic acid is a minor metabolite of the thyroid hormones (Roche *et al.*, 1956) and is able to depress the levels of serum lipids. It is extensively excreted in bile of rats and is eventually eliminated with the faeces. Thus rats injected subcutaneously with [^{131}I] triiodothyroacetic acid excrete about 15% of the dose in the urine and about 60% in the faeces within 72 h (Wilkinson, 1959). More than 40% of an injected dose of [^{131}I]-Triac appears in the bile of dogs within 24 h and about 20% in the urine (Flock *et al.*, 1962). In three days nearly 80% of the injected dose can be recovered from the faeces. The drug is excreted in the bile mainly in the form of its glucuronic acid conjugate together with smaller amounts of the glucuronide and sulphate conjugates of 3,3'-diiodothyroacetic acid.

Tetraiodothyropropionic acid (Tetraprop; mol. wt. 762)

Tetraiodothyropropionic acid is extensively excreted in the bile of dogs principally as its glucuronide together with the glucuronides of 3,3',5- and 3,5,3'-triiodothyropropionic acid and 3,3'-diiodothyropropionic acid. 3,5,3'-Triiodothyropropionic acid shows a similar pattern of metabolism and excretion; about one-third of an injected dose is excreted in the bile within 24 h mainly as the glucuronide conjugate of the parent compound and of 3,3'-diidothyropropionic acid. Small amounts of the sulfate conjugates of these two compounds, together with two other unidentified sulphate conjugates, (Flock *et al.*, 1962) also occur in thy bile.

3,5,3',5'-tetraiodothyroformic acid (mol. wt. 734)

3,5,3',5'-tetraiodothyroformic acid is a synthetic compound structurally related to the thyroid hormones. Its metabolism was originally investigated because of its hypocholesterolaemic activity. When injected into rats most of a dose of the 3',5'-^{131}I-labelled material is eliminated in the faeces (Culp and Rice, 1960). This arises from biliary excretion since biliary cannulated rats excrete about 80% of an injected dose in the bile within 24 h in the form of a metabolite which appears to be the ester glucuronide of the parent compound.

Tetraiodothyroformic acid

Tetraiodothyroformic acid ester glucuronide

REFERENCES

Albert, A. and Keating, F. R. Jr. (1952) *Endocrinology*, **51**, 427.
Briggs, F. N., Taurog, A. and Chaikoff, I. L. (1953) *Endocrinology*, **52**, 559.
Clayton, J. C., Free, A. E., Page, J. E., Somers, G. F. and Woollett, E. A. (1950) *Biochem. J.*, **46**, 598.
Culp, H. W. and Rice, C. N. (1960) *Endocrinology*, **67**, 563.

Fauvert, R., Roche, J., Michel, R., Thiéblemont, P. and Gruson, M. (1958) *Rev. franc. Études clin. biol.*, **3**, 372.

Flock, E. V., Bollman, J. L. and Grindlay, J. H. (1957) *Amer. J. Physiol.*, **189**, 420.

Flock, E. V. Bollman, J. L. and Stobie, G. H. C. (1962) *Biochem. Pharmacol.*, **11**, 627.

Flock, E. V. and Bollman, J. L. (1962) *Biochem. J.*, **84**, 621.

Goldstein, J. A. and Taurog, A. (1968) *Biochem. Pharmacol.*, **17**, 1049.

Grad, B. and Leblond, C. P. (1950) *Amer. J. Physiol.*, **162**, 17.

Johnson, P. C. and Beierwaltes, W. H. (1953) *J. Lab. clin. Med.*, **41**, 676.

Kellaway, P. E., Hoff, H. E. and Leblond, C. P. (1945) *Endocrinology*, **36**, 272.

Myant, N. B. (1956) *Clin. Sci.*, **15**, 227.

Roche, J., Michel. R. and Tata, J. (1953) *Biochim. biophys. Acta (Amst.)* **11**, 543.

Roche, J. Michel, R., Jouan, P. and Wolf, W. (1956) *Endocrinology*, **59**, 425.

Roche, J., Michel, R., Varrone, S. and Munoz de la Peña, A. (1961) *C. R. Soc. Biol. (Paris)*, **155**, 231.

Taurog, A., Briggs, F. N. and Chaikoff, I. L. (1952) *J. biol. Chem.*, **194**, 655.

Taurog, A. (1955) *Brookhaven Symposia in Biology*, **7**, 111.

Wilkinson, J. H. (1959) *Biochem. J.*, **73**, 334.

CHAPTER TWENTY-TWO

Vitamins

Biliary elimination is an important aspect of the overall fate of a number of vitamins particularly those having relatively high molecular weights such as retinal and retinol, vitamin K, vitamin D and cyanocobalamin. Whether or not other vitamins such as ascorbic acid, thiamine and other B vitamins are eliminated in the bile does not appear to have been investigated.

The discovery of the biliary excretion and ultimately faecal elimination of some vitamins was important in explaining the early discrepancies found in balance studies on vitamins between intake and excretion when the urinary pathway was considered as the only site of loss.

Some vitamins, such as vitamin A are excreted in the bile as physiologically active metabolites which undergo enterohepatic circulation and it has been suggested that the latter may be important in influencing the metabolic activity of the vitamin.

Vitamin A

The biliary route is important in several species for the elimination of vitamin A and its metabolites. Furthermore, some of the biliary metabolites have biological activity and undergo an enterohepatic circulation.

R = CH.CHO   Retinal (284)
R = CH.CH$_2$OH   Retinol (286)
R = CH.COOH   Retinoic acid (300)

Molecular weights are shown in parentheses

Rats excrete in the bile in 4 h about 10–15% of an intravenous dose of [6,7-^{14}C]retinal and about 40% of a dose of [^{14}C]retinoic acid. Both

242

retinal and retinoic acid appear in the bile as water-soluble metabolites which undergo absorption into an enterohepatic circulation. The latter may have a functional significance in the control of retinol metabolism (Zachman and Olson, 1964). The guinea pig and the chick also excrete both retinol and retinoic acid in the bile (Zachman *et al.*, 1966). The major biliary metabolite is retinoyl β-glucuronide together with some free retinoic acid and other products. The glucuronide has a vitamin biopotency of about 30—100% as great as all-*trans* retinol or all-*trans* retinoic acid (Nath and Olson, 1967). Retinoic acid, although incapable of fulfilling the visual and reproductive functions of retinol and retinal, effectively stimulates the growth of vitamin A-deficient animals. The faecal material consists largely of free retinoic acid indicating that the glucuronide is hydrolysed in the gut. The secretion of vitamin A derivatives in rat bile appears to be a normal physiological process.

Folic acid (mol. wt. 441)

Folic acid occurs in human bile at concentrations higher than those of the plasma. Baker *et al.* (1965) using a microbiological assay, found that folate levels in the bile (aspirated as duodenal juice) of eight fasting subjects to be about 2—14 times those of the serum. When [^{3}H] folic acid was injected intravenously into a patient with bile duct drainage following cholecystectomy the bile levels rose rapidly and were about 3—14 times those of the serum depending upon the time after injection.

Loss of folate in the bile may be one mechanism helping to produce folate depletion in those with defective absorption and in people with diarrhoea.

Dichloromethotrexate, an analogue of folic acid used in the treatment of cancer, is extensively excreted in human bile. One patient with a bile duct fistula excreted over 60% of an intravenous dose of [^{36}Cl] dichloromethotextrate in the bile in 8 h (Adamson, 1971).

Cyanocobalamin (mol. wt. 1357)

Cyanocobalamin is slowly excreted by several species, much of the dose appearing in the bile and ultimately the faeces. Rats injected with small doses of [^{60}Co] vitamin B_{12} eliminate the radioactivity very slowly; 30 days after dosing about 15% appears in the urine and about 37% in the faeces, the remainder being in the carcass. When the bile duct is ligated faecal elimination of radioactivity is markedly reduced showing that the bile is a major, but not the only, source of the radioactive cobalt in the faeces (Okuda *et al.*, 1958). The bile contains mainly unchanged cyanocobalamin and two metabolites which together account for about one quarter of the bile radioactivity (Stokes, 1961). The unchanged vitamin B_{12} but not its two metabolites is probably absorbed into an enterohepatic circulation.

Dogs excrete injected [^{60}Co] vitamin B_{12} very slowly; thus at 235 days after injection one dog had excreted a total of only 53% of the radioactivity, 36% of which was in the faeces and 17% in the urine. The vitamin slowly appears in the bile; about 3–7% of an intravenous dose is eliminated via this route over a period of several days (Willigan *et al.*, 1958).

In man large amounts of vitamin B_{12} appear in the bile. Thus, in one study following the intramuscular injection of [^{56}Co] vitamin B_{12} into human subjects with T-tube bile drainage, large amounts of radioactivity were excreted in the bile, faeces and urine shortly after injection. Later, the excretion pattern changed, more being excreted in the bile and faeces and less in the urine. It appears that at least two-thirds of the material excreted in the bile is re-absorbed into an enterohepatic circulation (Grasbeck *et al.*, 1958).

Vitamin D

Cholecalciferol
(vitamin D_3; mol. wt. 385)

Ergocalciferol
(vitamin D_2; mol. wt. 397)

A major route of excretion of metabolites of vitamin D in the rat is via the bile this explaining the finding of Kodicek (1960) that only 2% of an oral radioactive dose of the vitamin is found in the urine compared with about 80% in the faeces and intestinal contents. A young rat with a cannulated bile duct and given 0.34 mg of [1α-^{3}H] cholecalciferol by intravenous infusion eliminated 31% of the radioactivity in the bile within 24 h. The bile contained 5 polar metabolites, the major one being a glucuronic acid conjugate. A second rat excreted 13% of a dose of $[^{14}C]$ ergocalciferol in the bile in 24 h. This animal however developed obstructive jaundice so that possibly the value is low (Bell and Kodicek, 1969).

In humans, biliary excretion appears to be less important as Avioli et al. (1967) found that human subjects with bile fistulas excreted 3—6% of an intravenous dose of $[G-^{3}H]$ cholecalciferol in the bile within 48 h. In the same time only 2.4% of the dose was recovered in the urine. The bile contained little if any free vitamin D and most of the radioactivity was present as polar conjugates. In the patients with bile fistulas faecal excretion of radioactivity fell to negligible levels showing that the bile is the major source of faecal derivatives of vitamin D.

α-tocopherol (mol. wt. 431)

α-tocopherol when injected intravenously into rats is excreted in the bile for several days but not in the pancreatic juice (Schmandke and Proll, 1964). It also occurs in human bile in small amounts at levels similar to those of the plasma (Popper et al., 1949).

Whether or not conjugates or other metabolites of α-tocopherol occur in human and rat bile has not been investigated.

Vitamin K

Dogs excrete between 5—10% of an oral dose of $[^{14}C]$ menadione (vitamin K_3) in the bile in 12 h. No unchanged vitamin appears and all the excreted

Menadione (vitamin K_3; mol. wt. 172)

radioactivity is in the form of an unidentified polar form which does not appear to be a glucuronide conjugate (Losito et al., 1965).

The higher molecular weight vitamin K_1 (3-phytylmenadione; mol. wt. 451) appears to be extensively eliminated in rat bile and little is excreted in the urine (Taylor *et al.*, 1956). Only small amounts (1.5% of dose) of unchanged vitamin K_1 are found in the bile but ten times as much is found in the small intestine after intravenous injection, suggesting that the vitamin is excreted in the bile as conjugates which are hydrolysed in the gut.

Riboflavine (mol. wt. 376)

Riboflavine has been reported to be excreted in dog bile (Kagaya, 1956; Tedeschi, 1954).

Biotin (mol. wt. 244)

Biotin occurs normally in the bile of rabbits (Nogueira, 1962) at levels about 4 times those of the plasma. High levels are also found in the faeces.

REFERENCES

Adamson, R. H. (1971) *Ann. N. Y. Acad. Sci.*, **179**, 432.

Avioli, L. V., Lee, S. W., McDonald, J. E., Lund, J. and DeLuca, H. F. (1967) *J. clin. Invest.*, **46**, 983.

Baker, S. J., Kumar, S. and Swaminathan, S. P. (1965) *Lancet*, **1**, 685.

Bell, P. A. and Kodicek, E. (1969) *Biochem. J.*, **115**, 663.

Grasbeck, R., Nyberg, W. and Reizenstein, P. (1958) *Proc. Soc. exp. Biol. (N. Y.)*, **97**, 780.

Kagaya, A. (1956) *Vitamins (Kyoto)*, **11**, 303.

Kodicek, E. (1960) Proc. 4th int. Congr. Biochem., Vienna, vol 11, p. 198.

Losito, R., Millar, G. J. and Jacques, L. B. (1965) *Biochim. biophys. Acta., (Amst.)*, **107**, 123.

Nath, K. and Olson, J. A. (1967) *J. Nutr.*, **93**, 461.

Nogueira, D. M. (1962) *An. Farm. Quim. S. Paulo*, **13**, 5.

Okuda, K., Grasbeck, R. and Chow, B. F. (1958) *J. Lab. clin. Med.*, **51**, 17.

Popper, H., Dubin, A., Steigmann, F. and Hesser, F. P. (1949) *J. Lab. clin. Med.*, **34**, 648.

Schmandke, H. and Proll, J. (1964) *Int. Z. Vitamin-forsch.*, **34**, 312.

Stokes, J. B. (1961) *Nature (Lond.)*, **191**, 807.

Taylor, J. D., Millar, G. J. Jacques, L. B. and Spinks, J. W. T. (1965) *Canad. J. Biochem.*, **34**, 1143.

Tedeschi, G. G. (1954) *Boll. Soc. ital. Biol. sper.*, **30**, 663.

Willigan, D. A., Cronkite, E. P., Meyer, L. M. and Noto, S. L. (1958) *Proc. Soc. exp. Biol. (N.Y.)*, **99**, 81.

Zachman, R. D. and Olson, J. A. (1964) *Nature (Lond.)*, **201**, 1222.

Zachman, R. D., Singer, M. B. and Olson, J. A. (1966) *J. Nutr.*, **88**, 137.

CHAPTER TWENTY-THREE

Heterocyclic Compounds

INDOLE AND ITS DERIVATIVES

Indole and its metabolites are poorly excreted in the bile but a number of its derivatives including the ergot alkaloids, lysergic acid diethylamide and indomethacin and its analogues are extensively eliminated by this route.

Indole (mol. wt. 117)

Only about 5% of an injected dose of $[^{14}C]$indole is excreted in the bile and about 80% of the radioactivity is eliminated in the urine (King *et al.*, 1966).

| Indole | 5-hydroxyoxindole | Indoxyl sulphate |

The biliary material consists of indoxyl sulphate (0.8% of dose), which is also the main urinary metabolite of indole and some conjugated 5-hydroxy-oxindole (0.6% of dose); the nature of the remaining ^{14}C has not been determined.

Ergometrine (mol. wt. 325)

Ergometrine is an important alkaloid obtained from the fungus *Claviceps purpurea* which grows on rye. Its metabolic fate has not been fully investigated. Some data, however, indicate that biliary excretion is an important aspect of its overall fate. In rats, injected ergometrine (1 mg/kg) is excreted in the bile in the form of two polar metabolites which appear to be the glucuronides of 12-hydroxyergometrine and 12-hydroxyergometrinine.

At a higher dose level (45 mg/kg) the same two glucuronides appear in the bile together with ergometrine and ergometrinine and their respective glucuronides as well as four other minor unidentified metabolites (Slaytor and Wright, 1962).

Lysergic acid diethylamide (LSD; mol. wt. 323)

Lysergic acid diethylamide is a very potent chemical hallucinogen. As for the chemically related ergot alkaloids its metabolic fate has not been established but several workers have shown that the bile is the main channel for its elimination. Thus, Stoll et al. (1955) found that $[^{14}C]$ LSD injected intravenously into mice accumulates in the small intestine. They concluded that LSD is mainly metabolized and excreted via the liver and bile into the small intestine as water-soluble metabolites which have not been identified. Using a radioautographic method Idänpään-Heikkila and Schoolar (1969) have also observed that in pregnant mice injected $[^{14}C]$ LSD is excreted largely in the bile. Biliary cannulated rats eliminate most (60–80% of an injected dose) of $[^{14}C$-ethyl LSD] in the bile in 4 h. Intact rats excrete about 4% of the ^{14}C as CO_2 in the expired air, 8% in the urine and eventually about 80% in the faeces; the latter arising from biliary excretion (Boyd, 1959). The bile contains four metabolites and two of these appear to be glucuronic acid conjugates of phenols derived from LSD. Slaytor and Wright (1962) also found that LSD appears in rat bile in the form of two glucuronides of hydroxylated derivatives. Both metabolites had anti-5-HT activity but were less active in this respect than LSD.

Indomethacin ,(1-(*p*-chlorobenzoyl)-5-methoxy-2-methylindole-3-acetic acid; mol. wt. 358)

Indomethacin is a drug with anti-inflammatory, antipyretic and mild analgesic activity and is widely used for the treatment of rheumatoid arthritis. There occur marked species variations in the pattern of metabolism (Harman *et al.*, 1964) and excretion of the drug (Hucker *et al.*, 1966). The dog, guinea pig and rhesus monkey excrete about 50–60% of an intravenous dose of [^{14}C] indomethacin in the bile in 6 h. Unchanged indomethacin accounts for only 2–4% of the bile ^{14}C and the greater part of the radioactivity is associated with polar conjugated material. In the dog and possibly the monkey the main biliary metabolite appears to be the ester glucuronide of indomethacin. The drug appears to undergo an enterohepatic circulation following its excretion in the bile. In the monkey and guinea pig however, much of the material excreted in the bile is reabsorbed and eventually eliminated in the urine whereas in the dog most of the biliary material eventually appears in the faeces. In man some biliary excretion of indomethacin occurs but it may be at a lower level than in other species. In an investigation with a single subject with a biliary fistula about 15% of a dose of indomethacin appeared in the bile in 24 h.

Two analogues of indomethacin, namely 1-(*p*-chlorobenzoyl)-5-dimethylamin-2-methylindole-3-acetic acid (Hucker *et al.*, 1971) and 1-*p*-chlorobenzylidenyl-5-methoxy-2-methylindene-3-acetic acid (Hucker and Hoffman, 1971) are similarly extensively eliminated in the bile and ultimately in the faeces in both the dog and rat. In the dog, for both compounds, the main biliary material appears to be the ester glucuronide of the parent compound.

Vinblastine (vincaleukoblastine; mol. wt. 814)

Vinblastine is a alkaloid with antitumour properties which occurs in the plant *Vinca rosea* and is used in the treatment of cancer. Rats excrete 20–25% of an injected dose of [^{3}H] vinblastine in the bile and only traces in the urine. Most of the biliary material consists of metabolites of vinblastine as only 2% of dose appears in the bile as the unchanged alkaloid (Beer *et al.*, 1964).

THE NITROFURANS

The 5-nitrofurans are of special interest since a number have antibacterial properties. Several are excreted in the bile and the latter has appreciable antibacterial activity when collected from animals treated with 5-nitrofuran derivatives (Paul *et al.*, 1960). About 5% of an injected dose of **oxafuradene** can be recovered in the bile of dogs in 5 h (Conklin and Buzard, 1965). Following infusion of the drug, hepatic bile levels can be almost 100 times those of the plasma. The bile shows significant antibacterial activity against *E. coli.* **Nitrofurantoin** is also excreted in dog bile (Conklin and Wagner, 1971). Thus, about 17–23% of an intravenous dose, has been recovered in the bile in 6 h compared to 24–36% in the urine. The bile concentrations of the drug were high and about 200 times those of the plasma. The drug also has a marked hydrocholeretic effect in dogs and a dose of 12 mg/kg. intravenously can enhance the rate of bile flow about sevenfold. The biliary excretion of nitrofurantoin is reduced by hepatic dysfunction induced by carbon

Oxafuradene (mol. wt. 224)   Nitrofurantoin (mol. wt. 238)

tetrachloride. Thus, its administration to dogs reduced the biliary excretion of nitrofurantoin from 22% found in normal animals to 1%.

BARBITURATES

Although much is known concerning the metabolism of barbiturates (Mark, 1963; Williams and Parke, 1964; Bush and Sanders, 1967; Parke, 1971) there is relatively little information on their biliary excretion even though this may be an important aspect of their overall fate.

Phenobarbitone (mol. wt. 232)

Rats excrete about 18% of an injected dose of [^{14}C] phenobarbitone in the bile in 6 h (Klassen, 1971). The biliary material consists of a polar metabolite of phenobarbitone and it does not appear to be a glucuronic acid conjugate. The bile concentration of ^{14}C is about 10 times that of the plasma indicating that concentrative transfer occurs. Its biliary excretion is reduced by the concomitant administration of probenecid; this is probably due to competition for elimination in the bile. Biliary cannulated rats excrete about 28% of an injected dose of [^{14}C] pentobarbitone (mol. wt. 226) in the bile in 6 h. As with phenobarbitone the biliary material consists of a polar derivative of pentobarbitone. Concentrative transfer from plasma to bile occurs and the biliary excretion of the barbiturate is also reduced by probenecid administration.

Phenobarbitone   Pentobarbital   Methohexital

Methohexital (mol. wt. 262)

Methohexital is a barbiturate of ultra-short action used in both clinical and veterinary practice. When injected intravenously into rats about 20% of the dose appears in the urine and about 80% in the faeces (Welles et al., 1963). The latter arises from biliary excretion since cannulated rats eliminate 70% of an injected dose in the bile within 3 h. In the dog, biliary excretion is less: 22% of the dose appears in the bile at 2 h and 53% at 8 h after dosing.

Using a gas-chromatographic procedure Sunshine *et al.* (1966) found small amounts of unchanged methohexital in the bile of patients injected with the drug together with some unidentified metabolites.

It seems likely that other barbiturates undergo excretion in the bile. Thus, Block and Ebigt (1957) found varying amounts of radioactivity occurring in the faeces of mice following the intravenous injection of [^{14}C]-labelled barbiturates. In the case of thiopentone and 5-ethyl-5-(1-methylpropyl)thio-barbituric acid the faeces contained 20% and 45% respectively of the ^{14}C, this probably arising from extensive biliary excretion.

MORPHINE AND RELATED COMPOUNDS

Morphine (mol. wt. 285)

The investigation of the fate of morphine in the animal body has attracted the attention of numerous workers for it was thought that the results of such studies might provide an insight into the processes of morphine tolerance and addiction. In recent years it has been found that biliary excretion is an important aspect of the fate of morphine. Biliary elimination appears to be chiefly responsible for the appearance of morphine in the faeces and it is probable that the residual amounts of morphine excreted in the urine for several days arise from the enterohepatic circulation of the opiate.

The extent of biliary excretion of morphine varies markedly with species, being highest in the rat and dog and lowest in man and the rhesus monkey. Rats excrete about 60% of an injected dose of [N-^{14}C-methyl]morphine in the bile within 6 h after injection (March and Elliot, 1954; Bertagni *et al.*, 1972) mostly as bound morphine (probably morphine 3-glucuronide). Much of the biliary material is however, reabsorbed and eventually eliminated in the urine as only about 20–25% of the dose is recovered in the faeces. Most of the faecal material consists of bound morphine with only small amounts of free alkaloid.

Dogs eliminate a quarter to one third of an injected dose in the bile mainly as conjugated morphine (Woods, 1954). Tolerant animals may eliminate nearly

50% of an injected dose in the bile, also almost entirely in the conjugated form. Faecal excretion of both free and conjugated morphine is much less, being about 7% for non-tolerant and 16% in tolerant animals. Most of the faecal material consists of free morphine suggesting that the bound material eliminated with the bile is hydrolyzed in the intestine (Cochin *et al.*, 1954).

Significant biliary excretion of morphine occurs in the rhesus monkey although the main channel for its elimination is the urine (Mellett and Woods, 1956). Thus, in a non-tolerant monkey, nearly 20% of an injected dose of morphine was found in the gall-bladder at 90 min. In a second non-tolerant monkey the total biliary morphine at 4 h was equivalent to 11.5% of the dose. Over 99% of the opiate present in the bile was in the conjugated form. Biliary excretion may be prolonged since a bound morphine concentration of 300 μg/ml was found in the bile of a single animal sacrificed at 24 h. Tolerant monkeys may excrete less in the bile, for example, one tolerant animal eliminated 5.7% of the dose in the bile at 90 min and a second animal 5.6% in 4 h. Some enterohepatic circulation apparently occurs since only small quantities of morphine appear in the faeces chiefly in the free form.

In humans the biliary pathway seems less important for the disposal of morphine. Thus, in a single study Elliott *et al.* (1954) it was estimated that about 7% of an injected dose of labelled morphine was excreted in the bile. In this study a duodenal tube was passed and $[^{14}C]$ morphine sulphate injected intramuscularly. The radioactivity in the duodenal secretions was highest between 1½ and 6 h after administration of the dose. Assuming that the radioactivity in the duodenal samples originated in the bile and that the 24 h bile output was 500 ml it was estimated that 7.4% of the injected dose was eliminated by this route (Elliott *et al.*, 1954).

Biliary excretion also occurs in the cat; as much as 9% of an injected dose of morphine occurs in gall-bladder bile within 4 h mainly in a conjugated form (Chernov and Woods, 1965).

Dextromethorphan (*d*-3-methoxy-*N*-methylmorphinan; mol. wt. 271)

Dextromethorphan is a synthetic antitussive drug free of analgesic and addicting properties.

	R^1	R^2
Dextromethorphan	OCH$_3$	CH$_3$
(*d*)-3-hydroxy-*N*-methylmorphinan	OH	CH$_3$
(*d*)-3-methoxy-morphinan	OCH$_3$	H
(*d*)-3-hydroxymorphinan	OH	H

[^{3}H] Dextromethorphan when given orally or by injection to rats is eliminated mainly in the faeces. Thus about 36% of an oral or injected dose appears in the faeces in 4 days after dosing and about 18% in the urine. The faecal material arises mainly from biliary excretion since rats with bile fistulae eliminate 77% of an oral dose of [^{3}H] dextromethorphan in the bile in 24 h. The bile contains 3-hydroxy-*N*-methylmorphinan and 3-hydroxymorphinan and their respective glucuronide and sulphate conjugates (Kamm *et al.*, 1967).

Pentazocine (mol. wt. 285)

Pentazocine, R = —CH$_2$·CH=C$\genfrac{}{}{0pt}{}{\text{CH}_3}{\text{CH}_3}$; *cis* — 3—chloroallylnorpentazocine, R = —CH$_2$·CH=CHCl

Pentazocine is a synthetic non-addictive analgesic. Cats eliminate both pentazocine and its analogue, *cis*-3-chloroallylnorpentazocine in the bile. For the latter compound about 50% of an intramuscular dose is eliminated in the bile within 8 h and about 9% in the case of pentazocine. Large amounts of radioactivity are associated with the liver and gastrointestinal tract when the

[³H]-labelled drugs are given by intramuscular injection and this is a reflection of the importance of the biliary route for the elimination of these drugs (Ferrari, 1968).

PHENOTHIAZINES

A number of important compounds are derivatives of the tricyclic compound phenothiazine and they include the well-known dye methylene blue, the anthelmintic phenothiazine, and the phenothiazine based tranquillizing drugs such as chlorpromazine. Biliary excretion and enterohepatic circulation is an important aspect of their overall fate and this appears to be particularly significant for phenothiazines such as thioridazine and thiethylperazine which contain an additional ring system in their molecular structures. In most cases small amounts of the parent compound together with the sulphoxidation product, the sulphoxide, appear in the bile, but most of the drug is eliminated in the form of polar conjugates, presumably of metabolites arising from hydroxylation.

Promethazine (mol. wt. 284)

Promethazine is a phenothiazine derivative having antihistamine and sedative properties. Intact rats excrete about 50% of an injected dose in the urine in 72 h and some 20% in the faeces. The latter arises from biliary excretion as biliary cannulated rats eliminate about 18% of a dose of [³⁵S]promethazine in the bile in 4 h. Both the bile and urine contain unchanged promethazine and its sulphoxide and two unidentified polar metabolites which may be conjugates (Hansson and Schmiterlöw, 1961).

Chlorpromazine (mol. wt. 319)

Chlorpromazine is an important psychotherapeutic drug having sedative and anti-emetic actions. The drug and its metabolites have been reported to undergo excretion in the bile of a number of species including the rabbit (Franchi and Gianni, 1957), the dog (Van Loon et al., 1964) and man (Hall and Ryman, 1958). Thus, the bile of dogs given chlorpromazine by intraduodenal installation contains substantial amounts of chlorpromazine and its sulphoxide together with conjugated metabolites. Extensive biliary excretion probably also occurs in the rat since intact rats injected with [^{35}S] chlorpromazine excrete about 40–50% of the radioactivity in the urine in 48 h and about 40% in the faeces (Emmerson and Miya, 1962).

Chlorprothixene (mol. wt. 316)

$$\text{CH} \cdot \text{CH}_2\text{CH}_2\text{N(CH}_3)_2$$

Chlorprothixene is a drug with tranquillizing and antipsychotic properties. It is an analogue of chlorpromazine in which the phenothiazine ring has been replaced by the thiaxanthene ring system to which the dimethylaminopropyl side chain is attached by a double bond. Biliary excretion of the drug occurs in the rat and probably in man as well. In bile-fistula rats, after the intravenous injection of chlorprothixene, up to 24% of the dose has been recovered in the bile as the sulphoxide in 7 h. (Allgén et al., 1960).

Thioridazine (mol. wt. 371)

Thioridazine is used clinically as a tranquillizing agent. It is extensively excreted in the bile of both the rat and man. Thus, rats injected intravenously with [^{35}S] thioridazine excrete about 75% of the radioactivity in the bile in 24 h with only a few per cent in the urine. The material excreted in the bile does not appear to be reabsorbed since intact animals eliminate about 80% of an injected dose in the faeces and only 9% in the urine (Zehnder et al., 1962a). Most of the biliary material consists of glucuronide conjugates of hydroxylated derivatives of thioridazine and northioridazine and their sulphoxidation products. The drug is also extensively excreted in human bile. Thus, one patient who had received a single oral dose of 200 mg of $[^{35}S]$-thioridazine excreted about 60% of the radioactivity in the bile within 3 days. The highest bile level occurred at about 4 h after dosing. The drug appeared in the bile as metabolites and unchanged thioridazine was not detected (Eiduson and Geller, 1963).

The pyrrolidine analogue of thioridazine shows a pattern of biliary excretion in the rat similar to that of the parent drug. When injected intravenously into rats about 70% of the dose is eliminated in the bile. In intact animals, within 20 h of injection, nearly 60% of the dose is found in the faeces — arising from elimination with the bile, and only about 9% is excreted in the urine (Zehnder et al., 1962a).

Thiethylperazine (mol. wt. 400)

Thiethylperazine is used as an anti-emetic and anti-vertigo drug.

It is eliminated by rats mainly by the biliary-faecal pathway since biliary cannulated rats eliminate about 70% of an injected dose of $[^{35}S]$ thiethyl-perazine in the bile. This appears to be poorly reabsorbed since within 24—28 h of dosing nearly 90% of the radioactivity can be recovered from the faeces with only 8% in the urine. Most of the drug excreted in the bile is in the form of glucuronide conjugates (Zehnder et al., 1962b).

Imipramine (mol. wt. 280)

Imipramine is a synthetic tricyclic drug widely used in the treatment of depressive disorders.

CH₂CH₂CH₂N(CH₃)₂

A metabolite of the drug, *N*-desmethylimipramine or desimipramine, formed by *N*-dealkylation, is thought to be mainly responsible for the therapeutic activity of the drug. In the rat extensive biliary excretion and enterohepatic circulation of the drug and its metabolites occurs (Bickel and Weder, 1968). Intact rats eliminate about two-thirds of an injected dose in the urine and the remainder in the faeces whereas biliary cannulated animals excrete about 70% of the dose in the bile. Most of the biliary material consists of the glucuronide conjugates of 2-hydroxyimipramine and 2-hydroxydesmethylimipramine together with much smaller amounts of the unchanged drug, desmethyl-imipramine, and their 2-hydroxy derivatives, and a small amount of iminodibenzyl. The conjugates are split in the gut and the aglycones released together with the unconjugated metabolites present in the bile are absorbed into an enterohepatic circulation. In addition the gut flora converts imipramine to desmethylimipramine by dealkylation. According to Bickel and Weder (1968) up to 90% and 60% of the two therapeutically active compounds, imipramine and desmethylimipramine, may be sequestered for hours in the intestine as a consequence of enterohepatic circulation.

Both the glucuronides of 2-hydroxyimipramine and 2-hydroxydesmethyl-imipramine are transferred from plasma to bile against a concentration gradient of 1000 or more.

2-hydroxyimipramine glucuronide (R = CH₃)
2-hydroxydesmethylimipramine glucuronide (R = H)

The bile/plasma ratio for imipramine is about 50—90 showing that the drug is also concentratively transferred (Bickel and Minder, 1970a). Further studies have shown that both imipramine and desmethylimipramine, but not their hydrophilic metabolites, can be incorporated in the bile salt-phospholipid micelles which occur in bile and that this may have a bearing on their elimination with the bile (Bickel and Minder, 1970b).

A related antidepressive drug, **amitryptiline** has been reported to be excreted in the bile of mice as a glucuronide conjugate (Cassano *et al.*, 1965).

MISCELLANEOUS COMPOUNDS

Diphenylhydantoin (mol. wt. 252)

Diphenylhydantoin has anticonvulsant properties and is used in the treatment of epilepsy. Extensive biliary excretion and enterohepatic circulation of the drug and its metabolites occur in the rat. Thus, 24 h after injection of [^{14}C] diphenylhydantoin about half the radioactivity appears in the urine and half in the gastrointestinal tract, the latter arising through biliary excretion. However, the latter is largely reabsorbed and excreted by the kidneys since at 48 h after injection 94% of the ^{14}C is found in the urine. The bile contains little unchanged drug and most of the excreted material is in the form of polar acidic metabolites (Noach *et al.*, 1958).

Nicotine (mol. wt. 162)

Nicotine   Cotinine (mol. wt. 176)

The biliary route is of little importance for the clearance of the alkaloid for cannulated rats excrete only 3% of an injected dose of [^{14}C]nicotine in the bile in 6 h (Hansson and Schmiterlöw, 1962). The biliary material consists of unchanged nicotine together with some cotinine. Mice, dogs and rats eliminate up to 90% of a dose of nicotine in the urine showing that this is the main channel for the elimination of the alkaloid.

Mepivacaine (mol. wt. 246)

Mepivacaine is used as a local anaesthetic. The drug undergoes rapid and extensive biliary excretion in rats since about 30% of an injected dose appears in the bile in 30 min and 50% in 6 h. The bile contains only traces of mepivacaine and most of the drug is excreted as glucuronide conjugates probably of metabolites formed by hydroxylation of the aromatic or piperidine ring. Most of the material excreted in the bile is probably absorbed from the intestine since intact rats injected with the drug excrete about 55% of the dose in the urine in 24 h and only about 3% in the faeces (Hansson *et al.*, 1965).

Phenmetrazine (2-phenyl-3-methyl-morpholine, mol. wt. 177)

Phenmetrazine is a synthetic anorexigenic drug. Its use is now discouraged because of the misuse of the drug associated with its psycho-stimulating effects. Extensive biliary excretion and enterohepatic circulation of the injected drug occurs in rats. Thus, Engelhardt *et al.*, (1958) recovered 40% of an injected dose of [^{14}C] phenmetrazine in the bile of rats. Intact rats however eliminated 95–99% of an injected dose in the urine showing that extensive reabsorption of the material excreted in the bile must occur. The bile and urine contained three unidentified metabolites of phenmetrazine (Engelhardt *et al.*, 1957).

Triazine derivatives (mol. wt. 279)

2-[(*o*-phenoxyphenyl)amino]-
4-amino-1,3,5-triazine

Metabolite

A number of triazine derivatives are active against experimentally induced viral infections in mice. For, one of these compounds, namely, 2-[(*o*-phenoxyphenyl)amino]-4-amino-1,3,5-triazine, biliary excretion has been shown to be important for its elimination. When injected into rats only 6% of the dose is found in the urine in 48 h but 60–80% can be recovered from the faeces. The faecal excretion arises from biliary elimination since biliary cannulated rats eliminate 42% of an injected (subcutaneous) dose in the bile in 8 h. The biliary material consists of some unchanged drug together with a major metabolite identified as 2-[(o-phenoxyphenyl)-amino]-4-amino-6-hydroxy-1,3,5-triazine formed by hydroxylation of the triazine ring (Cresseri et al., 1966).

Terephthalanilides

Terephthalanilides have anti-tumour properties and have been used experimentally for the treatment of leukemia. The biliary excretion of one of these compounds labelled with ^{14}C, namely, 4′,4″-bis(2-imidazolin-2-yl)-2-chloro-terephthalanilide has been investigated in rats. When injected intravenously into biliary cannulated rats the drug is only slowly excreted and in 24 h only 11% appears in the bile and 15% in the urine. Intact rats eliminate 23% of an injected dose in the urine in 3 days and 24% in the faeces — the latter arising from biliary excretion (Kreis et al., 1963).

Indocyanine green (mol. wt. 775)

Indocyanine green is a water-soluble tricarbocyanine dye used to measure cardiac output. When injected intravenously it is rapidly extracted from the circulation by the liver and excreted in the bile. Its rate of disappearance from the blood is therefore sometimes used as a measure of liver function. It is almost quantitatively excreted in the bile of the rat (Levine et al., 1970), the dog (Wheeler et al., 1958) and the rabbit (Smith, 1971).

Following excretion in the bile it is probably eliminated with the faeces as Wheeler et al., (1958) found that in dogs only 2% of a dose given by intraduodenal infusion was recovered in the bile. Excretion in human bile is also extensive; two subjects with T-tube drainage and in which the bile collection was incomplete, excreted about 50% of an intravenous dose in the bile and none appeared in the urine (Hirom et al., 1972).

REFERENCES

Allgén, L.-G., Jönsson, B., Nauckhoff, B., Andersen, M.-L., Huus, I. and Møller Nielsen, I. (1960) *Experientia (Basel)*, **16**, 325.

Beer, C. T., Wilson, M. L. and Bell, J. (1964) *Canad. J. Physiol.*, **42**, 368.

Bertagni, P., Hirom, P. C., Millburn, P. and Smith, R. L. (1972) unpublished observations.

Bickel, M. H. and Weder, H. J. (1968) *Arch. int. Pharmacodyn.*, **173**, 433.

Bickel, M. H. and Minder, R. (1970a) *Biochem. Pharmacol.*, **19**, 2425.

Bickel, M. H. and Minder, R. (1970b) *Biochem. Pharmacol.*, **19**, 2437.

Block, W. and Ebigt, I. (1957) *Arzneimittel-Forsch.*, **7**, 572.

Boyd, E. S. (1959) *Arch. int. Pharmacodyn.*, **120**, 292.

Bush, M. T. and Sanders, E. (1967) *Ann. Rev. Pharmacol.*, **7**, 57.

Cassano, G. B., Sjöstrand, S. E. and Hansson, E. (1965) *Psychopharmacologia (Berl.)*, **8**, 1.

Chernov, H. I. and Woods, L. A. (1965) *J. Pharmacol. exp. Ther.*, **149**, 146.

Cochin, J., Haggart, J., Woods, L. A. and Seevers, M. H. (1954) *J. Pharmacol exp. Ther.*, **111**, 74.

Conklin, J. D. and Buzard, J. A. (1965) *J. pharm. Sci.*, **54**, 1766.

Conklin, J. D. and Wagner, D. L. (1971) *Brit. J. Pharmacol.*, **43**, 140.

Cresseri, A., Giraldi, P. N., Logemann, W., Tosolini, G. and Valzelli, G. (1966) *Brit. J. Pharmacol.*, **27**, 486.

Eiduson, S. and Geller, E. (1963) *Biochem. Pharmacol.*, **12**, 1429.

Elliott, H. W., Tolbert, B. M., Adler, T. K. and Anderson, H. H. (1954) *Proc. Soc. exp. Biol. (N.Y.)*, **85**, 77.

Emmerson, J. L. and Miya, T. S. (1962) *J. Pharmacol. exp. Ther.*, **137**, 148.

Engelhardt, A., Jerchel, D., Weidmann, H. and Wick, H. (1957) *Naunyn-Schmiedeberg's Arch. exp. Path. Pharmak.*, **232**, 326.

Engelhardt, A., Jerchel, D., Weidmann, H. and Wick, H. (1958) *Naunyn-Schmiedeberg's Arch. exp. Path. Pharmak.*, **235**, 10.

Ferrari, R. A. (1968) *Toxicol. appl. Pharmacol.*, **12**, 404.

Franchi, G. and Gianni, A. M. (1957) *Arch. ital. Sci. farmacol.*, **7**, 135.

Hall, G. H. and Ryman, B. E. (1968) *Arch. int. Pharmacodyn.*, **117**, 81.

Hansson, E. and Schmiterlöw, C. G. (1961) *Arch. int. Pharmacodyn.*, **131**, 309.

Hansson, E. and Schmiterlöw, C. G. (1962) *J. Pharmacol. exp. Ther.*, **137**, 91.

Hansson, E., Hoffman, P. and Kristerson, L. (1965) *Acta pharmacol. (Kbh.)*, **22**, 213.

Harman, R. E., Meisinger, M. A. P., Davis, G. E. and Kuehl, F. A. Jr. (1964) *J. Pharmacol. exp. Ther.*, **143**, 215.

Hirom, P. C., Millburn, P., Sever, P. and Smith, R. L. (1972) unpublished observations.

Hucker, H. B., Zacchei, A. G., Cox, S. V., Brodie, D. A. and Cantwell, N. H. R. (1966) *J. Pharmacol. exp. Ther.*, **153**, 237.

Hucker, H. B. and Hoffman, E. A. (1971) *J. pharm. Sci.*, **60**, 1049.

Hucker, H. B., Hochberg, A. and Hoffman, E. A. (1971) *J. pharm. Sci.*, **60**, 1053.

Idänpään-Heikkila, J. E. and Schoolar, J. C. (1969) *Science,* **164,** 1295.

Kamm, J. J., Taddeo, A. B. and Van Loon, E. J. (1967) *J. Pharmacol. exp. Ther.,* **158,** 437.

King, L. J., Parke, D. V. and Williams, R. T. (1966) *Biochem. J.,* **98,** 266.

Klaassen, C. D. (1971) *Brit. J. Pharmacol.,* **43,** 161.

Kreis, W., Bloch, R., Warkentin, D. L. and Burchenal, J. H. (1963) *Biochem. Pharmacol.,* **12,** 1165.

Levine, W. G., Millburn, P., Smith, R. L. and Williams, R. T. (1970) *Biochem. Pharmacol.,* **19,** 235.

March, C. H. and Elliott, H. W. (1954) *Proc. Soc. exp. Biol. (N.Y.),* **86,** 494.

Mark, L. C. (1963) *Clin. Pharmacol. Ther.,* **4,** 504.

Mellett, L. B. and Woods, L. A. (1956) *J. Pharmacol. exp. Ther.,* **116,** 77.

Noach, E. L., Woodbury, D. M. and Goodman, L. S. (1958) *J. Pharmacol. exp. Ther.,* **122,** 301.

Parke, D. V. (1971) In *Acute Barbiturate Poisoning,* p. 7, edited by H. Matthew, Excerpta Medica, Amsterdam.

Paul, M. F., Paul, H. E., Bender, R. C., Kopko, F., Harrington, C. M., Ellis, V. R. and Buzard, J. A. (1960) *Antibiot. and Chemother.,* **10,** 287.

Slaytor, M. B. and Wright, S. E. (1962) *J. med. pharm. Chem.,* **5,** 483.

Smith, R. L. (1971) *Handbook of Experimental Pharmacology,* 28/i, 354.

Stoll, A., Rothlin, E., Rutschmann, J. and Schalch, W. R. (1955) *Experientia (Basel),* **11,** 396.

Sunshine, I., Whitwam, J. G., Fike, W. W., Finkle, B. and LeBeau, J. (1966) *Brit. J. Anaesth.,* **38,** 23.

Van Loon, E. J., Flanagan, T. L., Novick, W. J. and Maass, A. R. (1964) *J. pharm. Sci.,* **53,** 1211.

Welles, J. S., McMahon, R. E. and Doran, W. J. (1963) *J. Pharmacol. exp. Ther.,* **139,** 166.

Wheeler, H. O., Cranston, W. I. and Meltzer, J. I. (1958) *Proc. Soc. exp. Biol. (N.Y.),* **99,** 11.

Williams, R. T. and Parke, D. V. (1964) *Ann. Rev. Pharmacol.,* **4,** 85.

Woods, L. A. (1954) *J. Pharmacol. exp. Ther.,* **112,** 158.

Zehnder, K., Kalberer, F., Kreis, W. and Rutschmann, J. (1962a) *Biochem. Pharmacol.,* **11,** 535.

Zehnder, K., Kalberer, F. and Rutschmann, J. (1962b) *Biochem. Pharmacol.,* **11,** 551.

Author Index

Subject Index

B5